Test Bank
Chapters 18-26

Accounting
Twenty Fifth Edition

Carl S. Warren
Professor Emeritus of Accounting
University of Georgia, Athens

James M. Reeve
Professor Emeritus of Accounting
University of Tennessee, Knoxville

Jonathan E. Duchac
Professor of Accounting
Wake Forest University

SOUTH-WESTERN
CENGAGE Learning

Australia • Brazil • Japan • Korea • Mexico • Singapore • Spain • United Kingdom • United States

ISBN-13: 978-1-285-07856-4
ISBN-10: 1-285-07856-X

South-Western Cengage Learning
5191 Natorp Boulevard
Mason, OH 45040
USA

Cengage Learning is a leading provider of customized learning solutions with office locations around the globe, including Singapore, the United Kingdom, Australia, Mexico, Brazil, and Japan. Locate your local office at: **international.cengage.com/region**.

Cengage Learning products are represented in Canada by Nelson Education, Ltd.

For your course and learning solutions, visit **www.cengage.com**.

Purchase any of our products at your local college store or at our preferred online store **www.CengageBrain.com**.

Printed in the United States of America
1 2 3 4 5   17 16 15 14 13

Table of Contents

Chapter 18—Managerial Accounting Concepts and Principles

TRUE/FALSE

1. Accounting is an information system that provides essential data about the economic activities of an entity to various users to aid them in making informed judgments and decisions.

    ANS: T   PTS: 1   DIF: Easy   OBJ: LO: 18-01
    NAT: BUSPROG: Analytic   KEY: Bloom's: Knowledge

2. Managerial accounting reports are prepared according to generally accepted accounting principles.

    ANS: F   PTS: 1   DIF: Easy   OBJ: LO: 18-01
    NAT: BUSPROG: Analytic   KEY: Bloom's: Knowledge

3. Managerial accounting information includes both historical and estimated data.

    ANS: T   PTS: 1   DIF: Easy   OBJ: LO: 18-01
    NAT: BUSPROG: Analytic   KEY: Bloom's: Knowledge

4. Since there are few rules to restrict how an organization chooses to arrange its own internal data for decision making, managerial accounting provides ample opportunity for creativity and change.

    ANS: T   PTS: 1   DIF: Easy   OBJ: LO: 18-01
    NAT: BUSPROG: Analytic   KEY: Bloom's: Knowledge

5. A diagram of the operating structure of an organization is called an organization chart.

    ANS: T   PTS: 1   DIF: Easy   OBJ: LO: 18-01
    NAT: BUSPROG: Analytic   KEY: Bloom's: Knowledge

6. In most business organizations, the chief accountant is called the treasurer.

    ANS: F   PTS: 1   DIF: Easy   OBJ: LO: 18-01
    NAT: BUSPROG: Analytic   KEY: Bloom's: Knowledge

7. In most business organizations, the chief accountant is called the controller.

    ANS: T   PTS: 1   DIF: Easy   OBJ: LO: 18-01
    NAT: BUSPROG: Analytic   KEY: Bloom's: Knowledge

8. A staff department or unit is one that provides services, assistance, and advice to the departments with line or other staff responsibilities.

    ANS: T   PTS: 1   DIF: Easy   OBJ: LO: 18-01
    NAT: BUSPROG: Analytic   KEY: Bloom's: Knowledge

9. The vice presidents of production and sales and the controller hold line positions in most large organizations.

    ANS: F   PTS: 1   DIF: Easy   OBJ: LO: 18-01
    NAT: BUSPROG: Analytic   KEY: Bloom's: Knowledge

10. A staff department has no direct authority over a line department.

    ANS: T   PTS: 1   DIF: Easy   OBJ: LO: 18-01
    NAT: BUSPROG: Analytic   KEY: Bloom's: Knowledge

11. The controller's staff consists of management accountants responsible for systems and procedures, general accounting, budgets, taxes, and cost accounting.

    ANS: T   PTS: 1   DIF: Easy   OBJ: LO: 18-01
    NAT: BUSPROG: Analytic   KEY: Bloom's: Knowledge

12. Managerial accounting reports must be useful to the user of the information.

    ANS: T   PTS: 1   DIF: Easy   OBJ: LO: 18-01
    NAT: BUSPROG: Analytic   KEY: Bloom's: Knowledge

13. Planning is the process of monitoring operating results and comparing actual results with the expected results.

    ANS: F   PTS: 1   DIF: Easy   OBJ: LO: 18-01
    NAT: BUSPROG: Analytic   KEY: Bloom's: Knowledge

14. Planning is the process of developing the company's objectives or goals and translating these objectives into courses of action.

    ANS: T   PTS: 1   DIF: Easy   OBJ: LO: 18-01
    NAT: BUSPROG: Analytic   KEY: Bloom's: Knowledge

15. Control is the process of monitoring operating results and comparing actual results with the expected results.

    ANS: T   PTS: 1   DIF: Easy   OBJ: LO: 18-01
    NAT: BUSPROG: Analytic   KEY: Bloom's: Knowledge

16. Managerial accounting provides useful information to managers on product costs.

    ANS: T   PTS: 1   DIF: Easy   OBJ: LO: 18-02
    NAT: BUSPROG: Analytic   KEY: Bloom's: Knowledge

17. The payment of dividends is an example of a cost.

    ANS: F   PTS: 1   DIF: Moderate   OBJ: LO: 18-02
    NAT: BUSPROG: Analytic   KEY: Bloom's: Knowledge

18.   A cost can be a payment of cash for the purpose of generating revenues.

ANS: T   PTS: 1   DIF: Easy   OBJ: LO: 18-02
NAT: BUSPROG: Analytic   KEY: Bloom's: Knowledge

19.   The cost of a manufactured product generally consists of direct materials cost, direct labor cost, and factory overhead cost.

ANS: T   PTS: 1   DIF: Easy   OBJ: LO: 18-02
NAT: BUSPROG: Analytic   KEY: Bloom's: Knowledge

20.   The cost of materials entering directly into the manufacturing process is classified as factory overhead cost.

ANS: F   PTS: 1   DIF: Easy   OBJ: LO: 18-02
NAT: BUSPROG: Analytic   KEY: Bloom's: Knowledge

21.   The cost of wages paid to employees directly involved in converting materials to finished product is classified as direct labor cost.

ANS: T   PTS: 1   DIF: Easy   OBJ: LO: 18-02
NAT: BUSPROG: Analytic   KEY: Bloom's: Knowledge

22.   If the cost of employee wages is not a significant portion of the total product cost, the wages are classified as direct materials cost.

ANS: F   PTS: 1   DIF: Easy   OBJ: LO: 18-02
NAT: BUSPROG: Analytic   KEY: Bloom's: Knowledge

23.   For a construction contractor, the wages of carpenters would be classified as factory overhead cost.

ANS: F   PTS: 1   DIF: Moderate   OBJ: LO: 18-02
NAT: BUSPROG: Analytic   KEY: Bloom's: Knowledge

24.   For an automotive repair shop, the wages of mechanics would be classified as direct labor cost.

ANS: T   PTS: 1   DIF: Moderate   OBJ: LO: 18-02
NAT: BUSPROG: Analytic   KEY: Bloom's: Knowledge

25.   Costs other than direct materials cost and direct labor cost incurred in the manufacturing process are classified as factory overhead cost.

ANS: T   PTS: 1   DIF: Easy   OBJ: LO: 18-02
NAT: BUSPROG: Analytic   KEY: Bloom's: Knowledge

26.   Depreciation on factory plant and equipment is an example of factory overhead cost.

ANS: T   PTS: 1   DIF: Moderate   OBJ: LO: 18-02
NAT: BUSPROG: Analytic   KEY: Bloom's: Knowledge

27. Cost of oil used to lubricate factory machinery and equipment is an example of a direct materials cost.

    ANS: F   PTS: 1   DIF: Moderate   OBJ: LO: 18-02
    NAT: BUSPROG: Analytic   KEY: Bloom's: Knowledge

28. If the cost of materials is not a significant portion of the total product cost, the materials may be classified as part of factory overhead cost.

    ANS: T   PTS: 1   DIF: Moderate   OBJ: LO: 18-02
    NAT: BUSPROG: Analytic   KEY: Bloom's: Knowledge

29. Factory overhead cost is sometimes referred to as factory burden.

    ANS: T   PTS: 1   DIF: Easy   OBJ: LO: 18-02
    NAT: BUSPROG: Analytic   KEY: Bloom's: Knowledge

30. Conversion cost is the combination of direct labor cost and factory overhead cost.

    ANS: T   PTS: 1   DIF: Easy   OBJ: LO: 18-02
    NAT: BUSPROG: Analytic   KEY: Bloom's: Knowledge

31. Conversion cost is the combination of direct materials cost and factory overhead cost.

    ANS: F   PTS: 1   DIF: Easy   OBJ: LO: 18-02
    NAT: BUSPROG: Analytic   KEY: Bloom's: Knowledge

32. Factory overhead is an example of a product cost.

    ANS: T   PTS: 1   DIF: Easy   OBJ: LO: 18-02
    NAT: BUSPROG: Analytic   KEY: Bloom's: Knowledge

33. Direct labor costs are included in the conversion costs of a product.

    ANS: T   PTS: 1   DIF: Easy   OBJ: LO: 18-02
    NAT: BUSPROG: Analytic   KEY: Bloom's: Knowledge

34. The costs of materials and labor that do not enter directly into the finished product are classified as factory overhead.

    ANS: T   PTS: 1   DIF: Easy   OBJ: LO: 18-02
    NAT: BUSPROG: Analytic   KEY: Bloom's: Knowledge

35. The costs of materials and labor that do not enter directly into the finished product are classified as cost of goods sold.

    ANS: F   PTS: 1   DIF: Easy   OBJ: LO: 18-02
    NAT: BUSPROG: Analytic   KEY: Bloom's: Knowledge

36. Indirect labor would be included in factory overhead.

     ANS: T   PTS: 1   DIF: Moderate   OBJ: LO: 18-02
     NAT: BUSPROG: Analytic   KEY: Bloom's: Knowledge

37. A cost object indicates how costs are related or identified.

     ANS: T   PTS: 1   DIF: Easy   OBJ: LO: 18-02
     NAT: BUSPROG: Analytic   KEY: Bloom's: Knowledge

38. Direct costs can be specifically traced to a cost object.

     ANS: T   PTS: 1   DIF: Easy   OBJ: LO: 18-02
     NAT: BUSPROG: Analytic   KEY: Bloom's: Knowledge

39. Indirect costs can be specifically identified to a cost object.

     ANS: F   PTS: 1   DIF: Easy   OBJ: LO: 18-02
     NAT: BUSPROG: Analytic   KEY: Bloom's: Knowledge

40. Nonmanufacturing costs are classified into two categories: selling and administrative.

     ANS: T   PTS: 1   DIF: Easy   OBJ: LO: 18-02
     NAT: BUSPROG: Analytic   KEY: Bloom's: Knowledge

41. Prime costs are the combination of direct labor costs and factory overhead costs.

     ANS: F   PTS: 1   DIF: Easy   OBJ: LO: 18-02
     NAT: BUSPROG: Analytic   KEY: Bloom's: Knowledge

42. Prime costs are the combination of direct materials and direct labor costs.

     ANS: T   PTS: 1   DIF: Easy   OBJ: LO: 18-02
     NAT: BUSPROG: Analytic   KEY: Bloom's: Knowledge

43. Conversion costs are the combination of direct labor, direct material and factory overhead costs.

     ANS: F   PTS: 1   DIF: Easy   OBJ: LO: 18-02
     NAT: BUSPROG: Analytic   KEY: Bloom's: Knowledge

44. Product costs are also referred to as inventoriable costs.

     ANS: T   PTS: 1   DIF: Easy   OBJ: LO: 18-02
     NAT: BUSPROG: Analytic   KEY: Bloom's: Knowledge

45. Period costs include direct materials and direct labor.

     ANS: F   PTS: 1   DIF: Easy   OBJ: LO: 18-02
     NAT: BUSPROG: Analytic   KEY: Bloom's: Knowledge

46.   Period costs can be found in the balance sheet or in the income statement.

      ANS: F   PTS: 1   DIF: Easy   OBJ: LO: 18-02
      NAT: BUSPROG: Analytic   KEY: Bloom's: Knowledge

47.   On the balance sheet for a manufacturing business, the cost of direct materials, direct labor, and
      factory overhead are categorized as either materials inventory, work in process inventory, or
      finished goods inventory.

      ANS: T   PTS: 1   DIF: Moderate   OBJ: LO: 18-03
      NAT: BUSPROG: Analytic   KEY: Bloom's: Knowledge

48.   Only the value of the inventory that is sold will appear in the income statement.

      ANS: T   PTS: 1   DIF: Moderate   OBJ: LO: 18-03
      NAT: BUSPROG: Analytic   KEY: Bloom's: Knowledge

49.   The statement of cost of goods manufactured is an extension of the income statement for a
      manufacturing company.

      ANS: T   PTS: 1   DIF: Moderate   OBJ: LO: 18-03
      NAT: BUSPROG: Analytic   KEY: Bloom's: Knowledge

50.   Managers use managerial information to evaluate performance of a company's operation.

      ANS: T   PTS: 1   DIF: Easy   OBJ: LO: 18-04
      NAT: BUSPROG: Analytic   KEY: Bloom's: Knowledge

51.   Managerial information is for external as well as internal stakeholders.

      ANS: F   PTS: 1   DIF: Easy   OBJ: LO: 18-04
      NAT: BUSPROG: Analytic   KEY: Bloom's: Knowledge

52.   A report analyzing how many products need to be sold to cover operating costs is not typically a
      managerial accounting report.

      ANS: F   PTS: 1   DIF: Easy   OBJ: LO: 18-04
      NAT: BUSPROG: Analytic   KEY: Bloom's: Knowledge

53.   A report analyzing the dollar savings of purchasing new equipment to speed up the production
      process is a managerial accounting report.

      ANS: T   PTS: 1   DIF: Easy   OBJ: LO: 18-04
      NAT: BUSPROG: Analytic   KEY: Bloom's: Knowledge

54.   A performance report that identifies the amount of employee downtime is a financial accounting
      report.

      ANS: F   PTS: 1   DIF: Easy   OBJ: LO: 18-04
      NAT: BUSPROG: Analytic   KEY: Bloom's: Knowledge

55. Controlling deals with choosing goals and deciding how to achieve them.

ANS: F   PTS: 1   DIF: Easy   OBJ: LO: 18-01
NAT: BUSPROG: Analytic   KEY: Bloom's: Knowledge

56. Goods that are partway through the manufacturing process, but not yet complete, are referred to as materials inventory.

ANS: F   PTS: 1   DIF: Easy   OBJ: LO: 18-02
NAT: BUSPROG: Analytic   KEY: Bloom's: Knowledge

57. Manufacturers use labor, plant, and equipment to convert direct materials into finished products.

ANS: T   PTS: 1   DIF: Easy   OBJ: LO: 18-02
NAT: BUSPROG: Analytic   KEY: Bloom's: Knowledge

58. Product costs are not expensed until the product is sold.

ANS: T   PTS: 1   DIF: Moderate   OBJ: LO: 18-02
NAT: BUSPROG: Analytic   KEY: Bloom's: Knowledge

59. The plant manager's salary in a manufacturing business would be considered an indirect cost.

ANS: T   PTS: 1   DIF: Moderate   OBJ: LO: 18-02
NAT: BUSPROG: Analytic   KEY: Bloom's: Knowledge

60. Operating expenses are product costs and are expensed when the product is sold.

ANS: F   PTS: 1   DIF: Moderate   OBJ: LO: 18-02
NAT: BUSPROG: Analytic   KEY: Bloom's: Knowledge

61. Period costs are operating costs that are expensed in the period in which the goods are sold.

ANS: F   PTS: 1   DIF: Moderate   OBJ: LO: 18-02
NAT: BUSPROG: Analytic   KEY: Bloom's: Knowledge

62. Factory overhead includes all manufacturing costs except direct materials and direct labor.

ANS: T   PTS: 1   DIF: Easy   OBJ: LO: 18-02
NAT: BUSPROG: Analytic   KEY: Bloom's: Knowledge

63. Labor costs that are directly traceable to the product are part of factory overhead.

ANS: F   PTS: 1   DIF: Easy   OBJ: LO: 18-02
NAT: BUSPROG: Analytic   KEY: Bloom's: Knowledge

64. Product costs include direct labor and advertising expense.

ANS: F   PTS: 1   DIF: Easy   OBJ: LO: 18-02
NAT: BUSPROG: Analytic   KEY: Bloom's: Knowledge

65.   Indirect labor and indirect materials would be part of factory overhead.

      ANS: T   PTS: 1   DIF: Easy   OBJ: LO: 18-02
      NAT: BUSPROG: Analytic   KEY: Bloom's: Knowledge

66.   Prime costs consist of factory overhead and direct labor.

      ANS: F   PTS: 1   DIF: Easy   OBJ: LO: 18-02
      NAT: BUSPROG: Analytic   KEY: Bloom's: Knowledge

67.   Conversion costs consist of product costs and period costs.

      ANS: F   PTS: 1   DIF: Easy   OBJ: LO: 18-02
      NAT: BUSPROG: Analytic   KEY: Bloom's: Knowledge

68.   Prime costs consists of direct materials, indirect materials, and direct labor.

      ANS: F   PTS: 1   DIF: Easy   OBJ: LO: 18-02
      NAT: BUSPROG: Analytic   KEY: Bloom's: Knowledge

69.   Managerial accounting uses only past data in reports to aid management in the decision making
      process.

      ANS: F   PTS: 1   DIF: Easy   OBJ: LO: 18-01
      NAT: BUSPROG: Analytic   KEY: Bloom's: Knowledge

MATCHING

The following are some of the costs incurred by Cupcake Company. Identify them as either:
a.   Direct Materials
b.   Direct Labor
c.   Factory Overhead
d.   Non manufacturing cost

1.   Salesman commissions
2.   Factory rent
3.   Depreciation expense – factory
4.   Frosting
5.   Baker's wages
6.   Depreciation expense – office
7.   Cupcake mix
8.   Sprinkles for decoration (indirect material)

1.   ANS: D   PTS: 1   DIF: Easy   OBJ: LO: 18-02
     NAT: BUSPROG: Analytic   KEY: Bloom's: Knowledge
2.   ANS: C   PTS: 1   DIF: Easy   OBJ: LO: 18-02
     NAT: BUSPROG: Analytic   KEY: Bloom's: Knowledge
3.   ANS: C   PTS: 1   DIF: Easy   OBJ: LO: 18-02
     NAT: BUSPROG: Analytic   KEY: Bloom's: Knowledge
4.   ANS: A   PTS: 1   DIF: Easy   OBJ: LO: 18-02
     NAT: BUSPROG: Analytic   KEY: Bloom's: Knowledge

5. ANS: B   PTS: 1   DIF: Easy   OBJ: LO: 18-02
   NAT: BUSPROG: Analytic   KEY: Bloom's: Knowledge
6. ANS: D   PTS: 1   DIF: Easy   OBJ: LO: 18-02
   NAT: BUSPROG: Analytic   KEY: Bloom's: Knowledge
7. ANS: A   PTS: 1   DIF: Easy   OBJ: LO: 18-02
   NAT: BUSPROG: Analytic   KEY: Bloom's: Knowledge
8. ANS: C   PTS: 1   DIF: Easy   OBJ: LO: 18-02
   NAT: BUSPROG: Analytic   KEY: Bloom's: Knowledge

The following are some of the costs incurred by Cupcake Company. Identify them as either:
a. Prime costs
b. Conversion costs
c. Both prime and conversion costs
d. Neither prime or conversion costs

9. Salesman commissions
10. Factory rent
11. Depreciation expense – factory
12. Frosting
13. Baker's wages
14. Depreciation expense – office
15. Cupcake mix
16. Sprinkles for decoration (indirect material)

9. ANS: D   PTS: 1   DIF: Easy   OBJ: LO: 18-02
   NAT: BUSPROG: Analytic   KEY: Bloom's: Knowledge
10. ANS: B   PTS: 1   DIF: Easy   OBJ: LO: 18-02
    NAT: BUSPROG: Analytic   KEY: Bloom's: Knowledge
11. ANS: B   PTS: 1   DIF: Easy   OBJ: LO: 18-02
    NAT: BUSPROG: Analytic   KEY: Bloom's: Knowledge
12. ANS: A   PTS: 1   DIF: Easy   OBJ: LO: 18-02
    NAT: BUSPROG: Analytic   KEY: Bloom's: Knowledge
13. ANS: C   PTS: 1   DIF: Easy   OBJ: LO: 18-02
    NAT: BUSPROG: Analytic   KEY: Bloom's: Knowledge
14. ANS: D   PTS: 1   DIF: Easy   OBJ: LO: 18-02
    NAT: BUSPROG: Analytic   KEY: Bloom's: Knowledge
15. ANS: A   PTS: 1   DIF: Easy   OBJ: LO: 18-02
    NAT: BUSPROG: Analytic   KEY: Bloom's: Knowledge
16. ANS: B   PTS: 1   DIF: Easy   OBJ: LO: 18-02
    NAT: BUSPROG: Analytic   KEY: Bloom's: Knowledge

Bartel Corporation produces bar stools for restaurants. For each of the following, indicate whether the cost would typically be considered direct or indirect cost for the cost object given.
a. Direct
b. Indirect

17. The production labor wages for the bar stool assemblers.
18. The factory supervisor's salary for the barstool factory.
19. Lubricants used on the bar stool manufacturing equipment
20. Manufacturing costs for wood and steel used in the bar stools.
21. Nails and screws used in the production of the bar stools.

17. ANS: A   PTS: 1   DIF: Easy   OBJ: LO: 18-02
    NAT: BUSPROG: Analytic   KEY: Bloom's: Knowledge
18. ANS: B   PTS: 1   DIF: Easy   OBJ: LO: 18-02
    NAT: BUSPROG: Analytic   KEY: Bloom's: Knowledge
19. ANS: B   PTS: 1   DIF: Easy   OBJ: LO: 18-02
    NAT: BUSPROG: Analytic   KEY: Bloom's: Knowledge
20. ANS: A   PTS: 1   DIF: Easy   OBJ: LO: 18-02
    NAT: BUSPROG: Analytic   KEY: Bloom's: Knowledge
21. ANS: A   PTS: 1   DIF: Easy   OBJ: LO: 18-02
    NAT: BUSPROG: Analytic   KEY: Bloom's: Knowledge

Brown Corporation produces bicycles. For each of the following, indicate whether the cost would typically be considered product or period cost for the cost object given.
    a. Product
    b. Period

22. Tires for the bicycles.
23. Electricity costs to run the factory.
24. Selling costs for the period.
25. Delivery costs to take the bicycles to stores.
26. Accountant salaries at Brown Corporation.

22. ANS: A   PTS: 1   DIF: Easy   OBJ: LO: 18-02
    NAT: BUSPROG: Analytic   KEY: Bloom's: Knowledge
23. ANS: A   PTS: 1   DIF: Easy   OBJ: LO: 18-02
    NAT: BUSPROG: Analytic   KEY: Bloom's: Knowledge
24. ANS: B   PTS: 1   DIF: Easy   OBJ: LO: 18-02
    NAT: BUSPROG: Analytic   KEY: Bloom's: Knowledge
25. ANS: B   PTS: 1   DIF: Easy   OBJ: LO: 18-02
    NAT: BUSPROG: Analytic   KEY: Bloom's: Knowledge
26. ANS: B   PTS: 1   DIF: Easy   OBJ: LO: 18-02
    NAT: BUSPROG: Analytic   KEY: Bloom's: Knowledge

MULTIPLE CHOICE

1. In order to be useful to managers, management accounting reports should possess all of the following characteristics EXCEPT:
    a. provide objective measures of past operations and subjective estimates about future decisions
    b. be prepared in accordance with generally accepted accounting principles
    c. be provided at any time management needs information
    d. be prepared to report information for any unit of the business to support decision making

    ANS: B   PTS: 1   DIF: Easy   OBJ: LO: 18-01
    NAT: BUSPROG: Analytic   KEY: Bloom's: Knowledge

2. What is the primary criterion for the preparation of managerial accounting reports?
    a. Relevance of the reports
    b. Meet the manager needs
    c. Timing of the reports
    d. Cost of the reports

ANS: B   PTS: 1   DIF: Easy   OBJ: LO: 18-01
NAT: BUSPROG: Analytic   KEY: Bloom's: Knowledge

3. Which of the following is most associated with managerial accounting?
   a. Must follow GAAP
   b. May rely on estimates and forecasts
   c. Is prepared for users outside the organization.
   d. Always reports on the entire entity

ANS: B   PTS: 1   DIF: Easy   OBJ: LO: 18-01
NAT: BUSPROG: Analytic   KEY: Bloom's: Knowledge

4. Which of the following is most associated with financial accounting?
   a. Can have both objective and subjective information
   b. Can be prepared periodically, or as needed
   c. Prepared in accordance with GAAP
   d. Can be prepared for the entity or segment

ANS: C   PTS: 1   DIF: Easy   OBJ: LO: 18-01
NAT: BUSPROG: Analytic   KEY: Bloom's: Knowledge

5. Which of the following statements is false?
   a. There is no overlap between financial and managerial accounting.
   b. Managerial accounting sometimes relies on past information.
   c. Managerial accounting does not need to conform to GAAP
   d. Financial accounting must conform to GAAP.

ANS: A   PTS: 1   DIF: Easy   OBJ: LO: 18-01
NAT: BUSPROG: Analytic   KEY: Bloom's: Knowledge

6. In most business organizations, the chief management accountant is called the:
   a. chief accounting officer
   b. controller
   c. chairman of the board
   d. chief executive officer

ANS: B   PTS: 1   DIF: Easy   OBJ: LO: 18-01
NAT: BUSPROG: Analytic   KEY: Bloom's: Knowledge

7. All of the following employees hold line positions in Anthea Electric EXCEPT:
   a. vice president of production
   b. vice president of finance
   c. manager of the Valhalla Plant
   d. vice president of sales

ANS: B   PTS: 1   DIF: Easy   OBJ: LO: 18-01
NAT: BUSPROG: Analytic   KEY: Bloom's: Knowledge

8. The controller's staff often consists of several management accountants. All of the following would most likely be on the controller's staff EXCEPT:
   a. general accountants
   b. budgets and budget analysts
   c. investments and shareholder relations managers
   d. cost accountants

ANS: C   PTS: 1   DIF: Easy   OBJ: LO: 18-01
NAT: BUSPROG: Analytic   KEY: Bloom's: Knowledge

9. Managerial accounting
    a. is prepared according to GAAP.
    b. is prepared according to management needs.
    c. is prepared periodically only.
    d. is related to the entire business entity only.

ANS: B   PTS: 1   DIF: Easy   OBJ: LO: 18-01
NAT: BUSPROG: Analytic   KEY: Bloom's: Knowledge

10. Who are the individuals charged with the responsibility for directing the day-to-day operations of a
     business?
     a. Investors
     b. Managers
     c. Shareholders
     d. Customers

ANS: B   PTS: 1   DIF: Easy   OBJ: LO: 18-01
NAT: BUSPROG: Analytic   KEY: Bloom's: Knowledge

11. Which of the following are basic phases of the management process?
     a. Supervising and directing
     b. Decision making and supervising
     c. Organizing and directing
     d. Planning and controlling

ANS: D   PTS: 1   DIF: Easy   OBJ: LO: 18-01
NAT: BUSPROG: Analytic   KEY: Bloom's: Knowledge

12. What term is used to describe the process of monitoring operating results and comparing actual
     results with the expected results?
     a. Improving
     b. Controlling
     c. Directing
     d. Planning

ANS: B   PTS: 1   DIF: Easy   OBJ: LO: 18-01
NAT: BUSPROG: Analytic   KEY: Bloom's: Knowledge

13. What term is used to describe the process of developing the organization's objectives and translating
     those into courses of action?
     a. Supervising
     b. Planning
     c. Improving
     d. Decision making

ANS: B   PTS: 1   DIF: Easy   OBJ: LO: 18-01
NAT: BUSPROG: Analytic   KEY: Bloom's: Knowledge

14. Which of the following is the principle reason for preparing managerial accounting reports?
     a. Usefulness to management
     b. Cost of preparation

c. Clarity
d. GAAP

ANS: A   PTS: 1   DIF: Easy   OBJ: LO: 18-01
NAT: BUSPROG: Analytic   KEY: Bloom's: Knowledge

15. Which of the following is not a characteristic of useful managerial accounting reports?
a. Accuracy
b. GAAP
c. historical and estimated data
d. reports prepared as needed

ANS: B   PTS: 1   DIF: Easy   OBJ: LO: 18-01
NAT: BUSPROG: Analytic   KEY: Bloom's: Knowledge

16. Compute conversion costs given the following data: Direct Materials, $347,500; Direct Labor, $186,300; Factory Overhead, $187,900; and Selling Expenses, $45,290.
a. $533,800
b. $187,900
c. $721,700
d. $374,200

ANS: D   PTS: 1   DIF: Moderate   OBJ: LO: 18-02
NAT: BUSPROG: Analytic   KEY: Bloom's: Application

17. Which of the following is false in regards to direct materials for an auto manufacturer?
a. Steel would probably be a direct material.
b. Upholstery fabric would probably be a direct material
c. Oil to lubricate factory machines would not be a direct material.
d. Small plastic clips to hold on door panels, that become part of the auto, must be accounted for as direct materials.

ANS: D   PTS: 1   DIF: Moderate   OBJ: LO: 18-02
NAT: BUSPROG: Analytic   KEY: Bloom's: Knowledge

18. The cost of a manufactured product generally consists of which of the following costs?
a. Direct materials cost and factory overhead cost
b. Direct labor cost and factory overhead cost
c. Direct labor cost, direct materials cost, and factory overhead cost
d. Direct materials cost and direct labor cost

ANS: C   PTS: 1   DIF: Easy   OBJ: LO: 18-02
NAT: BUSPROG: Analytic   KEY: Bloom's: Knowledge

19. Materials must have which two qualities in order to be classified as direct materials?
a. They must be classified as both prime costs and conversion costs.
b. They must be introduced into the process in both work-in-process inventories and finished goods inventories.
c. They must be an integral part of the finished product, but can be an insignificant portion of the total product cost.
d. They must be an integral part of the finished product and be a significant portion of the total product cost.

ANS: D   PTS: 1   DIF: Easy   OBJ: LO: 18-02
NAT: BUSPROG: Analytic   KEY: Bloom's: Knowledge

20. Which of the following is an example of direct materials cost for an automobile manufacturer?
     a.   Cost of oil lubricants for factory machinery
     b.   Cost of wages of assembly worker
     c.   Salary of production supervisor
     d.   Cost of interior upholstery

     ANS: D   PTS: 1   DIF: Moderate   OBJ: LO: 18-02
     NAT: BUSPROG: Analytic   KEY: Bloom's: Knowledge

21. If the cost of direct materials is a small portion of total production cost, it may be classified as part
     of:
     a.   direct labor cost
     b.   selling and administrative costs
     c.   miscellaneous costs
     d.   factory overhead cost

     ANS: D   PTS: 1   DIF: Easy   OBJ: LO: 18-02
     NAT: BUSPROG: Analytic   KEY: Bloom's: Knowledge

22. The cost of wages paid to employees directly involved in the manufacturing process in converting
     materials into finished product is classified as:
     a.   factory overhead cost
     b.   direct labor cost
     c.   miscellaneous costs
     d.   direct materials cost

     ANS: B   PTS: 1   DIF: Easy   OBJ: LO: 18-02
     NAT: BUSPROG: Analytic   KEY: Bloom's: Knowledge

23. Which of the following is an example of direct labor cost for an airplane manufacturer?
     a.   Cost of oil lubricants for factory machinery
     b.   Cost of wages of assembly worker
     c.   Salary of plant supervisor
     d.   Cost of jet engines

     ANS: B   PTS: 1   DIF: Moderate   OBJ: LO: 18-02
     NAT: BUSPROG: Analytic   KEY: Bloom's: Knowledge

24. Costs other than direct materials cost and direct labor cost incurred in the manufacturing process are
     classified as:
     a.   factory overhead cost
     b.   miscellaneous expense
     c.   product costs
     d.   period cost

     ANS: A   PTS: 1   DIF: Easy   OBJ: LO: 18-02
     NAT: BUSPROG: Analytic   KEY: Bloom's: Knowledge

25. Which of the following is an example of a factory overhead cost?
     a.   Repair and maintenance cost on the administrative building
     b.   Factory heating and lighting cost

c. Insurance premiums on salespersons' automobiles
d. President's salary

ANS: B   PTS: 1   DIF: Challenging   OBJ: LO: 18-02
NAT: BUSPROG: Analytic   KEY: Bloom's: Knowledge

26. Another term often used to refer to factory overhead is:
a. surplus
b. period cost
c. supervisory cost
d. factory burden

ANS: D   PTS: 1   DIF: Easy   OBJ: LO: 18-02
NAT: BUSPROG: Analytic   KEY: Bloom's: Knowledge

27. Which of the following costs are referred to as conversion costs?
a. Direct labor cost and factory overhead cost
b. Direct materials cost and direct labor cost
c. Factory overhead cost
d. Direct materials cost and factory overhead cost

ANS: A   PTS: 1   DIF: Easy   OBJ: LO: 18-02
NAT: BUSPROG: Analytic   KEY: Bloom's: Knowledge

28. What term is used to refer to the cost of changing direct materials into a finished manufactured product?
a. Factory overhead cost
b. Period cost
c. Conversion cost
d. Direct labor cost

ANS: C   PTS: 1   DIF: Easy   OBJ: LO: 18-02
NAT: BUSPROG: Analytic   KEY: Bloom's: Knowledge

29. Which of the following items would not be classified as part of factory overhead?
a. Direct labor used
b. Amortization of manufacturing patents
c. Production supervisors' salaries
d. Factory supplies used

ANS: A   PTS: 1   DIF: Challenging   OBJ: LO: 18-02
NAT: BUSPROG: Analytic   KEY: Bloom's: Knowledge

30. Which of the following is considered a part of factory overhead cost?
a. Sales commissions
b. Depreciation of factory buildings
c. Depreciation of office equipment
d. Direct materials used

ANS: B   PTS: 1   DIF: Challenging   OBJ: LO: 18-02
NAT: BUSPROG: Analytic   KEY: Bloom's: Knowledge

31. Which of the following manufacturing costs is an indirect cost of producing a product?
    a. Oil lubricants used for factory machinery
    b. Commissions for sales personnel
    c. Hourly wages of an assembly worker
    d. Memory chips for a microcomputer manufacturer

    ANS: A   PTS: 1   DIF: Challenging   OBJ: LO: 18-02
    NAT: BUSPROG: Analytic   KEY: Bloom's: Knowledge

32. Prime costs are
    a. direct materials and factory overhead
    b. direct materials and direct labor
    c. direct labor and factory overhead
    d. period costs and factory overhead

    ANS: B   PTS: 1   DIF: Easy   OBJ: LO: 18-02
    NAT: BUSPROG: Analytic   KEY: Bloom's: Knowledge

33. Conversion costs are
    a. direct materials and direct labor
    b. direct materials and factory overhead
    c. factory overhead and direct labor
    d. direct materials and indirect labor

    ANS: C   PTS: 1   DIF: Easy   OBJ: LO: 18-02
    NAT: BUSPROG: Analytic   KEY: Bloom's: Knowledge

34. Which of the following is not a prime cost?
    a. Supervisor's wages
    b. Direct labor wages
    c. Machine operator wages
    d. Assembly line wages

    ANS: A   PTS: 1   DIF: Moderate   OBJ: LO: 18-02
    NAT: BUSPROG: Analytic   KEY: Bloom's: Knowledge

35. The following are all product costs except:
    a. Direct materials
    b. Sales and administrative expenses
    c. Direct labor
    d. Factory overhead

    ANS: B   PTS: 1   DIF: Easy   OBJ: LO: 18-02
    NAT: BUSPROG: Analytic   KEY: Bloom's: Knowledge

36. Which one of the following will not be found on the balance sheet of a manufacturing company?
    a. cost of goods sold
    b. materials
    c. work in process
    d. finished goods

    ANS: A   PTS: 1   DIF: Moderate   OBJ: LO: 18-03
    NAT: BUSPROG: Analytic   KEY: Bloom's: Knowledge

37. In the income statement of a manufacturing company, what replaces purchases in the cost of goods section of a retail company?
   a. Finished goods
   b. Cost of merchandise available
   c. Cost of goods manufactured
   d. Work in process completed

   ANS: C   PTS: 1   DIF: Moderate   OBJ: LO: 18-03
   NAT: BUSPROG: Analytic   KEY: Bloom's: Knowledge

38. What is the purpose of the Statement of Cost of Goods Manufactured?
   a. to determine the ending materials inventory
   b. to determine the ending work in process inventory
   c. to determine the amounts transferred to finished goods
   d. all of the answers are true

   ANS: C   PTS: 1   DIF: Easy   OBJ: LO: 18-03
   NAT: BUSPROG: Analytic   KEY: Bloom's: Knowledge

39. Which of the following accounts will be found on the income statement?
   a. inventory
   b. work in process
   c. finished goods
   d. cost of goods sold

   ANS: D   PTS: 1   DIF: Easy   OBJ: LO: 18-03
   NAT: BUSPROG: Analytic   KEY: Bloom's: Knowledge

40. All of the following are ways that managers use managerial information except
   a. to evaluate the company's stock performance
   b. to evaluate the performance of a company's operations
   c. to support long-term planning decisions
   d. to determine the cost of manufacturing a product

   ANS: A   PTS: 1   DIF: Moderate   OBJ: LO: 18-04
   NAT: BUSPROG: Analytic   KEY: Bloom's: Knowledge

41.
Cost of Materials Used	$45,000
Direct Labor costs	$48,000
Factory Overhead	$39,000
Work in Process, beg.	$28,000
Work in Process, end.	$18,000

   What is Cost of Goods Manufactured?
   a. $178,000
   b. $132,000
   c. $122,000
   d. $142,000

   ANS: D   PTS: 1   DIF: Moderate   OBJ: LO: 18-03
   NAT: BUSPROG: Analytic   KEY: Bloom's: Application

42. Cost of Materials Used $45,000
    Direct Labor costs $48,000
    Factory Overhead $39,000
    Work in Process, beg. $28,000
    Work in Process, end. $18,000
    Finished Goods,beg. $28,000
    Finished Goods, end. $18,000

    What is Cost of Goods Sold?
    a. $152,000
    b. $142,000
    c. $10,000
    d. $128,000

    ANS: A   PTS: 1   DIF: Moderate   OBJ: LO: 18-03
    NAT: BUSPROG: Analytic   KEY: Bloom's: Application

43.

Beginning Raw Materials Inventory	$40,000
Materials purchased	$65,000
Ending Raw Materials Inventory	$30,000

    What is the amount of Raw Materials Used?

    a. $5,000
    b. $65,000
    c. $75,000
    d. $30,000

    ANS: C   PTS: 1   DIF: Easy   OBJ: LO: 18-03
    NAT: BUSPROG: Analytic   KEY: Bloom's: Application

44. A company manufactured 50,000 units of a product at a cost of $450,000.   They sold 40,000 units
    for $15 each.   What is the gross margin?
    a. $750,000
    b. $240,000
    c. $600,000
    d. $450,000

    ANS: B   PTS: 1   DIF: Moderate   OBJ: LO: 18-03
    NAT: BUSPROG: Analytic   KEY: Bloom's: Application

45.

Work in Process, Beginning	$14,000
Work in Process, Ending	$20,000
Direct Labor costs incurred	$ 4,000
Cost of Goods Manufactured	$ 8,000
Factory Overhead	$ 8,000

    What is the amount of Direct Materials used?
    a. $2,000
    b. $4,000
    c. $8,000
    d. $14,000

ANS: A   PTS: 1   DIF: Moderate   OBJ: LO: 18-03
NAT: BUSPROG: Analytic   KEY: Bloom's: Application

46. A company sells goods for $150,000 that cost $60,000 to manufacture. Which statement(s) are true?
   a. The company will recognize sales on the balance sheet of $150,000.
   b. The company will recognize $90,000 gross profit on the balance sheet.
   c. The company will decrease finished goods by $60,000.
   d. All of these are true.

ANS: C   PTS: 1   DIF: Challenging   OBJ: LO: 18-03
NAT: BUSPROG: Analytic   KEY: Bloom's: Knowledge

47. Product costs
   a. appear only on the balance sheet
   b. appear only on the income statement
   c. are expensed as costs are incurred for direct labor, direct material and factory overhead
   d. appear on both the income statement and balance sheet

ANS: D   PTS: 1   DIF: Moderate   OBJ: LO: 18-02
NAT: BUSPROG: Analytic   KEY: Bloom's: Knowledge

48. Which of the following would be least likely to be considered a managerial accounting report?
   a. a report to analyze potential efficiencies and savings for the purchase of new production equipment.
   b. a schedule of total manufacturing costs incurred
   c. a statement of cost of goods manufactured
   d. a statement of stockholders' equity

ANS: D   PTS: 1   DIF: Moderate   OBJ: LO: 18-04
NAT: BUSPROG: Analytic   KEY: Bloom's: Knowledge

49. Managerial accountants would most likely prepare all of the following reports except:
   a. A performance report identifying amounts of scrap.
   b. A control report comparing direct material usage over time.
   c. A sales report targeting monthly sales and potential bonuses.
   d. An annual report for external regulators such as the SEC.

ANS: D   PTS: 1   DIF: Moderate   OBJ: LO: 18-04
NAT: BUSPROG: Analytic   KEY: Bloom's: Knowledge

50. Accounting designed to meet the needs of decision-makers inside the business is referred to as:
   a. general accounting
   b. financial accounting
   c. managerial accounting
   d. external accounting

ANS: C   PTS: 1   DIF: Easy   OBJ: LO: 18-01
NAT: BUSPROG: Analytic   KEY: Bloom's: Knowledge

51. The primary goal of managerial accounting is to provide information to:
   a. investors
   b. creditors

   c. management
   d. external auditors

ANS: C   PTS: 1   DIF: Easy   OBJ: LO: 18-01
NAT: BUSPROG: Analytic   KEY: Bloom's: Knowledge

52.   Goods that are partially completed by a manufacturer are referred to as:
   a. merchandise inventory
   b. work in process inventory
   c. finished goods inventory
   d. materials inventory

ANS: B   PTS: 1   DIF: Easy   OBJ: LO: 18-02
NAT: BUSPROG: Analytic   KEY: Bloom's: Knowledge

53.   A plant manager's salary may be referred to as:
   a. either a direct cost or an indirect cost since managerial accounting is not restricted by GAAP
   b. a direct cost
   c. an indirect cost
   d. a period cost

ANS: C   PTS: 1   DIF: Moderate   OBJ: LO: 18-02
NAT: BUSPROG: Analytic   KEY: Bloom's: Knowledge

54.   All of the following would probably be considered a direct material except:
   a. steel
   b. fabric
   c. glue
   d. lumber

ANS: C   PTS: 1   DIF: Easy   OBJ: LO: 18-02
NAT: BUSPROG: Analytic   KEY: Bloom's: Knowledge

55.   Period costs include:
   a. current assets on the balance sheet
   b. current liabilities on the balance sheet
   c. operating costs that are shown on the income statement when products are sold
   d. operating costs that are shown on the income statement in the period in which they are incurred

ANS: D   PTS: 1   DIF: Moderate   OBJ: LO: 18-02
NAT: BUSPROG: Analytic   KEY: Bloom's: Knowledge

56.   A product cost is:
   a. expensed in the period in which it is incurred
   b. shown with current liabilities on the balance sheet
   c. shown on the income statement with the operating expenses
   d. expensed in the period the product is sold

ANS: D   PTS: 1   DIF: Moderate   OBJ: LO: 18-02
NAT: BUSPROG: Analytic   KEY: Bloom's: Knowledge

57. Indirect labor and indirect materials are classified as:
    a. factory overhead and product costs
    b. factory overhead and period costs
    c. operating costs and period costs
    d. operating costs and product costs

    ANS: A   PTS: 1   DIF: Moderate   OBJ: LO: 18-02
    NAT: BUSPROG: Analytic   KEY: Bloom's: Knowledge

58. An example of a period cost is:
    a. advertising expense
    b. indirect materials
    c. depreciation on factory equipment
    d. property taxes on plant facilities

    ANS: A   PTS: 1   DIF: Moderate   OBJ: LO: 18-02
    NAT: BUSPROG: Analytic   KEY: Bloom's: Knowledge

59. Direct labor and direct materials are classified as:
    a. product costs and expensed when the goods are sold
    b. product costs and expensed when incurred
    c. period costs and expensed when incurred
    d. period costs and expensed when the goods are sold

    ANS: A   PTS: 1   DIF: Moderate   OBJ: LO: 18-02
    NAT: BUSPROG: Analytic   KEY: Bloom's: Knowledge

60. Indirect costs incurred in a manufacturing environment that cannot be traced directly to a product are treated as:
    a. period costs and expensed when incurred
    b. product costs and expensed when the goods are sold
    c. product costs and expenses when incurred
    d. period costs and expensed when the goods are sold

    ANS: B   PTS: 1   DIF: Moderate   OBJ: LO: 18-02
    NAT: BUSPROG: Analytic   KEY: Bloom's: Knowledge

61. Rent expense on a factory building would be treated as a(n):
    a. period cost
    b. product cost
    c. direct cost
    d. both A and C are correct

    ANS: B   PTS: 1   DIF: Moderate   OBJ: LO: 18-02
    NAT: BUSPROG: Analytic   KEY: Bloom's: Knowledge

62. Rent expense incurred on a factory building would be treated as a(n):
    a. indirect cost
    b. period cost
    c. product cost
    d. both A and C are correct

    ANS: D   PTS: 1   DIF: Moderate   OBJ: LO: 18-02
    NAT: BUSPROG: Analytic   KEY: Bloom's: Knowledge

63.   Which of the following is not a factory overhead cost?
      a.   materials used directly in the manufacturing process of the product
      b.   insurance on factory equipment
      c.   salaries of production supervisors
      d.   property tax on factory building

      ANS: A   PTS: 1   DIF: Moderate   OBJ: LO: 18-02
      NAT: BUSPROG: Analytic   KEY: Bloom's: Knowledge

64.   All of the following are examples of indirect labor except:
      a.   maintenance personnel
      b.   janitorial personnel
      c.   machine operators
      d.   plant managers

      ANS: C   PTS: 1   DIF: Easy   OBJ: LO: 18-02
      NAT: BUSPROG: Analytic   KEY: Bloom's: Knowledge

65.   Factory overhead includes:
      a.   factory rent and direct labor
      b.   direct materials and direct labor
      c.   indirect materials and direct materials
      d.   indirect labor and indirect materials

      ANS: D   PTS: 1   DIF: Moderate   OBJ: LO: 18-02
      NAT: BUSPROG: Analytic   KEY: Bloom's: Knowledge

Williams Company reports production costs for 2015 as follows:

Direct materials used	$345,000
Direct labor incurred	250,000
Factory overhead incurred	400,000
Operating expenses	175,000

66.   Williams Company's period costs for 2015 amount to:
      a. $345,000
      b. $250,000
      c. $400,000
      d. $175,000

      ANS: D   PTS: 1   DIF: Moderate   OBJ: LO: 18-02
      NAT: BUSPROG: Analytic   KEY: Bloom's: Application

67.   Williams Company's product costs for 2015 amount to:
      a. $995,000
      b. $920,000
      c. $825,000
      d. $770,000

      ANS: A   PTS: 1   DIF: Moderate   OBJ: LO: 18-02
      NAT: BUSPROG: Analytic   KEY: Bloom's: Application

68. Costs which are reported on the income statement as part of cost of goods sold are referred to as:
    a. administrative expenses
    b. period costs
    c. cost of goods manufactured
    d. operating expenses

    ANS: C   PTS: 1   DIF: Easy   OBJ: LO: 18-03
    NAT: BUSPROG: Analytic   KEY: Bloom's: Knowledge

69. Costs on the income statement for both a merchandiser and a manufacturer would include:
    a. operating expenses
    b. direct materials
    c. direct labor incurred
    d. cost of goods manufactured

    ANS: A   PTS: 1   DIF: Easy   OBJ: LO: 18-03
    NAT: BUSPROG: Analytic   KEY: Bloom's: Knowledge

70. Cost of goods sold for a manufacturer equals cost of goods manufactured plus:
    a. beginning work in process inventory less ending work in process inventory
    b. ending work in process inventory less beginning work in process inventory
    c. beginning finished goods inventory less ending finished goods inventory
    d. ending finished goods inventory less beginning finished goods inventory

    ANS: C   PTS: 1   DIF: Moderate   OBJ: LO: 18-03
    NAT: BUSPROG: Analytic   KEY: Bloom's: Knowledge

71. Cost of goods manufactured is equal to:
    a. total manufacturing costs plus ending materials inventory less beginning materials
       inventory
    b. cost of goods sold plus beginning work in process inventory less ending work in process
       inventory
    c. total manufacturing costs plus ending work in process inventory less beginning work in
       process inventory
    d. total manufacturing costs plus beginning work in process inventory less ending work in
       process inventory

    ANS: D   PTS: 1   DIF: Moderate   OBJ: LO: 18-03
    NAT: BUSPROG: Analytic   KEY: Bloom's: Knowledge

72. Finished goods inventory is reported on the:
    a. income statement as a period cost
    b. balance sheet as a long-term asset
    c. balance sheet as a current asset
    d. income statement as revenue

    ANS: C   PTS: 1   DIF: Easy   OBJ: LO: 18-03
    NAT: BUSPROG: Analytic   KEY: Bloom's: Knowledge

73. Beginning work in process is equal to:
    a. cost of goods manufactured plus ending work in process minus manufacturing costs
       incurred during the current period
    b. cost of goods manufactured minus ending work in process plus manufacturing costs
       incurred during the current period

   c.   ending work in process plus manufacturing costs incurred during the current period
   d.   manufacturing costs incurred during the current period minus ending work in process

ANS: A   PTS: 1   DIF: Moderate   OBJ: LO: 18-03
NAT: BUSPROG: Analytic   KEY: Bloom's: Knowledge

74.   All of the following would be reported on the balance sheet as a current asset except:
   a.   factory overhead
   b.   materials inventory
   c.   finished goods inventory
   d.   work in process inventory

ANS: A   PTS: 1   DIF: Easy   OBJ: LO: 18-03
NAT: BUSPROG: Analytic   KEY: Bloom's: Knowledge

75.   Reedy Company reports the following information for 2012:

Cost of goods manufactured	$68,250
Direct materials used	27,000
Direct labor incurred	25,000
Work in process inventory, January 1, 2012	11,000

Factory overhead is 75% of the cost of direct labor. Work in process inventory on December 31, 2012, is:
   a. $16,250
   b. $8,500
   c. $18,750
   d. $13,500

ANS: D   PTS: 1   DIF: Moderate   OBJ: LO: 18-03
NAT: BUSPROG: Analytic   KEY: Bloom's: Application

76.   At the beginning of 2011, the Gilbert Company's work in process inventory account had a balance of $30,000. During 2011, $68,000 of direct materials were used in production, and $66,000 of direct labor costs were incurred. Factory overhead in 2011 amounted to $90,000. Cost of goods manufactured is $230,000 in 2011. The balance in work in process inventory on December 31, 2011, is:
   a. $24,000
   b. $44,000
   c. $66,000
   d. $36,000

ANS: A   PTS: 1   DIF: Moderate   OBJ: LO: 18-03
NAT: BUSPROG: Analytic   KEY: Bloom's: Application

77.   A company used $35,000 of direct materials, incurred $73,000 in direct labor cost, and $114,000 in factory overhead costs during the period. If beginning and ending work in process inventories were $28,000 and $32,000 respectively, the cost of goods manufactured was:
   a. $218,000
   b. $226,000
   c. $190,000
   d. $222,000

ANS: A   PTS: 1   DIF: Moderate   OBJ: LO: 18-03
NAT: BUSPROG: Analytic   KEY: Bloom's: Application

78. Cost of goods manufactured during 2011 is $240, work in process inventory on December 31, 2011, is $50. Work in process inventory during 2011 decreased by 60%. Total manufacturing costs incurred during 2011 amount to:
    a. $190
    b. $165
    c. $290
    d. $315

    ANS: B   PTS: 1   DIF: Moderate   OBJ: LO: 18-03
    NAT: BUSPROG: Analytic   KEY: Bloom's: Application

79. Work in process inventory on December 31, 2011, is $44,000. Work in process inventory increased by 60% during 2011. Cost of goods manufactured for 2011 amounts to $275,000. What are the total manufacturing costs incurred in 2011?
    a. $291,500
    b. $302,000
    c. $275,750
    d. $233,750

    ANS: A   PTS: 1   DIF: Moderate   OBJ: LO: 18-03
    NAT: BUSPROG: Analytic   KEY: Bloom's: Application

80. Work in process inventory on December 31, 2011, is $42,000. Work in process inventory decreased by 40% during 2011. Total manufacturing costs incurred in 2011 amount to $260,000. What is cost of goods manufactured?
    a. $232,000
    b. $302,000
    c. $288,000
    d. $190,000

    ANS: C   PTS: 1   DIF: Moderate   OBJ: LO: 18-03
    NAT: BUSPROG: Analytic   KEY: Bloom's: Application

81. Work in process inventory increased by $20,000 during 2011. Cost of goods manufactured was $180,000. Total manufacturing costs incurred in 2011 are:
    a. $198,000
    b. $160,000
    c. $189,000
    d. $200,000

    ANS: D   PTS: 1   DIF: Moderate   OBJ: LO: 18-03
    NAT: BUSPROG: Analytic   KEY: Bloom's: Application

82. The cost of goods sold for Heedy manufacturing in 2011 was $233,000. The January 1, 2011, finished goods inventory balance was $31,600, and the December 31, 2011, finished goods inventory balance was $24,200. Cost of goods manufactured during the period was:
    a. $233,000
    b. $225,600
    c. $288,800
    d. $240,400

    ANS: B   PTS: 1   DIF: Moderate   OBJ: LO: 18-03
    NAT: BUSPROG: Analytic   KEY: Bloom's: Application

Chapter 18—Managerial Accounting Concepts and Principles

83. The Sharpe Company reports the following information for 2015:

Sales	$76,500
Direct materials used	7,300
Depreciation on factory equipment	4,700
Indirect labor	5,900
Direct labor	10,500
Factory rent	4,200
Factory utilities	1,200
Sales salaries expense	15,600
Office salaries expense	8,900
Indirect materials	1,200

Determine product costs for 2015.
a. $24,500
b. $30,300
c. $29,200
d. $35,000

ANS: D   PTS: 1   DIF: Easy   OBJ: LO: 18-02
NAT: BUSPROG: Analytic   KEY: Bloom's: Application

84. The Sharpe Company reports the following information for 2015:

Sales	$76,500
Direct materials used	7,300
Depreciation on factory equipment	4,700
Indirect labor	5,900
Direct labor	10,500
Factory rent	4,200
Factory utilities	1,200
Sales salaries expense	15,600
Office salaries expense	8,900
Indirect materials	1,200

Determine period costs for 2015.
a. $24,500
b. $30,300
c. $29,200
d. $35,000

ANS: A   PTS: 1   DIF: Easy   OBJ: LO: 18-02
NAT: BUSPROG: Analytic   KEY: Bloom's: Application

OTHER

1. The aspects of the management process are listed below. Match each phase to the appropriate description.

_____ Planning
_____ Directing
_____ Controlling
_____ Improving
_____ Decision making

a) Used by managers for continuous improvement
b) Managers must decide how to respond to unfavorable performances

© 2014 Cengage Learning. All Rights Reserved. May not be scanned, copied or duplicated, or posted to a publicly accessible website, in whole or in part.

c) Used by management to develop the organization's objectives and goals

d) Monitoring the operating results of implemented plans and comparing actual results

e) Managers run their day to day activities

ANS:

c   Planning

e   Directing

d   Controlling

a   Improving

b   Decision making

PTS: 1   DIF: Moderate   OBJ: LO: 18-01   NAT: BUSPROG: Analytic
KEY: Bloom's: Knowledge

2.   Identify the following costs as (a) direct materials, (b) direct labor, or (c) factory overhead for a cake manufacturer.

1. _____ Frosting

2. _____ Depreciation on oven

3. _____ Wages of bakers

4. _____ Sprinkles for topping

ANS:

1. Direct material

2. Factory overhead

3. Direct labor

4. Factory overhead

PTS: 1   DIF: Easy   OBJ: LO: 18-02   NAT: BUSPROG: Analytic
KEY: Bloom's: Knowledge

3.   Identify the following costs as (a) prime cost, (b) conversion cost, (c) or both for a cake factory.

1. _____ Frosting

2. _____ Wages of the baker

3. _____ Sprinkles for the topping (considered an indirect material)

4. _____ Depreciation on oven

ANS:

1. a

2. c

3. b

4. b

PTS: 1   DIF: Easy   OBJ: LO: 18-02   NAT: BUSPROG: Analytic
KEY: Bloom's: Knowledge

4.   Identify the following costs as a (a) product cost or (b) period cost for a cake factory.

1. _____ Frosting

2. _____ Baker's wages

3. _____ Advertising fees

4. _____ Transportation out

ANS:
1. a
2. a
3. b
4. b

PTS: 1　　　DIF: Easy　　　OBJ: LO: 18-02　　NAT: BUSPROG: Analytic
KEY: Bloom's: Knowledge

5. The Zoe Corporation has the following information for the month March. Determine the (a) cost of goods manufactured, and (b) cost of goods sold.

Cost of materials placed in production	$69,000
Direct labor	27,000
Factory overhead	34,000
Work in process, March 1	15,000
Work in process, March 31	19,500
Finished goods inventory, March 1	25,000
Finished goods inventory, March 31	23,000

ANS:

(a)

Work in process inventory, March 1		$15,000
Cost of materials placed in production	$69,000	
Direct labor	27,000	
Factory overhead	34,000	
Total manufacturing costs added		130,000
Total manufacturing costs		145,000
Less: Work in process inventory, March 31		19,500
Cost of goods manufactured		125,500

(b)

Finished goods inventory, March 1	$25,000
Cost of goods manufactured	125,500
Cost of finished goods available for sale	150,500
Less: Finished good inventory, March 31	23,000
Cost of goods sold	127,500

PTS: 1　　　DIF: Moderate　　OBJ: LO: 18-03　　NAT: BUSPROG: Analytic
KEY: Bloom's: Application

6. Sienna Company has the following information for January.

Cost of materials placed in production	$20,000
Direct labor	15,000
Factory overhead	24,000
Work in process inventory, January 1	2,900
Work in process inventory, January 31	3,500

Show your calculations to find the cost of goods manufactured.

ANS:

Work in process inventory, January 1		$ 2,900
Cost of materials placed in production	$20,000	
Direct labor	15,000	
Factory overhead	24,000	
Total manufacturing costs incurred		59,000
Total manufacturing costs		61,900
Less: Work in process inventory, January 31		3,500
Cost of goods manufactured		$58,400

PTS: 1   DIF: Moderate   OBJ: LO: 18-03   NAT: BUSPROG: Analytic
KEY: Bloom's: Application

7.   Magnus Industries has the following data:

Beginning Raw Materials Inventory	$75,000
Materials purchased	$40,000
Ending Raw Materials Inventory	$60,000

Show how you would calculate Raw Materials Used.

ANS:
$75,000 + $40,000 − $60,000 = $55,000 Raw Materials Used

PTS: 1   DIF: Easy   OBJ: LO: 18-03   NAT: BUSPROG: Analytic
KEY: Bloom's: Application

8.   Watson Company has the following data:

Work in Process, Beginning	$18,000
Work in Process, Ending	$25,000
Direct Labor costs incurred	$ 5,000
Cost of Goods Manufactured	$ 9,000
Factory Overhead	$ 7,000

Show how you would calculate the amount of Direct Materials Used.

ANS:
[($25,000 − $18,000) + $9,000] − ($7,000 + $5,000) = $4,000

PTS: 1   DIF: Moderate   OBJ: LO: 18-03   NAT: BUSPROG: Analytic
KEY: Bloom's: Application

9.   Laramie Technologies had the following data:

Cost of Materials Used $50,000
Direct Labor costs $56,000
Factory Overhead $28,000
Work in Process, beg. $45,000
Work in Process, end. $32,000

Show your calculations to determine the Cost of Goods Manufactured.

ANS:
$50,000 + $56,000 + $28,000 + ($45,000 − $32,000) = $147,000

PTS: 1   DIF: Moderate   OBJ: LO: 18-03   NAT: BUSPROG: Analytic
KEY: Bloom's: Application

10. Keeton Company had the following data:

Cost of Materials Used $60,000
Direct Labor costs $58,000
Factory Overhead $33,000
Work in Process, beg. $29,000
Work in Process, end. $18,000
Finished Goods,beg. $32,000
Finished Goods, end. $18,000

Show your calculations to determine the Cost of Goods Sold.

ANS:
$60,000 + $58,000 + $33,000 + ($29,000 − $18,000) + ($32,000 − $18,000) = $176,000

PTS: 1   DIF: Moderate   OBJ: LO: 18-03   NAT: BUSPROG: Analytic
KEY: Bloom's: Application

PROBLEM

1. The Zoe Corporation has the following information for the month of March. Prepare a (a) schedule of cost of goods manufactured, (b) an income statement for the month ended March 31, and (c) prepare only the inventory section of the balance sheet.

Purchases	$92,000
Materials inventory, March 1	6,000
Materials inventory, March 31	8,000
Direct labor	25,000
Factory overhead	37,000
Work in process, March 1	22,000
Work in process, March 31	23,500
Finished goods inventory, March 1	21,000
Finished goods inventory, March 31	30,000
Sales	257,000
Sales and administrative expenses	79,000

ANS:

(a)

Zoe Corporation			
Statement of Cost of Goods Manufactured			
For Month Ended March 31, 20xx			
Work in process inventory March 1			$22,000
Direct Materials:			
Materials inventory, March 1	$6,000		
Purchases	92,000		
Cost of materials for use	98,000		
Less materials inventory, March 31	8,000		
Cost of materials placed in production		90,000	
Direct Labor		25,000	
Factory overhead		37,000	
Total manufacturing costs added			152,000
Total manufacturing costs			174,000
Less work in process inventory, March 31			23,500
Cost of goods manufactured			$150,500

(b)

Zoe Corporation		
Income Statement		
For Month Ended March 31, 20xx		
Sales		$257,000
Cost of goods sold:		
Finished goods inventory, March 1	$21,000	
Cost of goods manufactured	150,500	
Cost of finished goods available for sales	171,500	
Less finished goods inventory, March 31	30,000	
Cost of goods sold		141,500
Gross Profit		115,500
Operating expenses:		
Sales and administrative expenses		79,000
Net Income		$36,500

(c)

Inventory:	
Materials	$ 8,000
Work in process	23,500
Finished goods	30,000
Total Inventory	$61,500

PTS: 1   DIF: Challenging   OBJ: LO: 18-03   NAT: BUSPROG: Analytic
KEY: Bloom's: Application

2. The following data (in thousands of dollars) have been taken from the accounting records of
    Rayburn Corporation for the current year.

Sales	$1,980
Selling expenses	280
Manufacturing overhead	460
Direct labor	400
Administrative expenses	300
Purchases of raw materials	240
Finished goods inventory, beginning	240
Finished goods inventory, ending	320
Raw materials inventory, beginning	80
Raw materials inventory, ending	140
Work in process inventory, beginning	140
Work in process inventory, ending	100

Required: (Present all reports and calculations in thousands of dollars)

(a) What was the cost of the raw materials used in production during the year?
(b) What was the cost of goods manufactured (finished) for the year?
(c) What was the cost of goods sold for the year?
(d) What was the net income for the year?

ANS:

(a) The cost of the raw materials used in production during the year is determined as follows:

Raw materials inventory, beginning	$ 80
Purchases of raw materials	240
Less raw materials inventory, ending	(140)
Raw materials used in production	$ 180

(b) The cost of goods manufactured (finished) during the year is determined as follows:

Raw materials used in production	$ 180
Direct labor	400
Manufacturing overhead	460
Total manufacturing costs	1,040
Work in process inventory, beginning	140
	1,180
Less: work in process inventory, ending	(100)
Cost of goods manufactured	$1,080

(c) The cost of goods sold for the year is determined as follows:

Finished goods inventory, beginning	$ 240
Cost of goods manufactured	1,080
Less finished goods inventory, ending	(320)
Cost of goods sold	$1,000

(d) The net income for the year is determined as follows:

Sales		$1,980
Cost of goods sold		1,000
Gross profit		980
Operating expenses:		
Administrative expenses	$300	
Selling expenses	280	(580)
Net income		$ 400

PTS: 1 DIF: Moderate OBJ: LO: 18-02 | LO: 18-03
NAT: BUSPROG: Analytic KEY: Bloom's: Application

3. Differentiate between:
a) direct materials versus indirect materials
b) direct labor versus indirect labor

ANS:
a) Direct materials must become a physical part of the finished product and their costs must be separately and conveniently traceable through the manufacturing process to finished goods inventory. Examples include wood, leather, steel, etc.

Indirect materials become part of the finished product but their minor costs cannot conveniently be traced directly to particular finished products. They are included as part of factory overhead.

b) Direct labor cost is the compensation of employees who physically convert materials into the company's products and whose effort can be traced directly to finished goods inventory. Examples include machine operators and assemblers.

Indirect labor is factory labor that is difficult to trace to specific products. Instead, the cost is included in factory overhead. Examples include forklift operators, janitors, and plant managers.

PTS: 1 DIF: Moderate OBJ: LO: 18-02 NAT: BUSPROG: Analytic
KEY: Bloom's: Knowledge

4. Classify the following costs as direct, indirect, or neither:

a)	_____	indirect labor incurred
b)	_____	factory equipment depreciation
c)	_____	indirect materials used
d)	_____	office equipment depreciation
e)	_____	direct materials used
f)	_____	insurance expired on administrative facilities
g)	_____	direct labor incurred
h)	_____	administrative office salaries
i)	_____	salespersons' salaries
j)	_____	utilities on factory building
k)	_____	utilities on administrative facilities

ANS:
a) indirect
b) indirect
c) indirect

d) neither
e) direct
f) neither
g) direct
h) neither
i) neither
j) indirect
k) neither

PTS: 1   DIF: Moderate   OBJ: LO: 18-02   NAT: BUSPROG: Analytic
KEY: Bloom's: Knowledge

5.   Use the correct number to designate each item below:
1) direct materials
2) selling and administrative expense
3) factory overhead
4) direct labor

a)	_____	rent expense on factory building
b)	_____	sales supplies used
c)	_____	factory supplies used
d)	_____	indirect materials used
e)	_____	wages of assembly line personnel
f)	_____	cost of primary material used to make product
g)	_____	depreciation on office equipment
h)	_____	rent on office facilities
i)	_____	insurance expired on factory equipment
j)	_____	utilities incurred in the office
k)	_____	advertising expense

ANS:
a) 3
b) 2
c) 3
d) 3
e) 4
f) 1
g) 2
h) 2
i) 3
j) 2
k)2

PTS: 1   DIF: Moderate   OBJ: LO: 18-02   NAT: BUSPROG: Analytic
KEY: Bloom's: Knowledge

6. The Sharpe Company reports the following information for 2012:

Sales	$76,500
Direct materials used	7,300
Depreciation on factory equipment	4,700
Indirect labor	5,900
Direct labor	10,500
Factory rent	4,200
Factory utilities	1,200
Sales salaries expense	15,600
Office salaries expense	8,900
Indirect materials	1,200

Compute:
a) product costs
b) period costs

ANS:
a) $7,300 + $4,700 + $5,900 + $10,500 + $4,200 + $1,200 + $1,200 = $35,000

b) $15,600 + $8,900 = $24,500

PTS: 1   DIF: Moderate   OBJ: LO: 18-02   NAT: BUSPROG: Analytic
KEY: Bloom's: Application

7. Allen Company used $71,000 of direct materials and incurred $37,000 of direct labor costs during 2011. Indirect labor amounted to $2,700 while indirect materials used totaled $1,600. Other operating costs pertaining to the factory included utilities of $3,100; maintenance of $4,500; supplies of $1,800; depreciation of $7,900; and property taxes of $2,600. There was no beginning or ending finished goods inventory, but work in process inventory began the year with a $5,500 balance and ended the year with a $7,500 balance.

Prepare a statement of cost of goods manufactured.

ANS:

Allen Company
Statement of Cost of Goods Manufactured
For the Year Ended December 31, 2011

Beginning work in process			$ 5,500
Direct materials used		$71,000	
Direct labor incurred		37,000	
Factory overhead			
Indirect labor	$ 2,700		
Indirect materials	1,600		
Utilities	3,100		
Maintenance	4,500		
Supplies	1,800		
Depreciation	7,900		
Property taxes	2,600	24,200	
Total manufacturing costs incurred			132,200
Total manufacturing costs			137,700
Less ending work in process inventory			(7,500)
Cost of goods manufactured			$130,200

PTS: 1   DIF: Moderate   OBJ: LO: 18-03   NAT: BUSPROG: Analytic
KEY: Bloom's: Application

8. The following information is available for Carter Corporation for 2012:
    1) Materials inventory decreased $4,000 during 2012.
    2) Materials inventory on December 31, 2012, was 50% of materials inventory on January 1, 2012.
    3) Beginning work in process inventory was $145,000.
    4) Ending finished goods inventory was $65,000.
    5) Purchases of direct materials were $154,700.
    6) Direct materials used were 2.5 times the cost of direct labor.
    7) Total manufacturing costs incurred were $246,400, 80% of cost of goods manufactured and
    $156,000 less than cost of goods sold.

    Compute:
    a) finished goods inventory on January 1, 2012
    b) work in process inventory on December 31, 2012
    c) direct labor incurred
    d) factory overhead incurred
    e) direct materials used
    f) materials inventory on January 1, 2012
    g) materials inventory on December 31, 2012

    Note to students: The answers are not necessarily calculated in alphabetical order.

    ANS:
    a) cost of goods sold = $246,400 + $156,000 = $402,400
        $402,400 + $65,000 − $308,000 = $159,400

    b) cost of goods manufactured = $246,400/.80 = $308,000
        $246,400 + $145,000 − $308,000 = $83,400

    c) $158,700/2.5 = $63,480

    d) $246,400 − $158,700 − $63,480 = $24,220

    e) $8,000 + $154,700 − $4,000 = $158,700

    f) X = January 1, 2012 materials inventory
        $4,000 = .5X
        X = $8,000

    g) $8,000 − $4,000 = $4,000

    PTS: 1   DIF: Challenging   OBJ: LO: 18-02 | LO: 18-03
    NAT: BUSPROG: Analytic   KEY: Bloom's: Application

9. Rosalba Manufacturing Company had the following account balance for 2012:

	January 1	December 31
Accounts receivable	$27,000	$33,000
Materials inventory	22,500	6,000
Work in process inventory	70,200	48,000
Finished goods inventory	3,000	15,000

Collections on account were $625,000 in 2012.
Cost of goods sold was 68% of sales.
Direct materials purchased amounted to $90,000.
Factory overhead was 300% of the cost of direct labor.

Compute:

a) sales revenue (all sales were on account)
b) cost of goods sold
c) cost of goods manufactured
d) direct labor incurred
e) direct materials used
f) factory overhead incurred

ANS:
a) $33,000 + $625,000 − $27,000 = $631,000

b) $631,000 × .68 = $429,080

c) $15,000 + $429,080 − $3,000 = $441,080

d) $441,080 + $48,000 − $70,200 = $418,880 total manufacturing costs added
   $418,880 − $106,500 = $312,380
   $312,380 = factory overhead + direct labor
   Let X = direct labor
   3X + X = $312,380
   4X = $312,380
   X = $78,095

e) $22,500 + $90,000 − $6,000 = $106,500

f) $78,095 × 3 = $234,285

PTS: 1   DIF: Challenging   OBJ: LO: 18-03   NAT: BUSPROG: Analytic
KEY: Bloom's: Application

10. Sineath Industries had a fire and some of its accounting records were destroyed.   Available
     information is presented below for the year ended December 31, 2011.

Materials inventory, December 31, 2011	$15,000
Direct materials purchased	28,000
Direct materials used	22,900
Cost of goods manufactured	135,000

Additional information is as follows:
Factory overhead is 150% of direct labor cost.
Finished goods inventory decreased by $18,000 during the year.
Work in process inventory increased by $12,000 during the year.

Calculate:
a) materials inventory, January 1, 2011
b) direct labor cost
c) factory overhead incurred
d) cost of goods sold

ANS:
a) $15,000 + $22,900 − $28,000 = $9,900

b) $135,000 + $12,000 = $147,000 total manufacturing costs
    $147,000 − $22,900 = $124,100 direct labor and factory overhead
    Let X = direct labor cost
    X + 1.5X = $124,100
    2.5X = $124,100
    X = $49,640

c) $49,640 × 1.5 = $74,460

d) $135,000 + $18,000 = $153,000

PTS: 1   DIF: Challenging   OBJ: LO: 18-03   NAT: BUSPROG: Analytic
KEY: Bloom's: Application

11.   Classify the following costs as either a product cost or a period cost:

a)	_____	direct materials used
b)	_____	factory utilities
c)	_____	salespersons' commissions
d)	_____	salary of plant manager
e)	_____	indirect materials used
f)	_____	depreciation on store equipment
g)	_____	indirect labor incurred
h)	_____	advertising expense
i)	_____	direct labor incurred
j)	_____	factory machinery repairs and maintenance
k)	_____	depreciation on factory machinery
l)	_____	plant insurance expired

ANS:
a) product
b) product
c) period
d) product
e) product
f) period
g) product
h) period
i) product
j) product
k) product
l) product

PTS: 1   DIF: Moderate   OBJ: LO: 18-02   NAT: BUSPROG: Analytic
KEY: Bloom's: Knowledge

12. Differentiate between financial and managerial accounting, addressing such issues as what reports are generated, when, and for whom.

ANS:

	Managerial Accounting	Financial Accounting
Users	Internal managers	External investors, creditors, government
Reports	Detailed reports, not restricted by GAAP	Summary reports, restricted by GAAP
Timing	Future orientation	Past orientation

PTS: 1   DIF: Moderate   OBJ: LO: 18-01   NAT: BUSPROG: Analytic
KEY: Bloom's: Knowledge

TRUE/FALSE

1. Cost accounting systems are used to supply cost data information on costs incurred by a manufacturing process or department.

    ANS: T   PTS: 1   DIF: Easy   OBJ: LO: 19-01
    NAT: BUSPROG: Analytic   KEY: Bloom's: Knowledge

2. A manufacturer may employ a job order cost system for some of its products and a process cost system for others.

    ANS: T   PTS: 1   DIF: Easy   OBJ: LO: 19-01
    NAT: BUSPROG: Analytic   KEY: Bloom's: Knowledge

3. A job order cost accounting system provides for a separate record of the cost of each particular quantity of product that passes through the factory.

    ANS: T   PTS: 1   DIF: Easy   OBJ: LO: 19-01
    NAT: BUSPROG: Analytic   KEY: Bloom's: Knowledge

4. A process cost accounting system provides for a separate record of the cost of each particular quantity of product that passes through the factory.

    ANS: F   PTS: 1   DIF: Easy   OBJ: LO: 19-01
    NAT: BUSPROG: Analytic   KEY: Bloom's: Knowledge

5. A process cost accounting system accumulates costs for each of the departments or processes within the factory.

    ANS: T   PTS: 1   DIF: Easy   OBJ: LO: 19-01
    NAT: BUSPROG: Analytic   KEY: Bloom's: Knowledge

6. A process cost accounting system is best used by manufacturers of like units of product that are not distinguishable from each other during a continuous production process.

    ANS: T   PTS: 1   DIF: Easy   OBJ: LO: 19-01
    NAT: BUSPROG: Analytic   KEY: Bloom's: Knowledge

7. The process cost system is appropriate where few products are manufactured and each product is made to customers' specifications.

    ANS: F   PTS: 1   DIF: Easy   OBJ: LO: 19-01
    NAT: BUSPROG: Analytic   KEY: Bloom's: Knowledge

8. A job order cost system would be appropriate for a crude oil refining business.

    ANS: F   PTS: 1   DIF: Moderate   OBJ: LO: 19-01
    NAT: BUSPROG: Analytic   KEY: Bloom's: Knowledge

9.   A law firm would use a job order cost system to accumulate all of the costs associated with a
     particular client engagement, such as lawyer time, copying charges, filing fees, and overhead.

     ANS: T   PTS: 1   DIF: Easy   OBJ: LO: 19-01
     NAT: BUSPROG: Analytic   KEY: Bloom's: Knowledge

10. The job order costing system is not used by service organizations.

     ANS: F   PTS: 1   DIF: Easy   OBJ: LO: 19-01
     NAT: BUSPROG: Analytic   KEY: Bloom's: Knowledge

11. The job order costing system is used by service firms to determine revenues, expenses, and
     ultimately profit.

     ANS: T   PTS: 1   DIF: Moderate   OBJ: LO: 19-01
     NAT: BUSPROG: Analytic   KEY: Bloom's: Knowledge

12. Perpetual inventory controlling accounts and subsidiary ledgers are maintained for materials, work
     in process, and finished goods in cost accounting systems.

     ANS: T   PTS: 1   DIF: Easy   OBJ: LO: 19-02
     NAT: BUSPROG: Analytic   KEY: Bloom's: Knowledge

13. When the goods are sold, their costs are transferred from Work in Process to Finished Goods.

     ANS: F   PTS: 1   DIF: Easy   OBJ: LO: 19-02
     NAT: BUSPROG: Analytic   KEY: Bloom's: Knowledge

14. The materials requisition serves as the source document for debiting the accounts in the materials
     ledger.

     ANS: F   PTS: 1   DIF: Easy   OBJ: LO: 19-02
     NAT: BUSPROG: Analytic   KEY: Bloom's: Knowledge

15. Materials are transferred from the storeroom to the factory in response to materials requisitions.

     ANS: T   PTS: 1   DIF: Easy   OBJ: LO: 19-02
     NAT: BUSPROG: Analytic   KEY: Bloom's: Knowledge

16. The document that serves as the basis for recording direct labor on a job cost sheet is the time card.

     ANS: F   PTS: 1   DIF: Easy   OBJ: LO: 19-02
     NAT: BUSPROG: Analytic   KEY: Bloom's: Knowledge

17. The document that serves as the basis for recording direct labor on a job cost sheet is the time ticket.

     ANS: T   PTS: 1   DIF: Easy   OBJ: LO: 19-02
     NAT: BUSPROG: Analytic   KEY: Bloom's: Knowledge

18. Depreciation expense on factory equipment is part of factory overhead cost.

     ANS: T   PTS: 1   DIF: Moderate   OBJ: LO: 19-02
     NAT: BUSPROG: Analytic   KEY: Bloom's: Knowledge

19. Factory overhead is applied to production using a predetermined overhead rate.

ANS: T   PTS: 1   DIF: Easy   OBJ: LO: 19-02
NAT: BUSPROG: Analytic   KEY: Bloom's: Knowledge

20. If factory overhead applied exceeds the actual costs, the factory overhead account will have a credit balance.

ANS: T   PTS: 1   DIF: Moderate   OBJ: LO: 19-02
NAT: BUSPROG: Analytic   KEY: Bloom's: Knowledge

21. If factory overhead applied exceeds the actual costs, overhead is said to be underapplied.

ANS: F   PTS: 1   DIF: Moderate   OBJ: LO: 19-02
NAT: BUSPROG: Analytic   KEY: Bloom's: Knowledge

22. If the underapplied factory overhead amount is material, it is transferred to Cost of Goods Sold at the end of the fiscal year.

ANS: F   PTS: 1   DIF: Moderate   OBJ: LO: 19-02
NAT: BUSPROG: Analytic   KEY: Bloom's: Knowledge

23. If the underapplied factory overhead amount is immaterial, it is transferred to Cost of Goods Sold at the end of the fiscal year.

ANS: T   PTS: 1   DIF: Easy   OBJ: LO: 19-02
NAT: BUSPROG: Analytic   KEY: Bloom's: Knowledge

24. Each account in the cost ledger in a job order system is called a job cost sheet.

ANS: T   PTS: 1   DIF: Easy   OBJ: LO: 19-02
NAT: BUSPROG: Analytic   KEY: Bloom's: Knowledge

25. In the job order system, the finished goods account is the controlling account for the factory overhead ledger.

ANS: F   PTS: 1   DIF: Easy   OBJ: LO: 19-02
NAT: BUSPROG: Analytic   KEY: Bloom's: Knowledge

26. The inventory accounts generally maintained by a manufacturing firm are only finished goods and materials.

ANS: F   PTS: 1   DIF: Easy   OBJ: LO: 19-02
NAT: BUSPROG: Analytic   KEY: Bloom's: Knowledge

27. Generally accepted accounting principles require companies to use only one factory overhead rate for product costing.

ANS: F   PTS: 1   DIF: Easy   OBJ: LO: 19-02
NAT: BUSPROG: Analytic   KEY: Bloom's: Knowledge

28.   Activity-based costing is a method of accumulating and allocating costs by department.

ANS: F   PTS: 1   DIF: Easy   OBJ: LO: 19-02
NAT: BUSPROG: Analytic   KEY: Bloom's: Knowledge

29.   Interim financial statements for a manufacturing business would report overapplied factory
      overhead as a deferred item on the balance sheet.

ANS: T   PTS: 1   DIF: Easy   OBJ: LO: 19-02
NAT: BUSPROG: Analytic   KEY: Bloom's: Knowledge

30.   The debit to factory overhead for the cost of indirect materials is obtained from the summary of the
      materials requisitions.

ANS: T   PTS: 1   DIF: Easy   OBJ: LO: 19-02
NAT: BUSPROG: Analytic   KEY: Bloom's: Knowledge

31.   In a factory with several processing departments, a single factory overhead rate may not provide
      accurate product costs and effective cost control.

ANS: T   PTS: 1   DIF: Easy   OBJ: LO: 19-02
NAT: BUSPROG: Analytic   KEY: Bloom's: Knowledge

32.   Nonmanufacturing costs are generally classified into two categories: selling and administrative.

ANS: T   PTS: 1   DIF: Easy   OBJ: LO: 19-02
NAT: BUSPROG: Analytic   KEY: Bloom's: Knowledge

33.   The current year's advertising costs are normally considered period costs.

ANS: T   PTS: 1   DIF: Moderate   OBJ: LO: 19-02
NAT: BUSPROG: Analytic   KEY: Bloom's: Knowledge

34.   Direct labor cost is an example of a period cost.

ANS: F   PTS: 1   DIF: Easy   OBJ: LO: 19-02
NAT: BUSPROG: Analytic   KEY: Bloom's: Knowledge

35.   A manufacturing business reports just two types of inventory on its balance sheet: work in process
      inventory and finished goods inventory.

ANS: F   PTS: 1   DIF: Easy   OBJ: LO: 19-02
NAT: BUSPROG: Analytic   KEY: Bloom's: Knowledge

36.   On the balance sheet for a manufacturing business, the cost of direct materials, direct labor, and
      factory overhead, which have entered into the manufacturing process but are associated with
      products that have not been finished, is reported as direct materials inventory.

ANS: F   PTS: 1   DIF: Moderate   OBJ: LO: 19-02
NAT: BUSPROG: Analytic   KEY: Bloom's: Knowledge

37. As product costs are incurred in the manufacturing process, they are accounted for as assets and reported on the balance sheet as inventory.

ANS: T   PTS: 1   DIF: Easy   OBJ: LO: 19-02
NAT: BUSPROG: Analytic   KEY: Bloom's: Knowledge

38. A receiving report is prepared when purchased materials are first received by the manufacturing department.

ANS: F   PTS: 1   DIF: Easy   OBJ: LO: 19-02
NAT: BUSPROG: Analytic   KEY: Bloom's: Knowledge

39. Period costs are costs that are incurred for the production requirements of a certain period.

ANS: F   PTS: 1   DIF: Easy   OBJ: LO: 19-02
NAT: BUSPROG: Analytic   KEY: Bloom's: Knowledge

40. Job order cost systems can be used to compare unit costs of similar jobs to determine if costs are staying within expected ranges.

ANS: T   PTS: 1   DIF: Moderate   OBJ: LO: 19-03
NAT: BUSPROG: Analytic   KEY: Bloom's: Knowledge

41. Job cost sheets can provide information to managers on unit cost trends, the cost impact of continuous improvement in the manufacturing process, the cost impact of materials changes, and the cost impact of direct materials price or direct labor rate changes over time.

ANS: T   PTS: 1   DIF: Easy   OBJ: LO: 19-03
NAT: BUSPROG: Analytic   KEY: Bloom's: Knowledge

42. Job order cost accounting systems may be used to evaluate a company's efficiency.

ANS: T   PTS: 1   DIF: Easy   OBJ: LO: 19-03
NAT: BUSPROG: Analytic   KEY: Bloom's: Knowledge

43. Information about costs developed through a job order cost system can not be used to evaluate an organization's cost performance.

ANS: F   PTS: 1   DIF: Easy   OBJ: LO: 19-03
NAT: BUSPROG: Analytic   KEY: Bloom's: Knowledge

44. A staff department or unit is one directly involved in the basic objective of the organization.

ANS: F   PTS: 1   DIF: Moderate   OBJ: LO: 19-03
NAT: BUSPROG: Analytic   KEY: Bloom's: Knowledge

45. Job order cost accounting systems may be used for planning and controlling a service business.

ANS: T   PTS: 1   DIF: Easy   OBJ: LO: 19-04
NAT: BUSPROG: Analytic   KEY: Bloom's: Knowledge

46.   Job order cost accounting systems can be used only for companies that manufacture a product.

      ANS: F   PTS: 1   DIF: Easy   OBJ: LO: 19-04
      NAT: BUSPROG: Analytic   KEY: Bloom's: Knowledge

47.   The direct labor and overhead costs of providing services to clients are accumulated in a
      work-in-process account.

      ANS: T   PTS: 1   DIF: Easy   OBJ: LO: 19-04
      NAT: BUSPROG: Analytic   KEY: Bloom's: Knowledge

48.   In a job order cost accounting system for a service business, materials costs are normally included as
      part of overhead.

      ANS: T   PTS: 1   DIF: Easy   OBJ: LO: 19-04
      NAT: BUSPROG: Analytic   KEY: Bloom's: Knowledge

49.   A service organization will not use the job order costing method because it has no direct materials.

      ANS: F   PTS: 1   DIF: Easy   OBJ: LO: 19-04
      NAT: BUSPROG: Analytic   KEY: Bloom's: Knowledge

50.   Using the job order cost system, service organizations are able to bill customers on a weekly or
      monthly basis, even when the job has not been completed.

      ANS: T   PTS: 1   DIF: Moderate   OBJ: LO: 19-04
      NAT: BUSPROG: Analytic   KEY: Bloom's: Knowledge

MATCHING

      Identify the costs as one of the following:
      a.   Direct labor
      b.   Direct materials
      c.   Factory overhead
      d.   Not a product cost

   1.   Factory depreciation
   2.   President's salary
   3.   Salesmen commissions
   4.   Wood
   5.   Factory supervisor's salary
   6.   Assembler's wages
   7.   Plastic parts
   8.   Finished goods warehouse rent
   9.   Machine operator
  10.   Maintenance Supplies

   1.   ANS: C   PTS: 1   DIF: Moderate   OBJ: LO: 19-02
        NAT: BUSPROG: Analytic   KEY: Bloom's: Knowledge
   2.   ANS: D   PTS: 1   DIF: Moderate   OBJ: LO: 19-02
        NAT: BUSPROG: Analytic   KEY: Bloom's: Knowledge

3. ANS: D   PTS: 1   DIF: Moderate   OBJ: LO: 19-02
NAT: BUSPROG: Analytic   KEY: Bloom's: Knowledge

4. ANS: B   PTS: 1   DIF: Moderate   OBJ: LO: 19-02
NAT: BUSPROG: Analytic   KEY: Bloom's: Knowledge

5. ANS: C   PTS: 1   DIF: Moderate   OBJ: LO: 19-02
NAT: BUSPROG: Analytic   KEY: Bloom's: Knowledge

6. ANS: A   PTS: 1   DIF: Moderate   OBJ: LO: 19-02
NAT: BUSPROG: Analytic   KEY: Bloom's: Knowledge

7. ANS: B   PTS: 1   DIF: Moderate   OBJ: LO: 19-02
NAT: BUSPROG: Analytic   KEY: Bloom's: Knowledge

8. ANS: D   PTS: 1   DIF: Moderate   OBJ: LO: 19-02
NAT: BUSPROG: Analytic   KEY: Bloom's: Knowledge

9. ANS: A   PTS: 1   DIF: Moderate   OBJ: LO: 19-02
NAT: BUSPROG: Analytic   KEY: Bloom's: Knowledge

10. ANS: C   PTS: 1   DIF: Moderate   OBJ: LO: 19-02
NAT: BUSPROG: Analytic   KEY: Bloom's: Knowledge

Match each of the following terms with the phrase that most closely describes it. Each answer may be used only once.
a. Job order cost system
b. Process cost system
c. Activity based costing
d. Underapplied overhead
e. Overapplied overhead
f. Finished goods ledger
g. Period costs

11. System that uses a different overhead rate for each activity.
12. Expenses of the current period.
13. Applied overhead is more than actual overhead incurred.
14. Typically used by companies that make custom products.
15. Typically used by companies whose products are indistinguishable from each other.
16. The stock ledger.
17. Applied overhead is less than actual overhead incurred.

11. ANS: C   PTS: 1   DIF: Moderate   OBJ: LO: 19-01| LO: 19-02
NAT: BUSPROG: Analytic   KEY: Bloom's: Knowledge

12. ANS: G   PTS: 1   DIF: Moderate   OBJ: LO: 19-01| LO: 19-02
NAT: BUSPROG: Analytic   KEY: Bloom's: Knowledge

13. ANS: E   PTS: 1   DIF: Moderate   OBJ: LO: 19-01| LO: 19-02
NAT: BUSPROG: Analytic   KEY: Bloom's: Knowledge

14. ANS: A   PTS: 1   DIF: Moderate   OBJ: LO: 19-01| LO: 19-02
NAT: BUSPROG: Analytic   KEY: Bloom's: Knowledge

15. ANS: B   PTS: 1   DIF: Moderate   OBJ: LO: 19-01| LO: 19-02
NAT: BUSPROG: Analytic   KEY: Bloom's: Knowledge

16. ANS: F   PTS: 1   DIF: Moderate   OBJ: LO: 19-01| LO: 19-02
NAT: BUSPROG: Analytic   KEY: Bloom's: Knowledge

17. ANS: D   PTS: 1   DIF: Moderate   OBJ: LO: 19-01| LO: 19-02
NAT: BUSPROG: Analytic   KEY: Bloom's: Knowledge

Match each of the following terms with the phrase that most closely describes it.   Each answer may be used only once.

   a.   Job cost sheets
   b.   Material requisition
   c.   Receiving report
   d.   Time tickets
   e.   Cost of Services

18.   Service providers use this account similarly to the cost of merchandise sold account used by merchandisers.
19.   Subsidiary ledger for Work in Process.
20.   Serves as the basis for recording direct labor on a job cost sheet.
21.   Prepared when materials that have been ordered are received and inspected.
22.   Serves as the basis for recording materials used.

18.   ANS: E   PTS: 1   DIF: Moderate   OBJ: LO: 19-04
      NAT: BUSPROG: Analytic   KEY: Bloom's: Knowledge
19.   ANS: A   PTS: 1   DIF: Moderate   OBJ: LO: 19-01| LO: 19-02
      NAT: BUSPROG: Analytic   KEY: Bloom's: Knowledge
20.   ANS: D   PTS: 1   DIF: Moderate   OBJ: LO: 19-01| LO: 19-02
      NAT: BUSPROG: Analytic   KEY: Bloom's: Knowledge
21.   ANS: C   PTS: 1   DIF: Moderate   OBJ: LO: 19-01| LO: 19-02
      NAT: BUSPROG: Analytic   KEY: Bloom's: Knowledge
22.   ANS: B   PTS: 1   DIF: Moderate   OBJ: LO: 19-01| LO: 19-02
      NAT: BUSPROG: Analytic   KEY: Bloom's: Knowledge

MULTIPLE CHOICE

1.   Which of the following are the two main types of cost accounting systems for manufacturing operations?
   a.   Process cost and general accounting systems
   b.   Job order cost and process cost systems
   c.   Job order and general accounting systems
   d.   Process cost and replacement cost systems

   ANS: B   PTS: 1   DIF: Easy   OBJ: LO: 19-01
   NAT: BUSPROG: Analytic   KEY: Bloom's: Knowledge

2.   Which of the following would most likely use a job order costing system?
   a.   A paper mill
   b.   A swimming pool installer
   c.   A company that manufactures chlorine for swimming pools
   d.   An oil refinery

   ANS: B   PTS: 1   DIF: Easy   OBJ: LO: 19-01
   NAT: BUSPROG: Analytic   KEY: Bloom's: Knowledge

3.   Which of the following would be most likely to use process costing?
   a.   A custom furniture manufacturer.
   b.   An auto body repair shop.

    c. A law firm
    d. A lawn fertilizer manufacturer.

ANS: D   PTS: 1   DIF: Easy   OBJ: LO: 19-01
NAT: BUSPROG: Analytic   KEY: Bloom's: Knowledge

4.   Which of the following systems provides for a separate record of the cost of each particular quantity of product that passes through the factory?
    a. Job order cost system
    b. General cost system
    c. Replacement cost system
    d. Process cost system

ANS: A   PTS: 1   DIF: Easy   OBJ: LO: 19-01
NAT: BUSPROG: Analytic   KEY: Bloom's: Knowledge

5.   For which of the following businesses would the job order cost system be appropriate?
    a. Meat processor
    b. Automobile manufacturer
    c. Oil refinery
    d. Construction contractor

ANS: D   PTS: 1   DIF: Moderate   OBJ: LO: 19-01
NAT: BUSPROG: Analytic   KEY: Bloom's: Knowledge

6.   For which of the following businesses would the process cost system be appropriate?
    a. Book retailer
    b. Dress designer
    c. Lumber mill
    d. Printing firm

ANS: C   PTS: 1   DIF: Moderate   OBJ: LO: 19-01
NAT: BUSPROG: Analytic   KEY: Bloom's: Knowledge

7.   Which of the following is *not* a characteristic of a job order costing system?
    a. It accumulates cost for each department within the factory.
    b. It provides a separate record for the cost of each quantity of product that passes through the factory.
    c. It is best suited for industries that manufactures custom goods.
    d. Uses only one work in process account.

ANS: A   PTS: 1   DIF: Easy   OBJ: LO: 19-01
NAT: BUSPROG: Analytic   KEY: Bloom's: Knowledge

8.   Which of the following products probably would be manufactured using a job order costing system?
    a. Number 2 pencils
    b. Computer monitors.
    c. Wedding invitations.
    d. Paper.

ANS: C   PTS: 1   DIF: Easy   OBJ: LO: 19-01
NAT: BUSPROG: Analytic   KEY: Bloom's: Knowledge

9. Job order costing and process costing are
    a. pricing systems.
    b. cost accounting systems.
    c. cost flow systems.
    d. inventory tracking systems.

    ANS: B   PTS: 1   DIF: Easy   OBJ: LO: 19-01
    NAT: BUSPROG: Analytic   KEY: Bloom's: Knowledge

10. Which of the following is not true about why a service firm will use the job order costing system?
    a. to help control costs
    b. to determine client billing
    c. to determine department costs within the firm
    d. to determine profit

    ANS: C   PTS: 1   DIF: Moderate   OBJ: LO: 19-01
    NAT: BUSPROG: Analytic   KEY: Bloom's: Knowledge

11. Which of the following costs are NOT included in finished goods inventory?
    a. Direct labor
    b. Factory overhead
    c. Company president's salary
    d. Direct materials

    ANS: C   PTS: 1   DIF: Easy   OBJ: LO: 19-02
    NAT: BUSPROG: Analytic   KEY: Bloom's: Knowledge

12. Which of the following is the correct flow of manufacturing costs?
    a. Raw materials, work in process, finished goods, cost of goods sold
    b. Raw materials, finished goods, cost of goods sold, work in process.
    c. Work in process, finished goods, raw materials, cost of goods sold
    d. Cost of goods sold, raw materials, work in process, finished goods.

    ANS: A   PTS: 1   DIF: Easy   OBJ: LO: 19-02
    NAT: BUSPROG: Analytic   KEY: Bloom's: Knowledge

13. Which of the following would record the labor costs to an individual job?
    a. Clock card
    b. In-and-out cards
    c. Time tickets
    d. Payroll register

    ANS: C   PTS: 1   DIF: Moderate   OBJ: LO: 19-02
    NAT: BUSPROG: Analytic   KEY: Bloom's: Knowledge

14. The Thomlin Company forecasts that total overhead for the current year will be $15,000,000 and that total machine hours will be 300,000 hours. Year to date, the actual overhead is $16,000,000 and the actual machine hours are 330,000 hours. If the Thomlin Company uses a predetermined overhead rate based on machine hours for applying overhead, what is that overhead rate?
    a. $48 per machine hour
    b. $53 per machine hour
    c. $45 per machine hour
    d. $50 per machine hour

ANS: D   PTS: 1   DIF: Moderate   OBJ: LO: 19-02
NAT: BUSPROG: Analytic   KEY: Bloom's: Application

15. The Thomlin Company forecasts that total overhead for the current year will be $15,000,000 and that total machine hours will be 300,000 hours. Year to date, the actual overhead is $16,000,000 and the actual machine hours are 330,000 hours. If the Thomlin Company uses a predetermined overhead rate based on machine hours for applying overhead, as of this point in time (year to date) the overhead is over/under applied by
    a. $1,000,000 overapplied
    b. $1,000,000 underapplied
    c. $500,000 overapplied
    d. $500,000 underapplied

ANS: C   PTS: 1   DIF: Moderate   OBJ: LO: 19-02
NAT: BUSPROG: Analytic   KEY: Bloom's: Application

16. At the end of the year, overhead applied was $35,000,000. Actual overhead was $34,300,000. Closing over/under applied overhead into cost of goods sold would cause net income to:
    a. Increase by $700,000
    b. Decrease by $700,000
    c. Remain constant
    d. Decrease by $300,000

ANS: A   PTS: 1   DIF: Moderate   OBJ: LO: 19-02
NAT: BUSPROG: Analytic   KEY: Bloom's: Knowledge

17. Which of the following would most likely be a period cost?
    a. Depreciation on factory lunchroom furniture.
    b. Salary of telephone receptionist in the sales office.
    c. Salary of a security guard for the factory parking lot.
    d. Computer chips used by a computer manufacturer.

ANS: B   PTS: 1   DIF: Moderate   OBJ: LO: 19-02
NAT: BUSPROG: Analytic   KEY: Bloom's: Knowledge

18. Which of the following would most likely be a product cost?
    a. Salary of VP of sales.
    b. Advertising for a particular product.
    c. Drill bits for a drill press used in the plant assembly area.
    d. Salary of the company receptionist.

ANS: C   PTS: 1   DIF: Moderate   OBJ: LO: 19-02
NAT: BUSPROG: Analytic   KEY: Bloom's: Knowledge

19. The document authorizing the issuance of materials from the storeroom is the:
    a. materials requisition
    b. purchase requisition
    c. receiving report
    d. purchase order

ANS: A   PTS: 1   DIF: Easy   OBJ: LO: 19-02
NAT: BUSPROG: Analytic   KEY: Bloom's: Knowledge

20. The source of the data for debiting Work-in-Process for direct materials is the:
    a. purchase order
    b. purchase requisition
    c. materials requisition
    d. receiving report

    ANS: C   PTS: 1   DIF: Moderate   OBJ: LO: 19-02
    NAT: BUSPROG: Analytic   KEY: Bloom's: Knowledge

21. In a job order cost accounting system, the entry to record the flow of direct materials into production is:
    a. debit Work in Process, credit Materials
    b. debit Materials, credit Work in Process
    c. debit Factory Overhead, credit Materials
    d. debit Work in Process, credit Supplies

    ANS: A   PTS: 1   DIF: Moderate   OBJ: LO: 19-02
    NAT: BUSPROG: Analytic   KEY: Bloom's: Knowledge

22. A summary of the materials requisitions completed during a period serves as the basis for transferring the cost of the materials from the controlling account in the general ledger to the controlling accounts for:
    a. work in process and cost of goods sold
    b. work in process and factory overhead
    c. finished goods and cost of goods sold
    d. work in process and finished goods

    ANS: B   PTS: 1   DIF: Challenging OBJ: LO: 19-02
    NAT: BUSPROG: Analytic   KEY: Bloom's: Knowledge

23. In a job order cost accounting system, when goods that have been ordered are received, the receiving department personnel count, inspect the goods, and complete a:
    a. purchase order
    b. sales invoice
    c. receiving report
    d. purchase requisition

    ANS: C   PTS: 1   DIF: Easy   OBJ: LO: 19-02
    NAT: BUSPROG: Analytic   KEY: Bloom's: Knowledge

24. The amount of time spent by each employee and the labor cost incurred for each individual job or for factory overhead are recorded on:
    a. pay stubs.
    b. in-and-out cards.
    c. time tickets.
    d. employees' earnings records.

    ANS: C   PTS: 1   DIF: Easy   OBJ: LO: 19-02
    NAT: BUSPROG: Analytic   KEY: Bloom's: Knowledge

25. The amount of time spent by an employee in the factory is usually recorded on:
    a. time tickets
    b. job order cost sheets

    c.   employees' earnings records
    d.   statement of owners' equity

ANS: A   PTS: 1   DIF: Easy   OBJ: LO: 19-02
NAT: BUSPROG: Analytic   KEY: Bloom's: Knowledge

26.   The basis for recording direct and indirect labor costs incurred is a summary of the period's:
    a.   job order cost sheets
    b.   time tickets
    c.   employees' earnings records
    d.   clock cards

ANS: B   PTS: 1   DIF: Easy   OBJ: LO: 19-02
NAT: BUSPROG: Analytic   KEY: Bloom's: Knowledge

27.   The entry to record the flow of direct labor costs into production in a job order cost accounting system is:
    a.   debit Factory Overhead, credit Work in Process
    b.   debit Finished Goods, credit Wages Payable
    c.   debit Work in Process, credit Wages Payable
    d.   debit Factory Overhead, credit Wages Payable

ANS: C   PTS: 1   DIF: Moderate   OBJ: LO: 19-02
NAT: BUSPROG: Analytic   KEY: Bloom's: Knowledge

28.   At the end of July, the first month of the current fiscal year, the factory overhead account had a debit balance. Which of the following describes the nature of this balance and how it would be reported on the interim balance sheet?
    a.   Overapplied, deferred credit
    b.   Underapplied, deferred debit
    c.   Underapplied, deferred credit
    d.   Overapplied, deferred debit

ANS: B   PTS: 1   DIF: Moderate   OBJ: LO: 19-02
NAT: BUSPROG: Analytic   KEY: Bloom's: Knowledge

29.   At the end of the fiscal year, the balance in Factory Overhead is small. This balance would normally be:
    a.   transferred to Work in Process
    b.   transferred to Cost of Goods Sold
    c.   transferred to Finished Goods
    d.   allocated between Work in Process and Finished Goods

ANS: B   PTS: 1   DIF: Easy   OBJ: LO: 19-02
NAT: BUSPROG: Analytic   KEY: Bloom's: Knowledge

30.   The details concerning the costs incurred on each job order are accumulated in a work in process account, which is supported by a:
    a.   stock ledger
    b.   materials ledger
    c.   cost ledger
    d.   creditors ledger

31. Each account in the cost ledger is called a:
    a. finished goods sheet
    b. stock record
    c. materials requisition
    d. job cost sheet

32. Selected accounts with some debits and credits omitted are presented as follows:

Work in Process

Aug. 1	Balance	275,000	Aug. 31	Goods finished	1,030,000
31	Direct materials	X			
31	Direct labor	450,000			
31	Factory overhead	X			

Factory Overhead

Aug. 1-31	Costs incurred	145,000	Aug. 1	Balance	15,000
			31	Applied (30% of direct labor cost)	X

If the balance of Work in Process at August 31 is $220,000, what was the amount debited to Work in Process for direct materials in August?
a. $390,000
b. $170,000
c. $525,000
d. $580,000

33. Selected accounts with some debits and credits omitted are presented as follows:

Work in Process

Aug. 1	Balance	275,000	Aug. 31	Goods finished	1,030,000
31	Direct materials	X			
31	Direct labor	450,000			
31	Factory overhead	X			

Factory Overhead

Aug. 1-31	Costs incurred	145,000	Aug. 1	Balance	15,000
			31	Applied	X

If the balance of Work in Process at August 31 is $220,000, what was the amount debited to Work in Process for factory overhead in August, assuming a factory overhead rate of 30% of direct labor costs?

a. $135,000
b. $10,000
c. $120,000
d. $70,000

ANS: A   PTS: 1   DIF: Moderate   OBJ: LO: 19-02
NAT: BUSPROG: Analytic   KEY: Bloom's: Application

34.   Selected accounts with some debits and credits omitted are presented as follows:

Work in Process

Oct. 1	Balance	20,000	Oct. 31	Goods finished	X
31	Direct materials	96,700			
31	Direct labor	201,000			
31	Factory overhead	X			

Finished Goods

Oct. 1	Balance	52,000		
31	Goods finished	360,000		

If the balance of Work in Process at October 31 is $21,000, what was the amount of factory overhead applied in October?
a. $63,300
b. $21,300
c. $42,300
d. $11,300

ANS: A   PTS: 1   DIF: Challenging   OBJ: LO: 19-02
NAT: BUSPROG: Analytic   KEY: Bloom's: Application

35.   Selected accounts with a credit amount omitted are presented as follows:

Work in Process

Apr. 1	Balance	7,000	Apr. 30	Goods finished	X
30	Direct materials	78,400			
30	Direct labor	195,000			
30	Factory overhead	136,500			

Finished Goods

Apr. 1	Balance	42,000		
30	Goods finished	387,000		

What was the balance of Work in Process as of April 30?
a. $8,100
b. $35,000
c. $29,900
d. $22,900

ANS: C   PTS: 1   DIF: Challenging   OBJ: LO: 19-02
NAT: BUSPROG: Analytic   KEY: Bloom's: Application

36. If the amount of factory overhead cost incurred exceeds the amount applied, the factory overhead account will have a:
    a. debit balance and be underapplied
    b. credit balance and be underapplied
    c. credit balance and be overapplied
    d. debit balance and be overapplied

    ANS: A   PTS: 1   DIF: Moderate   OBJ: LO: 19-02
    NAT: BUSPROG: Analytic   KEY: Bloom's: Knowledge

37. The recording of the factory labor incurred for general factory use would include a debit to:
    a. Factory Overhead
    b. Wages Payable
    c. Wages Expense
    d. Cost of Goods Sold

    ANS: A   PTS: 1   DIF: Moderate   OBJ: LO: 19-02
    NAT: BUSPROG: Analytic   KEY: Bloom's: Knowledge

38. The recording of the application of factory overhead costs to jobs would include a credit to:
    a. Factory Overhead
    b. Wages Payable
    c. Work in Process
    d. Cost of Goods Sold

    ANS: A   PTS: 1   DIF: Moderate   OBJ: LO: 19-02
    NAT: BUSPROG: Analytic   KEY: Bloom's: Knowledge

39. The recording of the jobs completed would include a debit to:
    a. Factory Overhead
    b. Finished Goods
    c. Work in Process
    d. Cost of Goods Sold

    ANS: B   PTS: 1   DIF: Moderate   OBJ: LO: 19-02
    NAT: BUSPROG: Analytic   KEY: Bloom's: Knowledge

40. The recording of the jobs completed would include a credit to:
    a. Factory Overhead
    b. Finished Goods
    c. Work in Process
    d. Cost of Goods Sold

    ANS: C   PTS: 1   DIF: Moderate   OBJ: LO: 19-02
    NAT: BUSPROG: Analytic   KEY: Bloom's: Knowledge

41. The recording of the jobs shipped and customers billed would include a debit to:
    a. Accounts Payable
    b. Cash
    c. Finished Goods
    d. Cost of Goods Sold

    ANS: D   PTS: 1   DIF: Moderate   OBJ: LO: 19-02
    NAT: BUSPROG: Analytic   KEY: Bloom's: Knowledge

42. The recording of the jobs shipped and customers billed would include a credit to:
     a. Accounts Payable
     b. Cash
     c. Finished Goods
     d. Cost of Goods Sold

     ANS: C   PTS: 1   DIF: Moderate   OBJ: LO: 19-02
     NAT: BUSPROG: Analytic   KEY: Bloom's: Knowledge

43. The finished goods account is the controlling account for the:
     a. cost ledger
     b. materials ledger
     c. work in process ledger
     d. stock ledger

     ANS: D   PTS: 1   DIF: Moderate   OBJ: LO: 19-02
     NAT: BUSPROG: Analytic   KEY: Bloom's: Knowledge

44. The controlling account for the cost ledger is:
     a. Finished Goods
     b. Materials
     c. Work in Process
     d. Cost of Goods Sold

     ANS: C   PTS: 1   DIF: Easy   OBJ: LO: 19-02
     NAT: BUSPROG: Analytic   KEY: Bloom's: Knowledge

45. Poobah Manufacturers Inc. has estimated total factory overhead costs of $95,000 and 10,000 direct labor hours for the current fiscal year. If job number 117 incurred 2,300 direct labor hours, the work in process account will be debited and factory overhead will be credited for:
     a. $21,850
     b. $2,300
     c. $95,000
     d. cannot be determined

     ANS: A   PTS: 1   DIF: Moderate   OBJ: LO: 19-02
     NAT: BUSPROG: Analytic   KEY: Bloom's: Application

46. A widely used activity base for developing factory overhead rates in highly automated settings is:
     a. direct labor hours
     b. direct labor dollars
     c. direct materials
     d. machine hours

     ANS: D   PTS: 1   DIF: Easy   OBJ: LO: 19-02
     NAT: BUSPROG: Analytic   KEY: Bloom's: Knowledge

47. When job 711 was completed, direct materials totaled $4,000; direct labor, $5,600; and factory overhead, $2,400 respectively. Units produced totaled 1,000. Unit costs are:
     a. $12,000
     b. $1,200
     c. $120
     d. $12

ANS: D   PTS: 1   DIF: Moderate   OBJ: LO: 19-02
NAT: BUSPROG: Analytic   KEY: Bloom's: Application

48.   The entries to record cost and sale of a finished good on account is:
       a.   debit Cost of Goods Sold, credit Finished Goods
       b.   debit Cost of Goods Sold, credit Finished Goods, debit Accounts Receivable, credit Sales
       c.   debit Sales Expense, credit Finished Goods, credit Cash, credit Accounts Receivable
       d.   debit Work in Process, credit Finished Goods, debit Accounts Receivable, credit Sales

       ANS: B   PTS: 1   DIF: Easy   OBJ: LO: 19-02
       NAT: BUSPROG: Analytic   KEY: Bloom's: Knowledge

49.   All of the following are examples of activity bases except:
       a.   salaries of supervisors
       b.   quality inspections of products
       c.   number of machine setups
       d.   raw materials storage

       ANS: A   PTS: 1   DIF: Easy   OBJ: LO: 19-02
       NAT: BUSPROG: Analytic   KEY: Bloom's: Knowledge

50.   Materials purchased on account during the month amounted to $180,000. Materials requisitioned
       and placed in production totaled $165,000. From the following, select the entry to record the
       transaction on the day the materials were bought.
       a.   Materials   165,000
              Accounts Payable   165,000
       b.   Materials   180,000
              Accounts Payable   180,000
       c.   Materials   180,000
              Cash   180,000
       d.   Accounts Payable   180,000
              Materials   180,000

       ANS: B   PTS: 1   DIF: Moderate   OBJ: LO: 19-02
       NAT: BUSPROG: Analytic   KEY: Bloom's: Knowledge

51.   Materials purchased on account during the month amounted to $180,000. Materials requisitioned
       and placed in production totaled $165,000. From the following, select the entry to record the
       transaction on the day the materials were requisitioned by the production department.
       a.   Materials   165,000
              Work in Process   165,000
       b.   Work in Process   180,000
              Materials   180,000
       c.   Work in Process   165,000
              Materials   165,000
       d.   Work in Process   165,000
              Cash   165,000

       ANS: C   PTS: 1   DIF: Moderate   OBJ: LO: 19-02
       NAT: BUSPROG: Analytic   KEY: Bloom's: Knowledge

52. During the period, labor costs incurred on account amounted to $275,000 including $200,000 for production orders and $75,000 for general factory use. In addition, factory overhead charged to production was $32,000. From the following, select the entry to record the direct labor costs.

a. Work in Process   200,000
      Wages Payable   200,000
b. Work in Process   275,000
      Wages Payable   275,000
c. Wages Payable   275,000
      Work in Process   275,000
d. Wages Payable   200,000
      Work in Process   200,000

ANS: A   PTS: 1   DIF: Moderate   OBJ: LO: 19-02
NAT: BUSPROG: Analytic   KEY: Bloom's: Knowledge

53. During the period, labor costs incurred on account amounted to $275,000 including $200,000 for production orders and $75,000 for general factory use. In addition, factory overhead applied to production was $32,000. From the following, select the entry to record the actual factory overhead costs incurred.

a. Accounts Payable   75,000
      Factory Overhead   75,000
b. Factory Overhead   32,000
      Accounts Payable   32,000
c. Work in Process   75,000
      Wages Payable   75,000
d. Factory Overhead   75,000
      Wages Payable   75,000

ANS: D   PTS: 1   DIF: Moderate   OBJ: LO: 19-02
NAT: BUSPROG: Analytic   KEY: Bloom's: Knowledge

54. During the period, labor costs incurred on account amounted to $275,000 including $200,000 for production orders and $75,000 for general factory use. In addition, factory overhead applied to production was $32,000. From the following, select the entry to record the factory overhead applied to production.

a. Work in Process   75,000
      Factory Overhead   75,000
b. Factory Overhead   32,000
      Work in Process   32,000
c. Work in Process   32,000
      Factory Overhead   32,000
d. Factory Overhead   75,000
      Accounts Payable   75,000

ANS: C   PTS: 1   DIF: Moderate   OBJ: LO: 19-02
NAT: BUSPROG: Analytic   KEY: Bloom's: Knowledge

55. The cost of production of completed and finished goods during the period amounted to $450,000, and the finished products shipped to customers had total production costs of $357,000. From the following, select the entry to record the transfer of costs from work in process to finished goods.

    a. Finished Goods   357,000
           Work in Process   357,000
    b. Finished Goods   450,000
           Work in Process   450,000
    c. Work in Process   450,000
           Finished Goods   450,000
    d. Work in Process   357,000
           Finished Goods   357,000

    ANS: B   PTS: 1   DIF: Moderate   OBJ: LO: 19-02
    NAT: BUSPROG: Analytic   KEY: Bloom's: Knowledge

56. The cost of production of completed and finished goods during the period amounted to $450,000, and the finished products shipped to customers had total production costs of $357,000. From the following, select the entry to record the transfer of costs from finished goods to cost of goods sold.

    a. Finished Goods   450,000
           Cost of Goods Sold   450,000
    b. Finished Goods   357,000
           Cost of Goods Sold   357,000
    c. Cost of Goods Sold   357,000
           Finished Goods   357,000
    d. Cost of Goods Sold   450,000
           Finished Goods   450,000

    ANS: C   PTS: 1   DIF: Moderate   OBJ: LO: 19-02
    NAT: BUSPROG: Analytic   KEY: Bloom's: Knowledge

57. Costs that are used in generating revenues during the current period, but are not involved in the manufacturing process are often referred to as:
    a. period costs
    b. conversion costs
    c. factory overhead costs
    d. product costs

    ANS: A   PTS: 1   DIF: Easy   OBJ: LO: 19-02
    NAT: BUSPROG: Analytic   KEY: Bloom's: Knowledge

58. Costs that are treated as assets until the product is sold are called:
    a. product costs
    b. period costs
    c. conversion costs
    d. selling expenses

    ANS: A   PTS: 1   DIF: Easy   OBJ: LO: 19-02
    NAT: BUSPROG: Analytic   KEY: Bloom's: Knowledge

59. The period costs of a textbook publisher would include:
    a. wages of a press operator
    b. factory utility costs

c. advertising expenses
d. paper costs

ANS: C   PTS: 1   DIF: Easy OBJ: LO: 19-02
NAT: BUSPROG: Analytic   KEY: Bloom's: Knowledge

60. Which types of inventories does a manufacturing business report on the balance sheet?
a. Finished goods inventory and work in process inventory
b. Direct materials inventory and work in process inventory
c. Direct materials inventory, work in process inventory, and finished goods inventory
d. Direct materials inventory and finished goods inventory

ANS: C   PTS: 1   DIF: Easy   OBJ: LO: 19-02
NAT: BUSPROG: Analytic   KEY: Bloom's: Knowledge

61. For the manufacturing business, inventory which is in the process of being manufactured is referred to as:
a. supplies inventory
b. work in process inventory
c. finished goods inventory
d. direct materials inventory

ANS: B   PTS: 1   DIF: Easy   OBJ: LO: 19-02
NAT: BUSPROG: Analytic   KEY: Bloom's: Knowledge

62. The proper journal entry to record the purchase of $30,000 of raw materials on account would be:

a. Raw Material Inventory   30,000
      Accounts Receivable   30,000
b. Raw Material Inventory   30,000
      Accounts Payable   30,000
c. Inventory   30,000
      Accounts Receivable   30,000
d. Inventory   30,000
      Cash   30,000

ANS: B   PTS: 1   DIF: Easy   OBJ: LO: 19-02
NAT: BUSPROG: Analytic   KEY: Bloom's: Knowledge

63. Select the proper journal entry to record the movement of 1,700 units of part number 116B to work in process when each unit of 116B has a value of $2.00.

a. Raw Material Inventory   3,400
      Work in Process   3,400
b. Work in Process   3,400
      Factory Overhead   3,400
c. Work in Process   3,400
      Raw Material Inventory   3,400
d. Work in Process   3,400
      Cash   3,400

ANS: C   PTS: 1   DIF: Moderate   OBJ: LO: 19-02
NAT: BUSPROG: Analytic   KEY: Bloom's: Knowledge

64. Which of the following represents the factory overhead applied to a product?
    a. Predetermined factory overhead rate times estimated activity base.
    b. Actual factory overhead rate times estimated activity base.
    c. Predetermined factory overhead rate times actual activity base.
    d. Actual factory overhead rate times actual activity base.

ANS: C   PTS: 1   DIF: Moderate   OBJ: LO: 19-02
NAT: BUSPROG: Analytic   KEY: Bloom's: Knowledge

65. Which of the following is the correct formula to calculate the predetermined factory overhead rate?
    a. Estimated total factory overhead costs divided by estimated activity base.
    b. Actual total factory overhead costs divided by estimated activity base.
    c. Estimated total factory overhead costs divided by actual activity base.
    d. Actual total factory overhead costs divided by actual activity base.

ANS: A   PTS: 1   DIF: Moderate   OBJ: LO: 19-02
NAT: BUSPROG: Analytic   KEY: Bloom's: Knowledge

66. The following budget data are available for Oldest Company:

    Estimated direct labor hours   12,000
    Estimated direct labor dollars $ 90,000
    Estimated factory overhead costs $198,000

    If factory overhead is to be applied based on direct labor hours, the predetermined overhead rate is
    a. $7.50
    b. $.13
    c. $.061
    d. $16.50

ANS: D   PTS: 1   DIF: Moderate   OBJ: LO: 19-02
NAT: BUSPROG: Analytic   KEY: Bloom's: Application

67. A manufacturing company applies factory overhead based on direct labor hours. At the beginning of the year, it estimated that factory overhead costs would be $360,000 and direct labor hours would be 30,000. Actual factory overhead costs incurred were $377,200, and actual direct labor hours were 36,000. What is the amount of overapplied or underapplied manufacturing overhead at the end of the year?
    a. $6,000 overapplied.
    b. $6,000 underapplied.
    c. $54,800 overapplied.
    d. $54,800 underapplied.

ANS: C   PTS: 1   DIF: Moderate   OBJ: LO: 19-02
NAT: BUSPROG: Analytic   KEY: Bloom's: Application

68. A manufacturing company applies factory overhead based on direct labor hours. At the beginning of the year, it estimated that factory overhead costs would be $360,000 and direct labor hours would be 30,000. Actual manufacturing overhead costs incurred were $377,200, and actual direct labor hours were 36,000. What is the predetermined overhead rate per direct labor hour?
    a. $12.00
    b. $10.00

c. $12.57
d. $10.48

ANS: A   PTS: 1   DIF: Moderate   OBJ: LO: 19-02
NAT: BUSPROG: Analytic   KEY: Bloom's: Application

69. A manufacturing company applies factory overhead based on direct labor hours. At the beginning of the year, it estimated that factory overhead costs would be $360,000 and direct labor hours would be 30,000. Actual manufacturing overhead costs incurred were $377,200, and actual direct labor hours were 36,000. The entry to apply the factory overhead costs for the year would include a
   a. debit to factory overhead for $360,000.
   b. credit to factory overhead for $432,000.
   c. debit to factory overhead for $377,200.
   d. credit to factory overhead for $360,000.

ANS: B   PTS: 1   DIF: Moderate   OBJ: LO: 19-02
NAT: BUSPROG: Analytic   KEY: Bloom's: Knowledge

70. Bar code scanners are now being used to track incoming materials and to electronically transmit this data. Scanners have replaced which of the following:
   a. receiving report
   b. materials requisition
   c. materials ledger
   d. job cost sheet

ANS: A   PTS: 1   DIF: Moderate   OBJ: LO: 19-02
NAT: BUSPROG: Analytic   KEY: Bloom's: Knowledge

71. A separate account for each material is found in a
   a. general ledger
   b. materials ledger
   c. receiving report
   d. job cost sheet

ANS: B   PTS: 1   DIF: Easy   OBJ: LO: 19-02
NAT: BUSPROG: Analytic   KEY: Bloom's: Knowledge

72. The materials requisition is used to
   a. release materials from the storeroom to the factory
   b. release finished goods to the shipping department
   c. record the acquisition of materials from a vendor
   d. record and electronically transmit materials data in place of a receiving report

ANS: A   PTS: 1   DIF: Moderate   OBJ: LO: 19-02
NAT: BUSPROG: Analytic   KEY: Bloom's: Knowledge

73. Period costs are
   a. found on the balance sheet.
   b. not involved in the production process.
   c. classified as direct labor, direct material, or factory overhead.
   d. found on the job order cost sheets.

ANS: B   PTS: 1   DIF: Easy   OBJ: LO: 19-02
NAT: BUSPROG: Analytic   KEY: Bloom's: Knowledge

74. Generally, period costs are classified as either
    a. selling expenses or production expenses.
    b. administrative expense or production expenses.
    c. selling expenses or administrative expenses.
    d. general expenses or selling expenses.

    ANS: C   PTS: 1   DIF: Moderate   OBJ: LO: 19-02
    NAT: BUSPROG: Analytic   KEY: Bloom's: Knowledge

75. The following are true regarding product costs except
    a. product costs are found on the balance sheet until they are sold.
    b. product costs consist of direct labor, direct materials, and factory overhead.
    c. product costs can be found in three accounts in the balance sheet.
    d. product costs include sales and administrative expenses.

    ANS: D   PTS: 1   DIF: Moderate   OBJ: LO: 19-02
    NAT: BUSPROG: Analytic   KEY: Bloom's: Knowledge

76. Job cost sheets can provide information to managers for all but the following:
    a. cost impact of materials changes
    b. cost impact of continuous improvement in the manufacturing process
    c. cost impact of materials price or direct labor rate changes over time
    d. utilities, managerial salaries, and depreciation of computers in the corporate office

    ANS: D   PTS: 1   DIF: Moderate   OBJ: LO: 19-03
    NAT: BUSPROG: Analytic   KEY: Bloom's: Knowledge

77. A difference in quantity of materials used on two comparable jobs may be caused by:
    a. inadequately trained employees
    b. poor quality materials
    c. employee carelessness
    d. all of the above

    ANS: D   PTS: 1   DIF: Moderate   OBJ: LO: 19-03
    NAT: BUSPROG: Analytic   KEY: Bloom's: Knowledge

78. Which of the following would probably not be found in the accounting system of a service provider?
    a. Cost ledger
    b. Finished jobs ledger
    c. Deferred revenue account
    d. Job cost sheets

    ANS: B   PTS: 1   DIF: Moderate   OBJ: LO: 19-04
    NAT: BUSPROG: Analytic   KEY: Bloom's: Knowledge

79. Which of the following entries would probably not be found on the books of a service provider?
    a. Debit Work in Process; credit Materials
    b. Debit Work in Process; credit Wages Payable
    c. Debit Work in Process; credit Overhead
    d. Debit Cost of Services; credit Work in Process

    ANS: A   PTS: 1   DIF: Moderate   OBJ: LO: 19-04
    NAT: BUSPROG: Analytic   KEY: Bloom's: Knowledge

80. In a job order cost accounting system used by a service business, which of the following items would normally not be included as part of overhead?
    a. Materials
    b. Direct labor
    c. Rent
    d. Supplies

    ANS: B   PTS: 1   DIF: Easy   OBJ: LO: 19-04
    NAT: BUSPROG: Analytic   KEY: Bloom's: Knowledge

81. The direct labor and overhead costs of providing services to clients are accumulated in:
    a. finished services expense
    b. work in process
    c. administrative salaries expense
    d. overhead

    ANS: B   PTS: 1   DIF: Easy   OBJ: LO: 19-04
    NAT: BUSPROG: Analytic   KEY: Bloom's: Knowledge

82. When a job is completed in a service organization, the job costs are transferred to the
    a. work in process account.
    b. cost of services account.
    c. finished goods account.
    d. cost of goods sold account.

    ANS: B   PTS: 1   DIF: Moderate   OBJ: LO: 19-04
    NAT: BUSPROG: Analytic   KEY: Bloom's: Knowledge

83. The following budget data are available for Happy Company:

Estimated direct labor hours	12,000
Estimated direct labor dollars	$ 90,000
Estimated factory overhead costs	$179,000
Actual direct labor hours	11,500
Actual direct labor dollars	$ 92,000
Actual factory overhead costs	$180,000

    If factory overhead is to be applied based on direct labor dollars, the predetermined overhead rate is
    a. 199%
    b. 196%
    c. $14.92
    d. $15.65

    ANS: A   PTS: 1   DIF: Moderate   OBJ: LO: 19-02
    NAT: BUSPROG: Analytic   KEY: Bloom's: Application

84. The following budget data are available for Happy Company:

Estimated direct labor hours	12,000
Estimated direct labor dollars	$ 90,000
Estimated factory overhead costs	$180,000
Actual direct labor hours	11,500
Actual direct labor dollars	$ 92,000
Actual factory overhead costs	$181,000

If factory overhead is to be applied based on direct labor hours as the cost allocation base for the predetermined overhead rate, the amount of overhead applied into production is
a. $180,000
b. $181,000
c. $172,500
d. $184,000

ANS: C   PTS: 1   DIF: Moderate   OBJ: LO: 19-02
NAT: BUSPROG: Analytic   KEY: Bloom's: Application

85.   Scooby Company has applied $567,988 of overhead into production on Jobs in the Work in Process account.   Actual overhead at the end of the year is $575,000.   What is the adjustment for over or underapplied overhead?
a. $7012 Overapplied, increase Cost of Goods Sold
b. $7012 Underapplied, increase Cost of Goods Sold
c. $7012 Overapplied, decrease Cost of Goods Sold
d. $7012 Underapplied, decrease Cost of Goods Sold

ANS: B   PTS: 1   DIF: Moderate   OBJ: LO: 19-02
NAT: BUSPROG: Analytic   KEY: Bloom's: Application

Zeke Company is a manufacturing company that has worked on several production jobs during the 1st quarter of the year.   Below is a list of all the jobs for the quarter:

	Balance
Job 356	$ 450
Job 357	$1,235
Job 358	$ 378
Job 359	$ 689
Job 360	$ 456

Job 356, 357, 358 & 359 were completed.   Jobs 356 & 357 were sold at a profit of $500 on each job.

86.   What is the ending balance of Work in Process for Zeke Company as of the end of the 1st quarter?
a. $0
b. $456
c. $3,208
d. $2,752

ANS: B   PTS: 1   DIF: Moderate   OBJ: LO: 19-02
NAT: BUSPROG: Analytic   KEY: Bloom's: Application

87.   What is the ending balance of Finished Goods for Zeke Company as of the end of the 1st quarter?
a. $456
b. $1,067
c. $1,685
d. $2,752

ANS: B   PTS: 1   DIF: Moderate   OBJ: LO: 19-02
NAT: BUSPROG: Analytic   KEY: Bloom's: Application

88.   What is the ending balance of Cost of Goods sold for Zeke Company as of the end of the 1st quarter?
a. $456
b. $2,685

c. $1,685
d. $685

ANS: C   PTS: 1   DIF: Moderate   OBJ: LO: 19-02
NAT: BUSPROG: Analytic   KEY: Bloom's: Application

89. What is Sales for Zeke Company as of the end of the 1st quarter?
   a. $1,685
   b. $2,685
   c. $1,000
   d. $685

ANS: B   PTS: 1   DIF: Moderate   OBJ: LO: 19-02
NAT: BUSPROG: Analytic   KEY: Bloom's: Application

90. What is Gross Margin for Zeke Company as of the end of the 1st quarter?
   a. $1,685
   b. $2,685
   c. $1,000
   d. $685

ANS: C   PTS: 1   DIF: Moderate   OBJ: LO: 19-02
NAT: BUSPROG: Analytic   KEY: Bloom's: Application

91. The Cavy Company estimates that the factory overhead for the following year will be $1,250,000. The company has decided that the basis for applying factory overhead should be machine hours, which is estimated to be 40,000 hours. The machine hours for the month of April for all of the jobs was 4,780. If the actual factory overhead totaled $141,800, determine the over or under applied amount for the month.
   a. $7,575 underapplied   c. $7,575 overapplied
   b. $35,220 underapplied   d. $35,220 overapplied

ANS: C   PTS: 1   DIF: Moderate   OBJ: LO: 19-02
NAT: BUSPROG: Analytic   KEY: Bloom's: Application

92. The Winston Company estimates that the factory overhead for the following year will be $1,250,000. The company has decided that the basis for applying factory overhead should be machine hours, which is estimated to be 50,000 hours. The total machine hours for the year was 54,300. The actual factory overhead for the year was $1,375,000. Determine the over or under applied amount for the year.

   a. $17,500 overapplied   c. $118,250 overapplied
   b. $17,500 underapplied   d. $118,250 underapplied

ANS: B   PTS: 1   DIF: Moderate   OBJ: LO: 19-02
NAT: BUSPROG: Analytic   KEY: Bloom's: Application

OTHER

1. Record in good journal entry format the following transactions:

   1. April 10, 400 units of raw materials were purchased at $5.50.
   2. April 15, 300 units of raw materials were requisitioned at $6.00 for production, Job 345.
   3. April 25, 200 units of raw materials were requisitioned at $5.50 for production, Job 555.

ANS:

April 10	Materials	2,200	
	Accounts payable		2,200
April 15	Work in process	1,800	
	Materials		1,800
April 25	Work in process	1,100	
	Materials		1,100

PTS: 1   DIF: Moderate   OBJ: LO: 19-02   NAT: BUSPROG: Analytic
KEY: Bloom's: Knowledge

2. The Cavy Company accumulated 560 hours of direct labor on Job 345 and 800 hours on Job 777. The direct labor was incurred at a rate of $20 per direct labor hour for Job 345 and $21 per direct labor for Job 777. Journalize the entry to record the flow of labor costs into production.

ANS:

Work in process	28,000	
Wages payable		28,000

(560 * $20) + (800 * $21) = $28,000

PTS: 1   DIF: Moderate   OBJ: LO: 19-02   NAT: BUSPROG: Analytic
KEY: Bloom's: Knowledge

3. During the month of April, Cavy Company incurred factory overhead as follows:

Indirect materials	$11,000
Factory Supervision Labor	$ 4,000
Utilities	$ 500
Depreciation (factory)	$ 700
Small tools	$ 300
Equipment rental	$ 750

Journalize the entry to record the factory overhead incurred during April.

ANS:

Factory overhead	17,250	
Materials		11,000
Wages payable		4,000
Utilities		500
Accumulated depreciation		700
Small tools		300
Equipment rental		750

PTS: 1 DIF: Moderate OBJ: LO: 19-02 NAT: BUSPROG: Analytic
KEY: Bloom's: Knowledge

4. Cavy Company estimates that total factory overhead costs will be $660,000 for the year. Direct labor hours are estimated to be 100,000. Determine (a) the predetermined factory overhead rate, (b) the amount of factory overhead applied to Job 345 if the amount of direct labor hours is 560 and Job 777 if the amount of direct labor hours is 800, and (c) prepare the journal entry to apply factory overhead in April according to the predetermined overhead rate.

ANS:
(a) $660,000 / 100,000 = $6.60

(b) Job 345: 560 hrs * $6.60 = $3,696
    Job 777: 800 hrs * $6.60 = $5,280

(c)

Work in process	8,976	
Factory overhead		8,976

PTS: 1 DIF: Moderate OBJ: LO: 19-02 NAT: BUSPROG: Analytic
KEY: Bloom's: Knowledge

5. The Cavy Company estimates that the factory overhead for the following year will be $1,470,000. The company has decided that the basis for applying factory overhead should be machine hours, which is estimated to be 40,000 hours. Calculate the predetermined overhead rate to apply factory overhead.

ANS:
$1,470,000 / 40,000 = $36.75 per machine hour

PTS: 1 DIF: Easy OBJ: LO: 19-02 NAT: BUSPROG: Analytic
KEY: Bloom's: Application

6. The Cavy Company estimates that the factory overhead for the following year will be $1,250,000. The company has decided that the basis for applying factory overhead should be machine hours, which is estimated to be 40,000 hours. The machine hours for the month of April for all of the jobs was 4,780. What is the amount that will be applied to all of the jobs for the month of April?

ANS:
4,780 hours * $31.25 = $149,375

PTS: 1   DIF: Moderate   OBJ: LO: 19-02   NAT: BUSPROG: Analytic
KEY: Bloom's: Application

7.   The Cavy Company estimates that the factory overhead for the following year will be $1,470,000.
     The company has decided that the basis for applying factory overhead should be machine hours,
     which is estimated to be 40,000 hours. The machine hours for the month of April for all of the jobs
     was 4,780. Prepare the journal entry to apply factory overhead.

ANS:

Work in Process	175,665	
Factory Overhead		175,665

PTS: 1   DIF: Moderate   OBJ: LO: 19-02   NAT: BUSPROG: Analytic
KEY: Bloom's: Knowledge

8.   At the end of April, Cavy Company had completed Job 766 and 765. According to the individual job
     cost sheets the information is as follows:

Job	Direct Materials	Direct Labor	Machine Hours
Job 765	$5,670	$3,500	27
Job 766	$8,900	$4,775	44

Job 765 produced 152 units, and Job 766 consisted of 250 units.

Assuming that the predetermined overhead rate is applied by using machine hours at a rate of $200
per hour, determine the (a) balance on the job cost sheets for each job, and (b) the cost per unit at the
end of April.

ANS:
a) Job 765 = $14,570 ($5,670 + $3,500 + (27 * $200)
   Job 766 = $22,475 ($8,900 + $4,775 + (44 * $200)

b) Job 765 = $95.86 ($14,570 / 152)
   Job 766 = $89.90 ($22,475 / 250)

PTS: 1   DIF: Moderate   OBJ: LO: 19-02   NAT: BUSPROG: Analytic
KEY: Bloom's: Application

9.   Cavy Company completed 26,000 units during the year at a cost of $2,139,800. The beginning
     finished goods inventory was 5,000 units at $405,000. Determine the cost of goods sold for 20,000
     units, assuming a FIFO cost flow.

ANS:
$405,000 + (15,000 * $82.30) = $1,639,500

PTS: 1   DIF: Moderate   OBJ: LO: 19-02   NAT: BUSPROG: Analytic
KEY: Bloom's: Application

10. The Cavy Company estimates that the factory overhead for the following year will be $1,250,000. The company has decided that the basis for applying factory overhead should be machine hours, which is estimated to be 40,000 hours. The machine hours for the month of April for all of the jobs was 4,780. If the actual factory overhead totaled $141,800, determine the over or under applied amount for the month.

ANS:
$141,800 − $149,375 = $7,575 overapplied

PTS: 1　　DIF: Moderate　　OBJ: LO: 19-02　　NAT: BUSPROG: Analytic
KEY: Bloom's: Application

11. The Winston Company estimates that the factory overhead for the following year will be $1,250,000. The company has decided that the basis for applying factory overhead should be machine hours, which is estimated to be 50,000 hours. The total machine hours for the year was 54,300. The actual factory overhead for the year was $1,375,000.

a) Determine the total factory overhead amount applied.

b) Calculate the over or under applied amount for the year.

c) Prepare the journal entry to close factory overhead into Cost of Goods Sold.

ANS:
a) 54,300 hours * $25 = $1,357,500

b) $1,375,000 actual − $1,357,500 applied = $17,500 underapplied

c)

Cost of goods sold	17,500	
Factory overhead		17,500

PTS: 1　　DIF: Moderate　　OBJ: LO: 19-02　　NAT: BUSPROG: Analytic
KEY: Bloom's: Application

12. The Winston Company estimates that the factory overhead for the following year will be $1,250,000. The company has decided that the basis for applying factory overhead should be machine hours, which is estimated to be 50,000 hours. The total machine hours for the year was 54,300. The actual factory overhead for the year was $1,348,800.

a) Determine the total factory overhead amount applied.

b) Calculate the over or under applied amount for the year.

c) Prepare the journal entry to close factory overhead into Cost of Goods Sold.

ANS:
a) 54,300 hours * $25 = $1,357,500

b) $1,348,800 actual − $1,357,500 applied = $8,700 overapplied

c)

Factory Overhead	8,700	
Cost of Goods Sold		8,700

PTS: 1   DIF: Moderate   OBJ: LO: 19-02   NAT: BUSPROG: Analytic
KEY: Bloom's: Application

13.   Cranston Company estimates the following overhead costs for the coming year:

Equipment depreciation	$160,000
Equipment maintenance	60,000
Supervisory salaries	40,000
Factory rent	100,000
Total	$360,000

Cranston is also budgeting $600,000 in direct labor costs and 15,000 machine hours for the coming year.

Required:

a.   Calculate the predetermined overhead rate using direct labor costs as the allocation base.

b.   Calculate the predetermined overhead rate using machine hours as the allocation base.

ANS:

a. $360,000 / $600,000 = $ 0.60 per direct labor dollar

b. $360,000 / 15,000 machine hours = $24.00 per machine hour

PTS: 1   DIF: Easy   OBJ: LO: 19-02   NAT: BUSPROG: Analytic
KEY: Bloom's: Application

14.   Flagler Company allocates overhead based on machine hours.   They estimated overhead costs for the year to be $420,000.   Estimated machine hours were 50,000.   Actual hours and costs for the year were 46,000 machine hours and $380,000 of overhead.

Required:

a.   Calculate the overhead application rate for the year.

b.   What is the amount of applied overhead for the year?

c.   What is the amount of under or overapplied overhead for the year? Indicate whether it is over- or underapplied.

ANS:
a. $420,000/50,000 = $8.40/machine hour

b. $8.40 × 46,000 = $386,400

c. $380,000 − $386,400 = $6,400 overapplied

PTS: 1   DIF: Moderate   OBJ: LO: 19-02   NAT: BUSPROG: Analytic
KEY: Bloom's: Application

15. The Tulsa Company allocates overhead based on a predetermined overhead rate of $9.00 per direct labor hour. Job S35 required 8 tons of direct material at a cost of $600.00 per ton and took employees who earn $21.00 per hour a total of 80 hours to complete. What is the total cost of Job S35?

ANS:

Direct materials	8 tons @ $600	$4,800
Direct labor	80 hours @ $21	1,680
Manufacturing overhead	80 hours @ $9	720
Total cost of S35		$7,200

PTS: 1   DIF: Easy   OBJ: LO: 19-03   NAT: BUSPROG: Analytic
KEY: Bloom's: Knowledge

16. Technics Inc., a manufacturing company, utilizes job order costing. Each division establishes its own estimates regarding overhead which are as follows:

	Division A	Division B
Total estimated overhead	$128,000	$261,000
Total estimated machine hours	16,000	72,500
Total estimated direct labor costs	$155,000	$290,000

Required:

If Division A allocates overhead on the basis of machine hours, and Division B allocates overhead as a percentage of direct labor costs, what would the predetermined overhead rate be for each division?

ANS:
$128,000 / 16,000 = $8 per machine hour

$261,000 / $290,000 = 90% of direct labor costs

PTS: 1   DIF: Easy   OBJ: LO: 19-02   NAT: BUSPROG: Analytic
KEY: Bloom's: Application

17. Crain Company budgeted 35,000 direct labor hours and incurred 40,000 direct labor hours. It incurred $780,000 of overhead and estimated overhead was $735,000.

What is Crain's predetermined overhead rate? Was overhead overapplied or underapplied for the year? By how much?

ANS:
Predetermined overhead rate: $735,000 / 35,000 = $21.00 per direct labor hour

Applied overhead: $21.00 × 40,000 =	$840,000
Actual overhead	$780,000
Overapplied overhead	$ 60,000

PTS: 1   DIF: Moderate   OBJ: LO: 19-02   NAT: BUSPROG: Analytic
KEY: Bloom's: Application

18. Define and discuss the two main types of cost accounting systems for manufacturing operations. What are their similarities and differences?

ANS:
The two main cost accounting systems are job order cost and process cost.

A job order cost system provides product costs for each quantity of product that is manufactured. Each quantity of product that is produced is called a job. This type of system is used by companies that manufacture custom products or batches of similar products.

A process cost system provides product costs for each manufacturing department or process. Process cost systems are used by companies that manufacture products that are indistinguishable from each other and manufactured using a continuous process.

They are similar in that both systems are widely used and a company may use both -- job order for some products and process costing for others.

PTS: 1   DIF: Moderate   OBJ: LO: 17-01   NAT: BUSPROG: Analytic
KEY: Bloom's: Knowledge

19. Discuss how job order cost information is used in decision making. What are some possible reasons that actual cost of materials would exceed expected costs for a job?

ANS:
Since a job order cost system provides product costs for each quantity of product that is manufactured, total and unit product costs can be compared to similar jobs or expected costs. Thus, a job order cost system can be used by managers for cost evaluation and control.

Possible reasons that actual material costs would exceed expected cost include: poorly trained employees, poor quality materials, faulty equipment or incorrect instructions.

PTS: 1   DIF: Moderate   OBJ: LO: 17-03   NAT: BUSPROG: Analytic
KEY: Bloom's: Knowledge

20. Discuss the use of job order costing for professional services businesses. What are the similarities and differences between service and manufacturing business job order costing?

ANS:
Professional service providers -- attorneys, physicians, advertising agencies, etc. - may use job order cost accounting systems. In such cases, clients are considered jobs.

Like manufacturers, direct labor and overhead costs for service companies are accumulated in work in process accounts. Unlike manufacturers, material cost for service companies are usually insignificant and treated as overhead. When a job is completed it is transferred to Cost of Services which is similar to Cost of Goods Sold. Service companies do not use Finished Goods accounts.

PTS: 1   DIF: Moderate   OBJ: LO: 17-04   NAT: BUSPROG: Analytic
KEY: Bloom's: Knowledge

PROBLEM

1.   ABC Printing Company uses a job order cost system.

    (a)   Indicate the source of the data for debiting Work in Process for each of the following:
        (1)   Direct materials requisitioned
        (2)   Direct labor used

    (b)   Indicate the source of the data for crediting Work in Process for jobs completed.

    (c)   Present a list of the three controlling accounts used in the general ledger to record the inventories and, in each case, indicate the related subsidiary ledger.

ANS:
    (a)   (1)   Summary of materials requisitions
        (2)   Summary of time tickets

    (b)   Summary of job cost sheets for jobs completed

    (c)

Controlling Account	Subsidiary Ledger
Materials	Materials ledger
Work in Process	Cost ledger
Finished Goods	Finished goods ledger (or stock ledger)

PTS: 1   DIF: Moderate   OBJ: LO: 19-02   NAT: BUSPROG: Analytic
KEY: Bloom's: Knowledge

2.   During June, the receipts and issuances of Material No. A2FO are as follows:

		Received
June 3	Balance	1,100 units at $15
16		1,700 units at $17
29		900 units at $18

	Issued
June 11	700 units for Job No. 116
18	1,900 units for Job No. 117
30	800 units for Job No. 118

    (a)   Determine the cost of each of the three issues under a perpetual system, using the first-in, first-out method.

    (b)   Present the journal entry to record the issuance of the materials for the month, assuming that the cost of issuances is determined by the first-in, first-out method.

ANS:

(a)	June 11	issue:	700 at $15	$10,500
	18	issue:	400 at $15 plus 1,500 at $17	31,500
	31	issue:	200 at $17 plus 600 at $18	14,200
				$56,200

(b)   Work in Process   56,200
          Materials   56,200

PTS: 1   DIF: Moderate   OBJ: LO: 19-02   NAT: BUSPROG: Analytic
KEY: Bloom's: Application

3.   A summary of the time tickets for August follows:

Description	Amount	Description	Amount
Job No. 321	$11,000	Job No. 342	$8,300
Job No. 329	9,200	Job No. 346	5,700
Job No. 336	5,000	Indirect labor	8,000

Present the journal entries to record (a) the labor cost incurred and (b) the application of factory overhead to production for August. The factory overhead rate is 70% of direct labor cost.

ANS:
(a)   Work in Process   39,200
          Factory Overhead   8,000
             Wages Payable   47,200

(b)   Work in Process   27,440
          Factory Overhead   27,440

PTS: 1   DIF: Moderate   OBJ: LO: 19-02   NAT: BUSPROG: Analytic
KEY: Bloom's: Knowledge

4.   The following account appears in the ledger after only part of the postings have been completed for July, the first month of the current fiscal year:

Work in Process	
Balance, July 1	60,200
Direct materials	147,000
Direct labor	120,000

Factory overhead is applied to jobs at the rate of 60% of direct labor cost. The actual factory overhead incurred for July was $75,000. Jobs completed during the month totaled $301,200.

(a)   Prepare the journal entries to record (1) the application of factory overhead to production during July and (2) the jobs completed during July.

(b)   What is the balance of the factory overhead account on July 31?

(c)   Was factory overhead overapplied or underapplied on July 31?

(d)   Determine the cost of the unfinished jobs on July 31.

ANS:

(a) (1)   Work in Process   72,000
               Factory Overhead   72,000

     (2)   Finished Goods   301,200
               Work in Process   301,200

(b) $3,000 debit

(c)   Underapplied

(d)   Total debits to Work in Process:

Balance, July 1	$ 60,200	
Direct materials	147,000	
Direct labor	120,000	
Factory overhead	72,000	$399,200
Less cost of goods finished during July		301,200
Balance, Work in Process, July 31 (cost of unfinished jobs)		$ 98,000

PTS: 1   DIF: Challenging   OBJ: LO: 19-02   NAT: BUSPROG: Analytic
KEY: Bloom's: Application

5.   Present entries to record the following summarized operations related to production for a company
     using a job order cost system:

(a)	Materials purchased on account	$167,000
(b)	Prepaid expenses incurred on account	12,200
(c)	Materials requisitioned:	
	For production orders	153,700
	For general factory use	2,700
(d)	Factory labor used:	
	On production orders	141,300
	For general factory purposes	12,000
(e)	Depreciation on factory equipment	37,000
(f)	Expiration of prepaid expenses, chargeable to factory	6,100
(g)	Factory overhead costs incurred on account	67,000
(h)	Factory overhead applied, based on machine hours	105,300
(i)	Jobs finished	415,300
(j)	Jobs shipped to customers: cost, $412,000; selling price	638,000

ANS:

(a)	Materials	167,000	
	Accounts Payable		167,000
(b)	Prepaid Expenses	12,200	
	Accounts Payable		12,200
(c)	Work in Process	153,700	
	Factory Overhead	2,700	
	Materials		156,400
(d)	Work in Process	141,300	
	Factory Overhead	12,000	
	Wages Payable		153,300
(e)	Factory Overhead	37,000	
	Accumulated Depreciation - Factory Equipment		37,000
(f)	Factory Overhead	6,100	
	Prepaid Expenses		6,100
(g)	Factory Overhead	67,000	
	Accounts Payable		67,000
(h)	Work in Process	105,300	
	Factory Overhead		105,300
(i)	Finished Goods	415,300	
	Work in Process		415,300
(j)	Cost of Goods Sold	412,000	
	Finished Goods		412,000
	Accounts Receivable	638,000	
	Sales		638,000

PTS: 1   DIF: Moderate   OBJ: LO: 19-02   NAT: BUSPROG: Analytic
KEY: Bloom's: Knowledge

6.   The balance of Material Q on May 1 and the receipts and issuances during May are as follows:

Balance May 1   8 at $32
Received May 11   23 at $33
Received May 25   15 at $35

Issued May 17   14
Issued May 27   18

Determine the cost of each of the issuances under a perpetual system, using the first-in, first-out method.

ANS:

May 17 issue:	8 at $32 plus 6 at $33	$454
May 27 issue:	17 at $33 plus 1 at $35	$596

PTS: 1   DIF: Easy   OBJ: LO: 19-02   NAT: BUSPROG: Analytic
KEY: Bloom's: Application

7.   Prepare the journal entry for materials and labor, based on the following:

Raw materials issued:	$ 850	for Job 609
	600	for general use in the factory
Labor time tickets:	$1,600	for Job 609
	400	for supervision

ANS:

Work in Process	850	
Factory Overhead	600	
Raw Materials		1,450
Work in Process	1,600	
Factory Overhead	400	
Wages Payable		2,000

PTS: 1   DIF: Easy   OBJ: LO: 19-02   NAT: BUSPROG: Analytic
KEY: Bloom's: Application

8.   Six selected transactions for the current month are indicated by letters in the following T accounts in a job order cost accounting system:

Materials		Work in Process	
	(a)	(a)	(d)
		(b)	
		(c)	
Wages Payable		(f)	
	(b)		
Factory Overhead		**Finished Goods**	
(a)	(c)	(d)	(e)
(b)	(f)	(f)	
Cost of Goods Sold			
(e)			
(f)			

Describe each of the six transactions.

ANS:
(a)   Direct and indirect materials are issued.
(b)   Direct and indirect labor costs are incurred.
(c)   Factory overhead is applied.

(d) Completed goods are transferred to finished goods.

(e) Goods are sold.

(f) Underapplied overhead is allocated.

PTS: 1   DIF: Moderate   OBJ: LO: 19-02   NAT: BUSPROG: Analytic
KEY: Bloom's: Application

9. On January 2nd, Newsprint Manufacturing purchases 5 rolls of paper on account at $125.00 per roll
    for use within the production process. On January 5th 4 rolls of this paper are issued to Job 010507A
    in the Printing Department. The Printing Department records $675.00 in direct labor and $1,150.00
    of factory overhead to Job 010507A. On January 8th Printing transfers Job 010507A to the Folding
    Department. The folding department applies $450.00 in direct labor and $655.00 in factory
    overhead to Job 010507A. Job 010507A is transferred to Finished Goods Inventory on January 9th.

    (a) Journalize the purchasing of the paper to Raw Materials Inventory.

    (b) Journalize the transfer of raw materials to work in process, the application of direct
         labor, and the application of manufacturing overhead to Job 010507A while in the
         Printing Department.

    (c) Journalize the transfer of Job 010507A to the Folding Department at actual cost.

    (d) Journalize the application of direct labor, and the application of manufacturing
         overhead to Job 010507A while in the Folding Department.

    (e) Journalize the transfer of Job 010507A to Finished Goods Inventory at actual cost.

ANS:

(a) Jan 2nd	Raw Materials	625.00	
	Accounts Payable		625.00
(b) Jan 5th	Work in Process - Job 010507A - Printing	500.00	
	Raw Materials		500.00
Jan 5th	Work in Process - Job 010507A - Printing	675.00	
	Wages Payable		675.00
Jan 5th	Work in Process - Job 010507A - Printing	1,150.00	
	Factory Overhead		1,150.00
(c) Jan 8th	Work in Process - Job 010507A - Folding	2,325.00	
	Work in Process - Job 010507A - Printing		2,325.00
(d) Jan 8th	Work in Process - Job 010507A - Folding	450.00	
	Wages Payable		450.00
Jan 8th	Work in Process - Job 010507A - Folding	655.00	
	Factory Overhead		655.00
(e) Jan 9th	Finished Goods	3,430.00	
	Work in Process - Job 010507A - Folding		3,430.00

PTS: 1   DIF: Easy   OBJ: LO: 19-02   NAT: BUSPROG: Analytic
KEY: Bloom's: Knowledge

10. The Stamping Department accepted Job 051507A on May 15th to make 1,000 funnels.

To complete the job they requisitioned 1,100 sheets at $1.20 per sheet and 1,150 grommets at $0.15 per set.

The cost driver that the Stamping Department uses is drop-forge strokes which are counted on a machine mounted counter. $2.25 is applied as overhead for each drop-forge stroke. Additionally $375.00 of overhead is applied to each job due to setup and teardown.

Direct labor is applied at $22.50 per hour for the machine operator and $11.10 for the machine loader. The job required 6 1/2 hours of labor by the team.

When the job was complete Job 051507A was transferred to Semi-finished Goods Inventory (SFGI). When the job was transferred, 20 sheets were returned unused to raw material inventory, 75 grommet sets were returned, and there were 1,115 strokes on the counter.

Journalize all events depicted as of May 15th.

ANS:

May 15th	WIP - Job 051507A ($1,320.00 + $172.50)	1,492.50	
	Raw Material		1,492.50
May 15th	WIP - Job 051507A	375.00	
	WIP - Job 051507A (1,115 × $2.25)	2,508.75	
	Mfg Overhead		2,883.75
May 15th	WIP - Job 051507A (($22.50 + $11.10) × 6.5 hrs)	218.40	
	Wages Payable		218.40
May 15th	SFGI	4,559.40	
	Raw Materials ($24.00 + 11.25)	35.25	
	WIP - Job 051507A		4,594.65

PTS: 1   DIF: Challenging   OBJ: LO: 19-02   NAT: BUSPROG: Analytic
KEY: Bloom's: Knowledge

11. On November 14th the Milling Department has accepted Job 111407A for 1,000 pounds of Cereal Mix. The bill of materials (BOM) for the Cereal Mix is:

Material:	Standard Qty:	Standard Cost:
Oats	525 pounds	$1.25 per pound
Wheat	450 pounds	$1.15 per pound
Barley	85 pounds	$1.45 per pound
Malt	65 pounds	$2.15 per pound
Honey	25 quarts	$1.20 per quart
Water	25 gallons	$0.45 per gallon
Time:		
Miller	4 1/2 hours	$22.75 per hour
Loader	1 1/2 hours	$11.50 per hour

Manufacturing overhead is applied at $5.75 per pound completed, and $75.75 of materials are returned to Raw Materials Inventory. The recipe produced 1,025 pounds of cereal mix.

(a)   Write the journal entry to transfer raw materials to Job 111407A.

(b)   Write the journal entry to provide labor to Job 111407A.

(c)   Write the journal entry to return 50 pounds oats, 5 pounds of barley, and 5 quarts of honey back to raw materials inventory.

(d)   Write the journal entry to apply manufacturing overhead to Job 111407A.

(e)   Write the journal entry to transfer Job 111407A to finished goods on November 14th.

ANS:

(a) Nov 14th WIP - Job 111407A   1,478.00
                    Raw Materials   1,478.00

(525*$1.25) + (450*$1.15) + (85*$1.45) + (65*$2.15) + (25*$1.20) + (25*$0.45) = $1,478

(b) Nov 14th WIP - Job 111407A   119.63
                    Wages Payable or Wages Expense   119.63

(4.5*$22.75) + (1.5*$11.50) = $119.63

(c) Nov 14th Raw Materials   75.75
                    WIP - Job 111407A   75.75

(50*$1.25) + (5*$1.45) + (5*$1.20) = $75.75

(d) Nov 14th WIP - Job 111407A   5,893.75
                    Mfg Overhead   5,893.75

(1,025*$5.75)=$5,893.75)

(e) Nov 14th Finished Goods   7,415.63
                    WIP - Job 111407A   7,415.63

$1,478.00 + $119.63 − $75.75 +$5,893.75 =$7,415.63

PTS: 1   DIF: Challenging   OBJ: LO: 19-02   NAT: BUSPROG: Analytic
KEY: Bloom's: Knowledge

12.   Put the following in the order of the flow of manufacturing costs for a company
      a. Closing under/over applied factory overhead to cost of goods sold
      b. Materials purchased
      c. Factory labor used and factory overhead incurred in production
      d. Completed jobs moved to finished goods
      e. Factory overhead applied to jobs according to the predetermined overhead rate
      f. Materials requisitioned to jobs
      g. Selling of finished product
      h. Preparation of financial statements to determine gross profit

ANS:
b. Materials purchased
f. Materials requisitioned to jobs
c. Factory labor used and factory overhead incurred in production
e. Factory overhead applied to jobs according to the predetermined overhead rate
d. Completed jobs moved to finished goods
a. Closing under/over applied factory overhead to cost of goods sold
g. Selling of finished product
h. Preparation of financial statements to determine gross profit

PTS: 1 DIF: Moderate OBJ: LO: 19-02 NAT: BUSPROG: Analytic
KEY: Bloom's: Knowledge

13. The following is a list of costs incurred by several business organizations:

(a) Telephone cable for a telephone company.
(b) Subscription to a health club for executives.
(c) Salary of the Director of Internal Auditing.
(d) Long-distance telephone bill for calls made by salespersons.
(e) Carrying cases for a manufacturer of video camcorders.
(f) Cotton for a textile manufacturer of blue jeans.
(g) Bandages for the emergency room of a hospital.
(h) Cost of company holiday party.
(i) Electricity used to operate factory machinery.
(j) State unemployment compensation taxes for factory workers.
(k) Gloves for factory machine operators.
(l) Fees paid for lawn service for office grounds.
(m) Salary of secretary to vice-president of finance.
(n) Salary of secretary to vice-president of marketing.
(o) Production supervisor's salary.
(p) Engine oil for manufacturer and distributor of motorcycles.
(q) Oil lubricants for factory plant and equipment.
(r) Cost of a radio commercial.
(s) Depreciation on factory equipment.
(t) Wages of check-out clerk in company-owned retail outlet.
(u) Maintenance and repair costs for factory equipment.
(v) Depreciation on office equipment.
(w) Bonuses paid to salespersons.
(x) Insurance on factory building.
(y) Training for accounting personnel on use of microcomputer.
(z) Steel for a construction contractor.

Classify each of the preceding costs as product costs or period costs. For those costs classified as product costs, indicate whether the product cost is a direct materials cost, direct labor cost, or factory overhead cost. For those costs classified as period costs, indicate whether the period cost is a selling expense or an administrative expense. Use the following tabular headings for preparing your answer. Place an X in the appropriate column.

	Product Cost			Period Cost	
Cost	Direct Materials Cost	Direct Labor Cost	Factory Overhead Cost	Selling Expense	Administrative Expense

ANS:

	Product Cost			Period Cost	
Cost	Direct Materials Cost	Direct Labor Cost	Factory Overhead Cost	Selling Expense	Administrative Expense
(a)	X				
(b)					X
(c)					X
(d)				X	
(e)	X				
(f)	X				
(g)	X				
(h)					X
(i)			X		
(j)		X			
(k)			X		
(l)					X
(m)					X
(n)				X	
(o)			X		
(p)	X				
(q)			X		
(r)				X	
(s)			X		
(t)				X	
(u)			X		
(v)					X
(w)				X	
(x)			X		
(y)					X
(z)	X				

PTS: 1   DIF: Moderate   OBJ: LO: 19-03 | LO: 19-02
NAT: BUSPROG: Analytic   KEY: Bloom's: Knowledge

14.   List the accounts used in the cost flow for (a) a manufacturer and (b) a service provider.

ANS:
(a)   Materials
       Wages Payable
       Factory Overhead
       Work in Process
       Finished Goods
       Cost of Goods Sold

(b)   Supplies
       Wages Payable
       Overhead
       Work in Process
       Cost of Services

PTS: 1   DIF: Moderate   OBJ: LO: 19-02 | LO: 19-04
NAT: BUSPROG: Analytic   KEY: Bloom's: Knowledge

15. At the end of the period, Carson Company had the following balances in selected accounts:

Raw Materials Inventory	$ 80,000
Finished Goods	190,000
Work in Process Inventory	70,000
Cost of Goods Sold	1,000,000
Factory Overhead	30,000

Required:

a. Assuming the factory overhead balance is relatively small, prepare the journal entry to close the Factory Overhead account if the balance in the account is a debit balance. What does a debit balance mean?

b. Assuming the factory overhead balance is relatively small, prepare the journal entry to close the Factory Overhead account if the balance in the account is a credit balance. What does a credit balance mean?

ANS:

a.   Cost of Goods Sold   30,000
                 Factory Overhead   30,000

This means underapplied overhead in the factory overhead account.

b.   Factory Overhead   30,000
                 Cost of Goods Sold   30,000

This means overapplied overhead in the factory overhead account.

PTS: 1   DIF: Moderate   OBJ: LO: 19-02   NAT: BUSPROG: Analytic
KEY: Bloom's: Knowledge

TRUE/FALSE

1. Process cost systems use job order cost cards to accumulate cost data.

    ANS: F   PTS: 1   DIF: Easy   OBJ: LO: 20-01
    NAT: BUSPROG: Analytic   KEY: Bloom's: Knowledge

2. Both process and job order cost systems maintain perpetual inventory accounts with subsidiary ledgers.

    ANS: T   PTS: 1   DIF: Easy   OBJ: LO: 20-01
    NAT: BUSPROG: Analytic   KEY: Bloom's: Knowledge

3. If the principal products of a manufacturing process are identical, a process cost system is more appropriate than a job order cost system.

    ANS: T   PTS: 1   DIF: Easy   OBJ: LO: 20-01
    NAT: BUSPROG: Analytic   KEY: Bloom's: Knowledge

4. If the products of a manufacturing process are produced to customer specifications, a process cost system is more appropriate than a job order cost system.

    ANS: F   PTS: 1   DIF: Easy   OBJ: LO: 20-01
    NAT: BUSPROG: Analytic   KEY: Bloom's: Knowledge

5. Process manufacturers typically use large machines to process a continuous flow of raw materials into a finished state.

    ANS: T   PTS: 1   DIF: Easy   OBJ: LO: 20-01
    NAT: BUSPROG: Analytic   KEY: Bloom's: Knowledge

6. Industries that typically use process cost systems include chemicals, oil, metals, food, paper, and pharmaceuticals.

    ANS: T   PTS: 1   DIF: Easy   OBJ: LO: 20-01
    NAT: BUSPROG: Analytic   KEY: Bloom's: Knowledge

7. In a process cost system, product costs are accumulated by processing department rather than by job.

    ANS: T   PTS: 1   DIF: Easy   OBJ: LO: 20-01
    NAT: BUSPROG: Analytic   KEY: Bloom's: Knowledge

8. Conversion costs include materials, direct labor, and factory overhead.

    ANS: F   PTS: 1   DIF: Easy   OBJ: LO: 20-01
    NAT: BUSPROG: Analytic   KEY: Bloom's: Knowledge

9. The direct materials costs and direct labor costs incurred by a production department are referred to as conversion costs.

   ANS: F   PTS: 1   DIF: Easy   OBJ: LO: 20-01
   NAT: BUSPROG: Analytic   KEY: Bloom's: Knowledge

10. The direct labor costs and factory overhead costs incurred by a production department are referred to as conversion costs.

    ANS: T   PTS: 1   DIF: Easy   OBJ: LO: 20-01
    NAT: BUSPROG: Analytic   KEY: Bloom's: Knowledge

11. The first step in determining the cost of goods completed and ending inventory valuation using process costing is to calculate equivalent units of production.

    ANS: F   PTS: 1   DIF: Easy   OBJ: LO: 20-02
    NAT: BUSPROG: Analytic   KEY: Bloom's: Knowledge

12. Conversion costs are usually incurred evenly throughout a process.

    ANS: T   PTS: 1   DIF: Easy   OBJ: LO: 20-02
    NAT: BUSPROG: Analytic   KEY: Bloom's: Knowledge

13. Equivalent units of production are the number of units that could have been manufactured from start to finish during an accounting period.

    ANS: T   PTS: 1   DIF: Easy   OBJ: LO: 20-02
    NAT: BUSPROG: Analytic   KEY: Bloom's: Knowledge

14. Both job order and process cost accounting use equivalent units of production to determine costs.

    ANS: F   PTS: 1   DIF: Easy   OBJ: LO: 20-02
    NAT: BUSPROG: Analytic   KEY: Bloom's: Knowledge

15. If 30,000 units of materials enter production during the first year of operations, 25,000 of the units are finished, and 5,000 are 50% completed, the number of equivalent units of production would be 28,500.

    ANS: F   PTS: 1   DIF: Moderate   OBJ: LO: 20-02
    NAT: BUSPROG: Analytic   KEY: Bloom's: Application

16. If 16,000 units of materials enter production during the first year of operations, 12,000 of the units are finished, and 4,000 are 75% completed, the number of equivalent units of production would be 15,000.

    ANS: T   PTS: 1   DIF: Moderate   OBJ: LO: 20-02
    NAT: BUSPROG: Analytic   KEY: Bloom's: Application

17. If the costs for direct materials, direct labor, and factory overhead were $277,300, $52,600, and $61,000, respectively, for 14,000 equivalent units of production, the total conversion cost was $390,900.

ANS: F   PTS: 1   DIF: Moderate   OBJ: LO: 20-02
NAT: BUSPROG: Analytic   KEY: Bloom's: Application

18. If the costs for direct materials, direct labor, and factory overhead were $60,000, $35,000, and $25,000, respectively, for 20,000 equivalent units of production, the conversion cost per equivalent unit was $6.

ANS: F   PTS: 1   DIF: Moderate   OBJ: LO: 20-02
NAT: BUSPROG: Analytic   KEY: Bloom's: Application

19. If the costs for direct materials, direct labor, and factory overhead were $522,200, $82,700, and $45,300, respectively, for 16,000 equivalent units of production, the conversion cost per equivalent unit was $8.00.

ANS: T   PTS: 1   DIF: Moderate   OBJ: LO: 20-02
NAT: BUSPROG: Analytic   KEY: Bloom's: Application

20. If 10,000 units which were 50% completed are in process at November 1, 90,000 units were completed during November, and 20,000 were 20% completed at November 30, the number of equivalent units of production for November was 90,000. (Assume no loss of units in production and that inventories are costed by the first-in, first-out method.)

ANS: F   PTS: 1   DIF: Challenging   OBJ: LO: 20-02
NAT: BUSPROG: Analytic   KEY: Bloom's: Application

21. If 10,000 units which were 40% completed are in process at November 1, 80,000 units were completed during November, and 12,000 were 20% completed at November 30, the number of equivalent units of production for November was 75,600. (Assume no loss of units in production and that inventories are costed by the first-in, first-out method.)

ANS: F   PTS: 1   DIF: Challenging   OBJ: LO: 20-02
NAT: BUSPROG: Analytic   KEY: Bloom's: Application

22. In applying the first-in, first-out method of costing inventories, if 8,000 units which are 30% completed are in process at June 1, 28,000 units are completed during June, and 4,000 units were 75% completed at June 30, the number of equivalent units of production for June was 33,400.

ANS: F   PTS: 1   DIF: Challenging   OBJ: LO: 20-02
NAT: BUSPROG: Analytic   KEY: Bloom's: Application

23. In applying the first-in, first-out method of costing inventories, if 8,000 units which are 30% completed are in process at June 1, 28,000 units are completed during June, and 4,000 units were 80% completed at June 30, the number of equivalent units of production for June was 28,600.

ANS: F   PTS: 1   DIF: Challenging   OBJ: LO: 20-02
NAT: BUSPROG: Analytic   KEY: Bloom's: Application

24.   The cost of production report reports the cost of the goods sold.

      ANS: F   PTS: 1   DIF: Easy   OBJ: LO: 20-02
      NAT: BUSPROG: Analytic   KEY: Bloom's: Knowledge

25.   The cost of production report reports the cost charged to production and the costs allocated to
      finished goods and work in process.

      ANS: T   PTS: 1   DIF: Easy   OBJ: LO: 20-02
      NAT: BUSPROG: Analytic   KEY: Bloom's: Knowledge

26.   The cost of production report summarizes (1) the units for which the department is accountable and
      the units to be assigned costs and (2) the costs charged to the department and the allocation of those
      costs.

      ANS: T   PTS: 1   DIF: Easy   OBJ: LO: 20-02
      NAT: BUSPROG: Analytic   KEY: Bloom's: Knowledge

27.   The amount journalized showing the cost added to finished goods is taken from the cost of
      production report.

      ANS: T   PTS: 1   DIF: Easy   OBJ: LO: 20-02
      NAT: BUSPROG: Analytic   KEY: Bloom's: Knowledge

28.   One of the differences in accounting for a process costing system compared to a job order system is
      that the amounts used to transfer goods from one department to the next comes from the cost of
      production report instead of job cost cards.

      ANS: T   PTS: 1   DIF: Easy   OBJ: LO: 20-02
      NAT: BUSPROG: Analytic   KEY: Bloom's: Knowledge

29.   One of the primary uses of a cost of production report is to assist management in controlling
      production costs.

      ANS: T   PTS: 1   DIF: Easy   OBJ: LO: 20-02
      NAT: BUSPROG: Analytic   KEY: Bloom's: Knowledge

30.   Yield measures the ratio of the materials output quantity to the materials input quantity.

      ANS: T   PTS: 1   DIF: Easy   OBJ: LO: 20-04
      NAT: BUSPROG: Analytic   KEY: Bloom's: Knowledge

31.   Companies recognizing the need to simultaneously produce products with high quality, low cost,
      and instant availability have adopted a just-in-time processing philosophy.

      ANS: T   PTS: 1   DIF: Easy   OBJ: LO: 20-05
      NAT: BUSPROG: Analytic   KEY: Bloom's: Knowledge

32.   In a just-in-time system, processing functions are combined into work centers, sometimes called
      departments.

      ANS: F   PTS: 1   DIF: Easy   OBJ: LO: 20-05
      NAT: BUSPROG: Analytic   KEY: Bloom's: Knowledge

33. The FIFO method of process costing is simpler than the Average cost method.

ANS: F   PTS: 1   DIF: Easy   OBJ: 20-APP
NAT: BUSPROG: Analytic   KEY: Bloom's: Knowledge

34. Companies that use the average costing method for process costing have unit costs that include costs from more that one accounting period.

ANS: T   PTS: 1   DIF: Easy   OBJ: 20-APP
NAT: BUSPROG: Analytic   KEY: Bloom's: Knowledge

35. If a company uses average costing instead of FIFO they will still get the same unit costs.

ANS: F   PTS: 1   DIF: Easy   OBJ: 20-APP
NAT: BUSPROG: Analytic   KEY: Bloom's: Knowledge

36. The closer a company moves towards Just in Time production, the differences in unit costs between average costing and FIFO will be reduced.

ANS: T   PTS: 1   DIF: Moderate   OBJ: 20-APP
NAT: BUSPROG: Analytic   KEY: Bloom's: Knowledge

37. Custom-made goods would be accounted for using a process costing system.

ANS: F   PTS: 1   DIF: Easy   OBJ: LO: 20-01
NAT: BUSPROG: Analytic   KEY: Bloom's: Knowledge

38. In a process costing system, a separate work in process inventory account is maintained for each customer's job.

ANS: F   PTS: 1   DIF: Easy   OBJ: LO: 20-01
NAT: BUSPROG: Analytic   KEY: Bloom's: Knowledge

39. Direct materials, direct labor, and factory overhead are assigned to each manufacturing process in a process costing system.

ANS: T   PTS: 1   DIF: Easy   OBJ: LO: 20-01
NAT: BUSPROG: Analytic   KEY: Bloom's: Knowledge

40. In a process costing system, costs flow into finished goods inventory only from the work in process inventory of the last manufacturing process.

ANS: T   PTS: 1   DIF: Moderate   OBJ: LO: 20-02
NAT: BUSPROG: Analytic   KEY: Bloom's: Knowledge

41. Equivalent units are the sum of direct materials used and direct labor incurred.

ANS: F   PTS: 1   DIF: Easy   OBJ: LO: 20-01
NAT: BUSPROG: Analytic   KEY: Bloom's: Knowledge

42. Conversion costs are generally added evenly throughout the process.

    ANS: T   PTS: 1   DIF: Easy   OBJ: LO: 20-02
    NAT: BUSPROG: Analytic   KEY: Bloom's: Knowledge

43. Equivalent units should be computed separately for direct materials and conversion costs.

    ANS: T   PTS: 1   DIF: Easy   OBJ: LO: 20-02
    NAT: BUSPROG: Analytic   KEY: Bloom's: Knowledge

44. Costs are transferred, along with the units, from one work in process inventory account to the next in a process costing system.

    ANS: T   PTS: 1   DIF: Moderate   OBJ: LO: 20-02
    NAT: BUSPROG: Analytic   KEY: Bloom's: Knowledge

45. In a process costing system, each process will have a work in process inventory account.

    ANS: T   PTS: 1   DIF: Easy   OBJ: LO: 20-01
    NAT: BUSPROG: Analytic   KEY: Bloom's: Knowledge

46. In a process costing system, the cost per equivalent unit is computed before computing equivalent units.

    ANS: F   PTS: 1   DIF: Easy   OBJ: LO: 20-02
    NAT: BUSPROG: Analytic   KEY: Bloom's: Knowledge

47. Costs of ending work in process inventory are included in the cost per equivalent unit computation.

    ANS: T   PTS: 1   DIF: Moderate   OBJ: LO: 20-02
    NAT: BUSPROG: Analytic   KEY: Bloom's: Knowledge

48. Conversion and direct materials are generally both added at the end of the production process.

    ANS: F   PTS: 1   DIF: Moderate   OBJ: LO: 20-02
    NAT: BUSPROG: Analytic   KEY: Bloom's: Knowledge

49. Gilbert Corporation had 25,000 finished units and 8,000 units were 35% complete.   The equivalent units totaled 30,200.

    ANS: F   PTS: 1   DIF: Moderate   OBJ: LO: 20-02
    NAT: BUSPROG: Analytic   KEY: Bloom's: Application

50. The entry to transfer goods in process from Department X to Department Y includes a debit to Work in Process-Department X.

    ANS: F   PTS: 1   DIF: Moderate   OBJ: LO: 20-03
    NAT: BUSPROG: Analytic   KEY: Bloom's: Knowledge

51. Process manufacturing usually reflects a manufacturer that produces small quantities of unique items.

    ANS: F   PTS: 1   DIF: Easy   OBJ: LO: 20-01
    NAT: BUSPROG: Analytic   KEY: Bloom's: Knowledge

52. Equivalent units of production are always the same as the total number of physical units finished during the period.

ANS: F   PTS: 1   DIF: Moderate   OBJ: LO: 20-02
NAT: BUSPROG: Analytic   KEY: Bloom's: Knowledge

53. The last step in the accounting procedure for process costing is the calculation of equivalent units of production.

ANS: F   PTS: 1   DIF: Moderate   OBJ: LO: 20-02
NAT: BUSPROG: Analytic   KEY: Bloom's: Knowledge

54. The FIFO method separates work done on beginning inventory in the previous period from work done on it in the current period.

ANS: T   PTS: 1   DIF: Moderate   OBJ: LO: 20-02
NAT: BUSPROG: Analytic   KEY: Bloom's: Knowledge

55. When a process cost accounting system records the purchase of materials, the Materials account is credited.

ANS: F   PTS: 1   DIF: Moderate   OBJ: LO: 20-03
NAT: BUSPROG: Analytic   KEY: Bloom's: Knowledge

56. In a process costing system, indirect materials are charged to Work in Process.

ANS: F   PTS: 1   DIF: Moderate   OBJ: LO: 20-03
NAT: BUSPROG: Analytic   KEY: Bloom's: Knowledge

57. A process cost accounting system records all actual factory overhead costs directly in the Work in Process account.

ANS: F   PTS: 1   DIF: Moderate   OBJ: LO: 20-03
NAT: BUSPROG: Analytic   KEY: Bloom's: Knowledge

58. Once equivalent units are calculated for materials, this number will also be used for direct labor and factory overhead.

ANS: F   PTS: 1   DIF: Moderate   OBJ: LO: 20-02
NAT: BUSPROG: Analytic   KEY: Bloom's: Knowledge

59. If a department that applies FIFO process costing starts the reporting period with 50,000 physical units that were 25% complete with respect to direct materials and 40% complete with respect to conversion, it must add 12,500 equivalent units of direct materials and 20,000 equivalent units to direct labor to complete them.

ANS: F   PTS: 1   DIF: Moderate   OBJ: LO: 20-02
NAT: BUSPROG: Analytic   KEY: Bloom's: Application

60. All costs of the processes in a process costing system ultimately pass through the Cost of Goods
     Sold account.

     ANS: T   PTS: 1   DIF: Moderate   OBJ: LO: 20-03
     NAT: BUSPROG: Analytic   KEY: Bloom's: Knowledge

MULTIPLE CHOICE

1. For which of the following businesses would a process cost system be appropriate?
    a. Auto repair service
    b. Paint manufacturer
    c. Specialty printer
    d. Custom furniture manufacturer

    ANS: B   PTS: 1   DIF: Easy   OBJ: LO: 20-01
    NAT: BUSPROG: Analytic   KEY: Bloom's: Knowledge

2. Which of the following is NOT a way in which process and job order cost systems are similar?
    a. Both accumulate product costs--direct materials, direct labor, and factory overhead
    b. Both allocate product cost to units produced
    c. Both maintain perpetual inventories
    d. Both use job order cost cards

    ANS: D   PTS: 1   DIF: Easy   OBJ: LO: 20-01
    NAT: BUSPROG: Analytic   KEY: Bloom's: Knowledge

3. The cost system best suited to industries that manufacture a large number of identical units of
    commodities on a continuous basis is:
    a. process
    b. departmental
    c. first-in, first-out
    d. job order

    ANS: A   PTS: 1   DIF: Easy   OBJ: LO: 20-01
    NAT: BUSPROG: Analytic   KEY: Bloom's: Knowledge

4. In a process cost system, the amount of work in process inventory is valued by:
    a. finding the sum of all open job costs
    b. allocating departmental costs between completed and partially completed units
    c. multiplying units in ending inventory by the direct materials cost per unit
    d. all of the above

    ANS: B   PTS: 1   DIF: Moderate   OBJ: LO: 20-01
    NAT: BUSPROG: Analytic   KEY: Bloom's: Knowledge

5. In process cost accounting, the costs of direct materials and direct labor are charged directly to:
    a. service departments
    b. processing departments
    c. customer accounts receivable
    d. job orders

    ANS: B   PTS: 1   DIF: Easy   OBJ: LO: 20-01
    NAT: BUSPROG: Analytic   KEY: Bloom's: Knowledge

6. The two categories of cost comprising conversion costs are:
   a. direct labor and indirect labor
   b. direct labor and factory overhead
   c. factory overhead and direct materials
   d. direct labor and direct materials

   ANS: B   PTS: 1   DIF: Easy   OBJ: LO: 20-01
   NAT: BUSPROG: Analytic   KEY: Bloom's: Knowledge

7. In a process cost system, the cost of completed production in Department A is transferred to Department B by which of the following entries?
   a. Debit Work in Process--Dept. B; credit Work in Process--Dept. A.
   b. Debit Work in Process--Dept. B; credit Finished Goods--Dept. A.
   c. Debit Work in Process--Dept. B; credit Cost of Goods Sold--Dept. A.
   d. Debit Finished Goods; credit Work in Process--Dept. B.

   ANS: A   PTS: 1   DIF: Easy   OBJ: LO: 20-01
   NAT: BUSPROG: Analytic   KEY: Bloom's: Knowledge

8. The three categories of manufacturing costs comprising the cost of work in process are direct labor, direct materials, and:
   a. office expenses
   b. direct expenses
   c. sales salaries expense
   d. factory overhead

   ANS: D   PTS: 1   DIF: Easy   OBJ: LO: 20-01
   NAT: BUSPROG: Analytic   KEY: Bloom's: Knowledge

9. For which of the following businesses would a process cost system be appropriate?
   a. An oil refinery
   b. Yacht builder
   c. Specialty furniture company
   d. Custom electronics manufacturer

   ANS: A   PTS: 1   DIF: Easy   OBJ: LO: 20-01
   NAT: BUSPROG: Analytic   KEY: Bloom's: Knowledge

10. Which of the following is not characteristic of a process cost system?
    a. The system may use several work in process inventory accounts.
    b. Manufacturing costs are grouped by department rather than by jobs.
    c. The system accumulates costs per job.
    d. The system emphasizes time periods rather than the time it takes to complete a job.

    ANS: C   PTS: 1   DIF: Easy   OBJ: LO: 20-01
    NAT: BUSPROG: Analytic   KEY: Bloom's: Knowledge

11. Which of the following entities would probably use a process costing system?
    a. A custom boat builder
    b. A custom furniture manufacturer
    c. A one of a kind jewelry creator
    d. An oil refinery.

    ANS: D   PTS: 1   DIF: Easy   OBJ: LO: 20-01
    NAT: BUSPROG: Analytic   KEY: Bloom's: Knowledge

12. Which of the following is *not* a characteristic of a process cost system?
    a. Manufacturing costs are grouped by departments.
    b. The system may use several Work-in-Process accounts.
    c. The system measures costs for each completed job.
    d. The system allocates costs between completed and partially completed units within a department.

    ANS: C   PTS: 1   DIF: Easy   OBJ: LO: 20-01
    NAT: BUSPROG: Analytic   KEY: Bloom's: Knowledge

13. If a company uses a process costing system to account for the costs in its four production departments, how many Work-in-Process will it use?
    a. 3
    b. 4
    c. 1
    d. 2

    ANS: B   PTS: 1   DIF: Easy   OBJ: LO: 20-01
    NAT: BUSPROG: Analytic   KEY: Bloom's: Knowledge

14. The four steps necessary to determine the cost of goods completed and the ending inventory valuation in a process cost system are:

    1. allocate costs to transferred and partially completed units
    2. determine the units to be assigned costs
    3. determine the cost per equivalent unit
    4. calculate equivalent units of production

    The correct ordering of the steps is:
    a. 2, 4, 3, 1
    b. 4, 2, 3, 1
    c. 2, 3, 4, 1
    d. 2, 3, 1, 4

    ANS: A   PTS: 1   DIF: Easy   OBJ: LO: 20-02
    NAT: BUSPROG: Analytic   KEY: Bloom's: Knowledge

15. Which of the following costs incurred by a paper manufacturer would be included in the group of costs referred to as conversion costs?
    a. Advertising costs
    b. Raw lumber (direct materials)
    c. Machine operator's wages (direct labor)
    d. Sales salaries

    ANS: C   PTS: 1   DIF: Easy   OBJ: LO: 20-02
    NAT: BUSPROG: Analytic   KEY: Bloom's: Knowledge

16. Which of the following costs incurred by a paper manufacturer would NOT be included in the group of costs referred to as conversion costs?
    a. Factory supervisor's salary
    b. Machine operator's wages (direct labor)
    c. Raw lumber (direct materials)
    d. Factory maintenance personnel supplies

ANS: C   PTS: 1   DIF: Easy   OBJ: LO: 20-02
NAT: BUSPROG: Analytic   KEY: Bloom's: Knowledge

17. In the manufacture of 15,000 units of a product, direct materials cost incurred was $165,000, direct labor cost incurred was $105,000, and applied factory overhead was $53,500. What is the total conversion cost?
    a. $270,000
    b. $158,500
    c. $323,500
    d. $53,500

ANS: B   PTS: 1   DIF: Easy   OBJ: LO: 20-02
NAT: BUSPROG: Analytic   KEY: Bloom's: Application

18. If Department H had 600 units, 60% completed, in process at the beginning of the period, 6,000 units were completed during the period, and 700 units were 30% completed at the end of the period, what was the number of equivalent units of production for conversion costs for the period, if the first-in, first-out method is used to cost inventories?
    a. 7,300
    b. 5,640
    c. 6,700
    d. 5,850

ANS: D   PTS: 1   DIF: Moderate   OBJ: LO: 20-02
NAT: BUSPROG: Analytic   KEY: Bloom's: Application

19. If Department K had 2,000 units, 40% completed, in process at the beginning of the period, 12,000 units were completed during the period, and 1,200 units were 25% completed at the end of the period, what was the number of equivalent units of production for conversion costs for the period if the first-in, first-out method is used to cost inventories?
    a. 11,500
    b. 11,200
    c. 15,200
    d. 10,000

ANS: A   PTS: 1   DIF: Moderate   OBJ: LO: 20-02
NAT: BUSPROG: Analytic   KEY: Bloom's: Application

Department G had 3,600 units, 25% completed at the beginning of the period, 11,000 units were completed during the period, 3,000 units were one-fifth completed at the end of the period, and the following manufacturing costs were debited to the departmental work in process account during the period:

Work in process, beginning of period	$40,000
Costs added during period:	
Direct materials (10,400 at $8)	83,200
Direct labor	63,000
Factory overhead	25,000

20. Assuming that all direct materials are placed in process at the beginning of production and that the first-in, first-out method of inventory costing is used, what is the total cost of the departmental work in process inventory at the end of the period (round unit cost calculations to four decimal places)?
   a. $16,163
   b. $21,432
   c. $35,670
   d. $28,935

ANS: D   PTS: 1   DIF: Challenging   OBJ: LO: 20-02
NAT: BUSPROG: Analytic   KEY: Bloom's: Application

21. Assuming that all direct materials are placed in process at the beginning of production and that the first-in, first-out method of inventory costing is used, what is the total cost of 3,600 units of beginning inventory which were completed during the period (round unit cost calculations to four decimal places)?
   a. $62,206
   b. $16,163
   c. $40,000
   d. $19,275

ANS: A   PTS: 1   DIF: Challenging   OBJ: LO: 20-02
NAT: BUSPROG: Analytic   KEY: Bloom's: Application

22. Assuming that all direct materials are placed in process at the beginning of production and that the first-in, first-out method of inventory costing is used, what is the total cost of the units "started and completed" during the period (round unit cost calculations to four decimal places)?
   a. $211,200
   b. $120,060
   c. $190,275
   d. $20,934

ANS: B   PTS: 1   DIF: Challenging   OBJ: LO: 20-02
NAT: BUSPROG: Analytic   KEY: Bloom's: Application

23. Department R had 5,000 units in work in process that were 75% completed as to labor and overhead at the beginning of the period, 30,000 units of direct materials were added during the period, 32,000 units were completed during the period, and 3,000 units were 40% completed as to labor and overhead at the end of the period. All materials are added at the beginning of the process. The first-in, first-out method is used to cost inventories. The number of equivalent units of production for conversion costs for the period was:
   a. 32,450
   b. 29,450
   c. 31,950
   d. 26,000

ANS: B   PTS: 1   DIF: Moderate   OBJ: LO: 20-02
NAT: BUSPROG: Analytic   KEY: Bloom's: Application

Department S had no work in process at the beginning of the period. 12,000 units of direct materials were added during the period at a cost of $84,000, 9,000 units were completed during the period, and 3,000 units were 30% completed as to labor and overhead at the end of the period. All materials are added at the beginning of the process. Direct labor was $49,500 and factory overhead was $9,900.

24. The total conversion costs for the period were:
   a. $59,400
   b. $49,500
   c. $143,400
   d. $9,900

ANS: A   PTS: 1   DIF: Easy   OBJ: LO: 20-02
NAT: BUSPROG: Analytic   KEY: Bloom's: Application

25. The total cost of units completed during the period were:
   a. $117,000
   b. $143,400
   c. $121,000
   d. $127,450

ANS: A   PTS: 1   DIF: Challenging   OBJ: LO: 20-02
NAT: BUSPROG: Analytic   KEY: Bloom's: Application

26. The following production data were taken from the records of the Finishing Department for June:

Inventory in process, 6-1, 25% completed	1,500 units
Transferred to finished goods during June	5,000 units
Equivalent units of production during June	5,200 units

Determine the number of equivalent units of production in the June 30 Finishing Department inventory, assuming that the first-in, first-out method is used to cost inventories. Assume the completion percentage of 25% applies to both direct materials and conversion costs.
   a. 575 units
   b. 200 units
   c. 1,000 units
   d. 300 units

ANS: A   PTS: 1   DIF: Challenging   OBJ: LO: 20-02
NAT: BUSPROG: Analytic   KEY: Bloom's: Application

27. The debits to Work in Process--Assembly Department for April, together with data concerning production, are as follows:

April 1, work in process:	
Materials cost, 3,000 units	$ 8,000
Conversion costs, 3,000 units, 66.7% completed	6,000
Materials added during April, 10,000 units	30,000
Conversion costs during April	31,000
Goods finished during April, 11,500 units	---
April 30 work in process, 1,500 units, 50% completed	---

All direct materials are placed in process at the beginning of the process and the first-in, first-out method is used to cost inventories. The materials cost per equivalent unit for April is:
a. $3.00
b. $3.80
c. $2.92
d. $2.31

ANS: A   PTS: 1   DIF: Moderate   OBJ: LO: 20-02
NAT: BUSPROG: Analytic   KEY: Bloom's: Application

28. Department E had 4,000 units in Work in Process that were 40% completed at the beginning of the period at a cost of $12,500. 14,000 units of direct materials were added during the period at a cost of $28,700. 15,000 units were completed during the period, and 3,000 units were 75% completed at the end of the period. All materials are added at the beginning of the process. Direct labor was $32,450 and factory overhead was $18,710. The number of equivalent units of production for the period for conversion if the first-in, first-out method is used to cost inventories was:
a. 15,650
b. 14,850
c. 14,150
d. 14,650

ANS: A   PTS: 1   DIF: Moderate   OBJ: LO: 20-02
NAT: BUSPROG: Analytic   KEY: Bloom's: Application

29. Department A had 1,000 units in Work in Process that were 60% completed at the beginning of the period at a cost of $7,000. 4,000 units of direct materials were added during the period at a cost of $8,200. 4,500 units were completed during the period, and 500 units were 40% completed at the end of the period. All materials are added at the beginning of the process. Direct labor was $28,700 and factory overhead was $4,510. The cost of the 500 units in process at the end of the period if the first-in, first-out method is used to cost inventories was:
a. $3,240
b. $5,175
c. $2,569
d. $2,645

ANS: D   PTS: 1   DIF: Challenging   OBJ: LO: 20-02
NAT: BUSPROG: Analytic   KEY: Bloom's: Application

30. In the manufacture of 10,000 units of a product, direct materials cost incurred was $145,800, direct labor cost incurred was $82,000, and applied factory overhead was $45,500. What is the total conversion cost?
a. $127,500
b. $145,800
c. $272,200
d. $273,300

ANS: A   PTS: 1   DIF: Easy   OBJ: LO: 20-02
NAT: BUSPROG: Analytic   KEY: Bloom's: Application

31. If Department H had 600 units, 60% completed, in process at the beginning of the period, 8,000 units were completed during the period, and 500 units were 30% completed at the end of the period, what was the number of equivalent units of production for the period for conversion if the first-in, first-out method is used to cost inventories? Assume the completion percentage applies to both direct materials and conversion cost.
    a. 7,790
    b. 8,390
    c. 8,600
    d. 8,000

    ANS: A   PTS: 1   DIF: Moderate   OBJ: LO: 20-02
    NAT: BUSPROG: Analytic   KEY: Bloom's: Application

32. If Department K had 2,500 units, 45% completed, in process at the beginning of the period, 15,000 units were completed during the period, and 1,200 units were 40% completed at the end of the period, what was the number of equivalent units of production for the period for conversion if the first-in, first-out method is used to cost inventories? Assume the completion percentage applies to both direct materials and conversion cost.
    a. 16,855
    b. 16,605
    c. 13,460
    d. 14,355

    ANS: D   PTS: 1   DIF: Moderate   OBJ: LO: 20-02
    NAT: BUSPROG: Analytic   KEY: Bloom's: Application

Department A had 4,000 units in work in process that were 60% completed as to labor and overhead at the beginning of the period, 29,000 units of direct materials were added during the period, 31,000 units were completed during the period, and 2,000 units were 80% completed as to labor and overhead at the end of the period. All materials are added at the beginning of the process. The first-in, first-out method is used to cost inventories.

33. The number of equivalent units of production for conversion costs for the period was:
    a. 30,200
    b. 29,800
    c. 33,800
    d. 33,000

    ANS: A   PTS: 1   DIF: Moderate   OBJ: LO: 20-02
    NAT: BUSPROG: Analytic   KEY: Bloom's: Application

34. The number of equivalent units of production for material costs for the period was:
    a. 33,000
    b. 29,800
    c. 29,000
    d. 32,000

    ANS: C   PTS: 1   DIF: Moderate   OBJ: LO: 20-02
    NAT: BUSPROG: Analytic   KEY: Bloom's: Application

The following production data were taken from the records of the Finishing Department for June:

Inventory in process, 6-1 (30% completed)	4,000 units
Completed units during June	65,000 units
Ending inventory (60% complete)	7,000 units

35. Determine the number of conversion equivalent units of production in the June 30 Finishing Department inventory, assuming that the first-in, first-out method is used to cost inventories.
    a. 68,000 units
    b. 70,400 units
    c. 66,200 units
    d. 4,200 units

    ANS: A   PTS: 1   DIF: Moderate   OBJ: LO: 20-02
    NAT: BUSPROG: Analytic   KEY: Bloom's: Application

36. Determine the number of material equivalent units of production in the June 30 Finishing Department inventory, assuming that the first-in, first-out method is used to cost inventories and materials were added at the beginning of the process.
    a. 7,000 units
    b. 68,000 units
    c. 72,000 units
    d. 76,000 units

    ANS: B   PTS: 1   DIF: Moderate   OBJ: LO: 20-02
    NAT: BUSPROG: Analytic   KEY: Bloom's: Application

37. The debits to Work in Process--Assembly Department for April, together with data concerning production, are as follows:

April 1, work in process:	
Materials cost, 3,000 units	$ 7,200
Conversion costs, 3,000 units,	
60% completed	6,000
Materials added during April, 10,000 units	25,000
Conversion costs during April	35,750
Goods finished during April, 12,000 units	---
April 30 work in process, 1,000 units,	
40% completed	---

    All direct materials are placed in process at the beginning of the process and the first-in, first-out method is used to cost inventories. The materials cost per equivalent unit for April is:
    a. $2.48
    b. $2.08
    c. $2.50
    d. $5.25

    ANS: C   PTS: 1   DIF: Challenging   OBJ: LO: 20-02
    NAT: BUSPROG: Analytic   KEY: Bloom's: Application

38. The debits to Work in Process--Assembly Department for April, together with data concerning production, are as follows:

April 1, work in process:
  Materials cost, 3,000 units $ 7,200
  Conversion costs, 3,000 units,
    40% completed 6,000
Materials added during April, 10,000 units 25,000
Conversion costs during April 30,800
Goods finished during April, 12,000 units ---
April 30 work in process, 1,000 units,
  40% completed ---

All direct materials are placed in process at the beginning of the process and the first-in, first-out method is used to cost inventories. The conversion cost per equivalent unit for April is:
a. $2.48
b. $2.75
c. $2.50
d. $5.25

ANS: B   PTS: 1   DIF: Moderate   OBJ: LO: 20-02
NAT: BUSPROG: Analytic   KEY: Bloom's: Application

Department B had 3,000 units in Work in Process that were 25% completed at the beginning of the period at a cost of $12,500. 13,700 units of direct materials were added during the period at a cost of $28,700. 15,000 units were completed during the period, and 1,700 units were 95% completed at the end of the period. All materials are added at the beginning of the process. Direct labor was $32,450 and factory overhead was $18,710.

39. The number of equivalent units of production for the period for conversion if the first-in, first-out method is used to cost inventories was:
a. 14,365
b. 13,615
c. 12,000
d. 15,865

ANS: D   PTS: 1   DIF: Moderate   OBJ: LO: 20-02
NAT: BUSPROG: Analytic   KEY: Bloom's: Application

40. The number of equivalent units of production for the period for materials if the first-in, first-out method is used to cost inventories was:
a. 16,700
b. 12,000
c. 1,700
d. 13,700

ANS: D   PTS: 1   DIF: Moderate   OBJ: LO: 20-02
NAT: BUSPROG: Analytic   KEY: Bloom's: Application

The following unit data were assembled for the assembly process of the Super Co. for the month of June. Direct materials are added at the beginning of the process. Conversion costs are added uniformly over the production process. The company uses the FIFO process.

	Units
Beginning work in process (60% complete)	5,000
Units started in September	48,000
Ending work in process (30% complete)	4,000

41. The number of equivalent units produced with respect to conversion costs is:
   a. 50,200
   b. 48,000
   c. 53,000
   d. 47,200

   ANS: D   PTS: 1   DIF: Moderate   OBJ: LO: 20-02
   NAT: BUSPROG: Analytic   KEY: Bloom's: Application

42. The number of equivalent units produced with respect to direct materials costs is:
   a. 48,000
   b. 49,000
   c. 43,000
   d. 53,000

   ANS: A   PTS: 1   DIF: Moderate   OBJ: LO: 20-02
   NAT: BUSPROG: Analytic   KEY: Bloom's: Application

Carmelita Inc., has the following information available:

	Costs from Beginning Inventory	Costs from Current Period
Direct materials	$2,500	$22,252
Conversion Costs	6,200	150,536

43. At the beginning of the period, there were 500 units in process that were 60 percent complete as to conversion costs and 100 percent complete as to direct materials costs. During the period 4,500 units were started and completed. Ending inventory contained 340 units that were 30 percent complete as to conversion costs and 100 percent complete as to materials costs. (Assume that the company uses the FIFO process cost method.)

   The equivalent units of production for direct materials and conversion costs, respectively, were
   a. 5,340 for direct materials and 4,902 for conversion costs.
   b. 4,840 for direct materials and 4,802 for conversion costs.
   c. 4,602 for direct materials and 4,802 for conversion costs.
   d. 4,902 for direct materials and 4,802 for conversion costs.

   ANS: B   PTS: 1   DIF: Moderate   OBJ: LO: 20-02
   NAT: BUSPROG: Analytic   KEY: Bloom's: Application

44. At the beginning of the period, there were 500 units in process that were 60 percent complete as to conversion costs and 100 percent complete as to direct materials costs. During the period 4,500 units were started and completed. Ending inventory contained 340 units that were 30 percent complete as to conversion costs and 100 percent complete as to materials costs. (Assume that the company uses the FIFO process cost method.)

The cost of completing a unit during the current period was
a. $36.19
b. $34.88
c. $35.95
d. $35.89

ANS: C   PTS: 1   DIF: Challenging   OBJ: LO: 20-02
NAT: BUSPROG: Analytic   KEY: Bloom's: Application

45. At the beginning of the period, there were 500 units in process that were 60 percent complete as to conversion costs and 100 percent complete as to direct materials costs. During the period 4,500 units were started and completed. Ending inventory contained 340 units that were 30 percent complete as to conversion costs and 100 percent complete as to materials costs. (Assume that the company uses the FIFO process cost method.   Round cost per unit figures to two cents, i.e. $2.22 when calculating total costs.)

The total costs that will be transferred into Finished Goods for units started and completed were
a. $161,775
b. $156,960
c. $162,855
d. $161,505

ANS: A   PTS: 1   DIF: Challenging   OBJ: LO: 20-02
NAT: BUSPROG: Analytic   KEY: Bloom's: Application

46. Equivalent production units, usually are determined for
a. direct materials and conversion costs.
b. direct materials only.
c. conversion costs only.
d. direct materials and direct labor costs only.

ANS: A   PTS: 1   DIF: Moderate   OBJ: LO: 20-02
NAT: BUSPROG: Analytic   KEY: Bloom's: Knowledge

47. The portion of whole units that were completed with respect to either materials or conversion costs within a given accounting period is the definition of
a. units started and completed.
b. equivalent units.
c. conversion costs.
d. ending work in process.

ANS: B   PTS: 1   DIF: Moderate   OBJ: LO: 20-02
NAT: BUSPROG: Analytic   KEY: Bloom's: Knowledge

48. Which of the following is *not* included in conversion costs?
     a. Direct labor.
     b. Factory overhead.
     c. Indirect labor.
     d. Direct materials.

     ANS: D   PTS: 1   DIF: Easy   OBJ: LO: 20-02
     NAT: BUSPROG: Analytic   KEY: Bloom's: Knowledge

49. A form prepared periodically for each processing department summarizing (1) the units for which
     the department is accountable and the units to be assigned costs and (2) the costs charged to the
     department and the allocation of these costs is termed a:
     a. factory overhead production report
     b. manufacturing cost report
     c. process cost report
     d. cost of production report

     ANS: D   PTS: 1   DIF: Easy   OBJ: LO: 20-03
     NAT: BUSPROG: Analytic   KEY: Bloom's: Knowledge

Department W had 2,400 units, one-third completed at the beginning of the period, 16,000 units
were transferred to Department X from Department W during the period, and 1,800 units were
one-half completed at the end of the period.   Assume the completion ratios apply to direct materials
and conversion costs.

50. What are the total gross number of units to be assigned cost on the cost of production report for
     Department W?
     a. 12,000 units
     b. 13,600 units
     c. 18,500 units
     d. 17,800 units

     ANS: D   PTS: 1   DIF: Moderate   OBJ: LO: 20-03
     NAT: BUSPROG: Analytic   KEY: Bloom's: Application

51. What is the equivalent units of production used to compute unit conversion cost on the cost of
     production report for Department W (Assuming the company uses FIFO)?
     a. 16,100 units
     b. 13,600 units
     c. 15,000 units
     d. 18,500 units

     ANS: A   PTS: 1   DIF: Moderate   OBJ: LO: 20-03
     NAT: BUSPROG: Analytic   KEY: Bloom's: Application

Department J had no work in process at the beginning of the period, 18,000 units were completed
during the period, 2,000 units were 30% completed at the end of the period, and the following
manufacturing costs were debited to the departmental work in process account during the period
(Assuming the company uses FIFO and rounds average cost per unit to two decimal places):

Direct materials (20,000 at $5)	$ 100,000
Direct labor	142,300
Factory overhead	57,200

52. Assuming that all direct materials are placed in process at the beginning of production, what is the total cost of the departmental work in process inventory at the end of the period?
   a. $90,000
   b. $283,140
   c. $199,500
   d. $16,438

   ANS: D   PTS: 1   DIF: Challenging   OBJ: LO: 20-03
   NAT: BUSPROG: Analytic   KEY: Bloom's: Application

53. Assuming that all direct materials are placed in process at the beginning of production, what is the total cost of the 18,000 units completed during the period?
   a. $90,000
   b. $193,140
   c. $16,438
   d. $283,140

   ANS: D   PTS: 1   DIF: Challenging   OBJ: LO: 20-03
   NAT: BUSPROG: Analytic   KEY: Bloom's: Application

Mocha Company manufactures a single product by a continuous process, involving three production departments. The records indicate that direct materials, direct labor, and applied factory overhead for Department 1 were $100,000, $125,000, and $150,000, respectively. The records further indicate that direct materials, direct labor, and applied factory overhead for Department 2 were $55,000, $65,000, and $80,000, respectively. In addition, work in process at the beginning of the period for Department 1 totaled $75,000, and work in process at the end of the period totaled $60,000.

54. The journal entry to record the flow of costs into Department 1 during the period for direct materials is:
   a. Work in Process--Department 1   100,000
       Materials   100,000
   b. Work in Process--Department 1   55,000
       Materials   55,000
   c. Materials   100,000
       Work in Process--Department 1   100,000
   d. Materials   55,000
       Work in Process--Department 1   55,000

   ANS: A   PTS: 1   DIF: Moderate   OBJ: LO: 20-03
   NAT: BUSPROG: Analytic   KEY: Bloom's: Application

55. The journal entry to record the flow of costs into Department 2 during the period for direct materials is:
   a. Work in Process--Department 2   100,000
       Materials   100,000
   b. Work in Process--Department 2   55,000
       Materials   55,000
   c. Work in Process--Department 2   150,000
       Materials   150,000
   d. Materials   55,000
       Work in Process--Department 2   55,000

   ANS: B   PTS: 1   DIF: Moderate   OBJ: LO: 20-03
   NAT: BUSPROG: Analytic   KEY: Bloom's: Application

56. The journal entry to record the flow of costs into Department 1 during the period for direct labor is:
    a. Work in Process--Department 1   65,000
            Wages Payable   65,000
    b. Wages Payable   125,000
            Work in Process--Department 1   125,000
    c. Work in Process--Department 1   125,000
            Wages Payable   125,000
    d. Wages Payable   65,000
            Work in Process--Department 1   65,000

    ANS: C   PTS: 1   DIF: Moderate   OBJ: LO: 20-03
    NAT: BUSPROG: Analytic   KEY: Bloom's: Application

57. The journal entry to record the flow of costs into Department 2 during the period for direct labor is:
    a. Work in Process--Department 2   65,000
            Wages Payable   65,000
    b. Wages Payable   65,000
            Work in Process--Department 2   65,000
    c. Work in Process--Department 2   125,000
            Wages Payable   125,000
    d. Work in Process--Department 2   185,000
            Wages Payable   185,000

    ANS: A   PTS: 1   DIF: Moderate   OBJ: LO: 20-03
    NAT: BUSPROG: Analytic   KEY: Bloom's: Application

58. The journal entry to record the flow of costs into Department 1 during the period for applied overhead is:
    a. Factory Overhead--Department 1   150,000
            Work in Process--Department 1   150,000
    b. Work in Process--Department 1   125,000
            Factory Overhead--Department 1   125,000
    c. Work in Process--Department 1   80,000
            Factory Overhead--Department 1   80,000
    d. Work in Process--Department 1   150,000
            Factory Overhead--Department 1   150,000

    ANS: D   PTS: 1   DIF: Moderate   OBJ: LO: 20-03
    NAT: BUSPROG: Analytic   KEY: Bloom's: Application

59. The journal entry to record the flow of costs into Department 2 during the period for applied overhead is:
    a. Factory Overhead--Department 2   80,000
            Work in Process--Department 2   80,000
    b. Work in Process--Department 2   230,000
            Factory Overhead--Department 2   230,000
    c. Work in Process--Department 2   80,000
            Factory Overhead--Department 2   80,000
    d. Work in Process--Department 2   150,000
            Factory Overhead--Department 2   150,000

    ANS: C   PTS: 1   DIF: Moderate   OBJ: LO: 20-03
    NAT: BUSPROG: Analytic   KEY: Bloom's: Application

60. The journal entry to record the flow of costs from Department 1 into Department 2 during the period is:

a.	Work in Process--Department 2	390,000	
	Work in Process--Department 1		390,000
b.	Work in Process--Department 2	330,000	
	Work in Process--Department 1		330,000
c.	Work in Process--Department 2	215,000	
	Work in Process--Department 1		215,000
d.	Work in Process--Department 2	375,000	
	Work in Process--Department 1		375,000

ANS: A   PTS: 1   DIF: Moderate   OBJ: LO: 20-03
NAT: BUSPROG: Analytic   KEY: Bloom's: Application

61. Mocha Company manufactures a single product by a continuous process, involving three production departments. The records indicate that direct materials, direct labor, and applied factory overhead for Department 1 were $100,000, $125,000, and $150,000, respectively. Work in process at the beginning of the period for Department 1 was $75,000, and work in process at the end of the period totaled $60,000. The records indicate that direct materials, direct labor, and applied factory overhead for Department 2 were $50,000, $60,000, and $70,000, respectively. In addition, work in process at the beginning of the period for Department 2 totaled $75,000, and work in process at the end of the period totaled $60,000. The journal entry to record the flow of costs into Department 3 during the period is:

a.	Work in Process--Department 3	585,000	
	Work in Process--Department 2		585,000
b.	Work in Process--Department 3	570,000	
	Work in Process--Department 2		570,000
c.	Work in Process--Department 3	555,000	
	Work in Process--Department 2		555,000
d.	Work in Process--Department 3	165,000	
	Work in Process--Department 2		165,000

ANS: A   PTS: 1   DIF: Moderate   OBJ: LO: 20-03
NAT: BUSPROG: Analytic   KEY: Bloom's: Application

62. Mocha Company manufactures a single product by a continuous process, involving three production departments. The records indicate that direct materials, direct labor, and applied factory overhead for Department 1 were $100,000, $125,000, and $150,000, respectively. The records further indicate that direct materials, direct labor, and applied factory overhead for Department 2 were $50,000, $60,000, and $70,000, respectively. Department 2 has transferred-in costs of $390,000 for the current period. In addition, work in process at the beginning of the period for Department 2 totaled $75,000, and work in process at the end of the period totaled $90,000. The journal entry to record the flow of costs into Department 3 during the period is:

a.	Work in Process--Department 3	375,000	
	Work in Process--Department 2		375,000
b.	Work in Process--Department 3	570,000	
	Work in Process--Department 2		570,000
c.	Work in Process--Department 3	490,000	
	Work in Process--Department 2		490,000
d.	Work in Process--Department 3	555,000	
	Work in Process--Department 2		555,000

ANS: D   PTS: 1   DIF: Moderate   OBJ: LO: 20-03
NAT: BUSPROG: Analytic   KEY: Bloom's: Application

63. Mocha Company manufactures a single product by a continuous process, involving three production departments. The records indicate that direct materials, direct labor, and applied factory overhead for Department 2 were $100,000, $125,000, and $150,000, respectively. The records further indicate that direct materials, direct labor, and applied factory overhead for Department 3 were $50,000, $60,000, and $70,000, respectively. In addition, work in process at the beginning of the period for Department 3 totaled $75,000, and work in process at the end of the period totaled $60,000. The journal entry to record the flow of costs into Department 3 during the period for direct materials is:

a. Work in Process--Department 3   100,000
    Materials   100,000

b. Work in Process--Department 3   125,000
    Materials   125,000

c. Work in Process--Department 3   50,000
    Materials   50,000

d. Work in Process--Department 3   70,000
    Materials   70,000

ANS: C   PTS: 1   DIF: Moderate   OBJ: LO: 20-03
NAT: BUSPROG: Analytic   KEY: Bloom's: Application

Department G had 3,600 units, 40% completed at the beginning of the period, 12,000 units were completed during the period, 2,000 units were one-fifth completed at the end of the period, and the following manufacturing costs were debited to the departmental work in process account during the period:

Work in process, beginning of period	$60,000
Costs added during period:	
Direct materials (10,400 at $9.8365)	102,300
Direct labor	79,800
Factory overhead	25,200

64. Assuming that all direct materials are placed in process at the beginning of production and that the first-in, first-out method of inventory costing is used, what is the equivalent units for materials and conversion costs, respectively.
a. 14,000 and 12,160
b. 10,400 and 10,960
c. 14,000 and 13,600
d. 10,400 and 10,240

ANS: B   PTS: 1   DIF: Moderate   OBJ: LO: 20-02
NAT: BUSPROG: Analytic   KEY: Bloom's: Application

65. Assuming that all direct materials are placed in process at the beginning of production and that the first-in, first-out method of inventory costing is used, what is the material and conversion cost per unit (to the nearest penny), respectively.
a. $5.94 and $5.86
b. $5.94 and $6.38
c. $8.00 and $8.68
d. $9.84 and $9.58

ANS: D   PTS: 1   DIF: Moderate   OBJ: LO: 20-02
NAT: BUSPROG: Analytic   KEY: Bloom's: Application

66. Which of the following is not a use of the cost of production report?
    a. To help managers control operations.
    b. To help managers isolate problems.
    c. To project production.
    d. To help managers improve operations.

    ANS: C   PTS: 1   DIF: Easy   OBJ: LO: 20-04
    NAT: BUSPROG: Analytic   KEY: Bloom's: Knowledge

67. Which of the following measures would *not* help managers to control and improve operations?
    a. Units produced per time period
    b. Cost trends of a product
    c. Yield trends
    d. Commissions paid per time period

    ANS: D   PTS: 1   DIF: Moderate   OBJ: LO: 20-04
    NAT: BUSPROG: Analytic   KEY: Bloom's: Knowledge

68. Just-in-time processing is a business philosophy that focuses on reducing time and cost and eliminating poor quality. This is accomplished in manufacturing and non-manufacturing processes by:
    a. moving a product from process to process as each function is completed
    b. combining processing functions into work centers and cross-training workers to perform more than one function
    c. having production supervisors attempt to enter enough materials into manufacturing to keep all manufacturing departments operating
    d. having workers typically perform one function on a continuous basis

    ANS: B   PTS: 1   DIF: Easy   OBJ: LO: 20-05
    NAT: BUSPROG: Analytic   KEY: Bloom's: Knowledge

69. When a firm adopts a just-in-time operating environment,
    a. new, more efficient machinery and equipment must be purchased and installed in the original layout.
    b. machinery and equipment are moved into small autonomous production lines called manufacturing cells.
    c. new machinery and equipment must be purchased from franchised JIT dealers.
    d. employees are retrained on different equipment but the plant layout generally stays unchanged.

    ANS: B   PTS: 1   DIF: Easy   OBJ: LO: 20-05
    NAT: BUSPROG: Analytic   KEY: Bloom's: Knowledge

70. Which of the following best describes the effect on direct labor when management adopts a just-in-time environment?
    a. Workers typically perform one function.
    b. The environment becomes more labor intensive.
    c. Each employee runs a single machine.
    d. Workers are often cross-trained to perform more than one function.

    ANS: D   PTS: 1   DIF: Easy   OBJ: LO: 20-05
    NAT: BUSPROG: Analytic   KEY: Bloom's: Knowledge

71. According to the just-in-time philosophy,
    a. finished goods should always be available in case a customer wants something.
    b. employees should be expert at one function rather than be cross-trained for multiple functions.
    c. movement of the product and material is reduced.
    d. the product moves from process to process until completion.

    ANS: C   PTS: 1   DIF: Easy   OBJ: LO: 20-05
    NAT: BUSPROG: Analytic   KEY: Bloom's: Knowledge

72. Just-in-time operations attempt to significantly reduce
    a. profits.
    b. inventory needed to produce products.
    c. inspection time and moving time.
    d. processing time.

    ANS: C   PTS: 1   DIF: Moderate   OBJ: LO: 20-05
    NAT: BUSPROG: Analytic   KEY: Bloom's: Knowledge

The debits to Work in Process--Assembly Department for April, together with data concerning production, are as follows:

April 1, work in process:	
Materials cost, 3,000 units	$ 7,500
Conversion costs, 3,000 units,	
80% completed	6,000
Materials added during April, 10,000 units	29,000
Conversion costs during April	35,000
Goods finished during April, 11,500 units	---
April 30 work in process, 1,500 units,	
60% completed	---

All direct materials are placed in process at the beginning of the process and the <u>average cost method</u> is used to cost inventories.

73. The materials cost per equivalent unit (to the nearest cent) for April is:
    a. $2.60
    b. $2.81
    c. $3.02
    d. $2.26

    ANS: B   PTS: 1   DIF: Moderate   OBJ: 20-APP
    NAT: BUSPROG: Analytic   KEY: Bloom's: Application

74. The conversion cost per equivalent unit (to the nearest cent) for April is:
    a. $2.70
    b. $2.53
    c. $3.31
    d. $5.60

    ANS: C   PTS: 1   DIF: Moderate   OBJ: 20-APP
    NAT: BUSPROG: Analytic   KEY: Bloom's: Application

Department E had 4,000 units in Work in Process that were 40% completed at the beginning of the period at a cost of $12,500. 14,000 units of direct materials were added during the period at a cost of $28,700. 15,000 units were completed during the period, and 3,000 units were 75% completed at the end of the period. All materials are added at the beginning of the process. Direct labor was $32,450 and factory overhead was $18,710.

75. The number of equivalent units of production for the period for conversion if the average cost method is used to cost inventories was:
a. 15,650
b. 14,850
c. 18,000
d. 17,250

ANS: D   PTS: 1   DIF: Moderate   OBJ: 20-APP
NAT: BUSPROG: Analytic   KEY: Bloom's: Application

76. The number of equivalent units of production for the period for materials if the average cost method is used to cost inventories was:
a. 15,650
b. 18,000
c. 17,250
d. 17,700

ANS: B   PTS: 1   DIF: Moderate   OBJ: 20-APP
NAT: BUSPROG: Analytic   KEY: Bloom's: Application

Department E had 4,000 units in Work in Process that were 40% completed at the beginning of the period at a cost of $12,500. Of the $12,500, $8,000 was for material and $4,500 was for conversion costs. 14,000 units of direct materials were added during the period at a cost of $28,700. 15,000 units were completed during the period, and 3,000 units were 75% completed at the end of the period. All materials are added at the beginning of the process. Direct labor was $32,450 and factory overhead was $18,710.

77. If the average cost method is used the material cost per unit (to the nearest cent) would be:
a. $2.04
b. $1.59
c. $1.91
d. $2.00

ANS: A   PTS: 1   DIF: Challenging   OBJ: 20-APP
NAT: BUSPROG: Analytic   KEY: Bloom's: Application

78. If the average cost method is used the conversion cost per unit (to the nearest cent) would be:
a. $3.71
b. $2.84
c. $2.97
d. $3.23

ANS: D   PTS: 1   DIF: Challenging   OBJ: 20-APP
NAT: BUSPROG: Analytic   KEY: Bloom's: Application

79. Carolwood Company manufactures widgets and uses process costing. The status of their beginning and ending inventory is as follows:

Beginning Inventory	30% of the manufacturing process is complete.
Ending Inventory	55% of the manufacturing process is complete.

Direct materials are added to the manufacturing process in stages. None are added when production begins. Approximately 1/2 of the materials are added when the product is 25% complete. The other half is added when the product is 50% complete.

What percentage complete are Beginning Inventory and Ending Inventory with respect to Direct materials(DM) and Conversion Costs(CC)?

   a.   Beg.Inventory DM-50% CC-30%
       End.Inventory DM-100% CC-55%
   b.   Beg.Inventory DM-50% CC-30%
       End.Inventory DM-55% CC-55%
   c.   Beg.Inventory DM-30% CC-30%
       End.Inventory DM-55% CC-55%
   d.   Beg.Inventory DM-50% CC-70%
       End.Inventory DM-100% CC-45%

ANS: A   PTS: 1   DIF: Challenging   OBJ: LO: 20-02
NAT: BUSPROG: Analytic   KEY: Bloom's: Application

Penny, Inc. employs a process costing system. Direct materials are added at the beginning of the process. Here is information about July's activities:

On July 1:	
Beginning inventories	850 units, 60% complete
Direct materials cost	$5,000
Conversion costs	$4,000
During July:	
Number of units started	15,000
Direct materials added	$155,000
Conversion costs added	$83,520
On July 31:	
Ending inventories	1,600 units, 40% complete

80. Using the FIFO method, the number of units started and completed in July was
   a. 14,250
   b. 15,000
   c. 13,400
   d. 15,740

ANS: C   PTS: 1   DIF: Moderate   OBJ: LO: 20-02
NAT: BUSPROG: Analytic   KEY: Bloom's: Application

81. Using the FIFO method, the number of equivalent units of conversion costs was
   a. 14,400
   b. 14,380

c. 14,550
d. 15,850

ANS: B   PTS: 1   DIF: Moderate   OBJ: LO: 20-02
NAT: BUSPROG: Analytic   KEY: Bloom's: Application

82. Using the FIFO method, the cost per equivalent unit for materials used during July was
   a. $10.78
   b. $10.33
   c. $9.78
   d. $10.65

ANS: B   PTS: 1   DIF: Moderate   OBJ: LO: 20-02
NAT: BUSPROG: Analytic   KEY: Bloom's: Application

83. Using the FIFO method, the cost of goods completed and transferred out during July was (use average cost per unit rounded to four decimal places in computations)
   a. $227,270
   b. $225,060
   c. $236,905
   d. $228,200

ANS: A   PTS: 1   DIF: Challenging   OBJ: LO: 20-02
NAT: BUSPROG: Analytic   KEY: Bloom's: Application

84. The Mountain Springs Water Company has two departments. Purifying and Bottling. The Bottling Department received 67,000 liters from the Purifying Department. During the period, the Bottling Department completed 65,000 liters, including 3,000 liters of work in process at the beginning of the period. The ending work in process was 5,000 liters. How many liters were started and completed during the period?
   a. 62,000   c. 60,000
   b. 64,000   d. 70,000

ANS: A   PTS: 1   DIF: Moderate   OBJ: LO: 20-02
NAT: BUSPROG: Analytic   KEY: Bloom's: Application

OTHER

1. Which of the following industries would normally use job order costing systems and which would normally use process costing systems?

   Business consulting
   Chemicals
   Food
   Movie
   Soap and cosmetics
   Web designing

ANS:

Business consulting	Job Order
Chemicals	Process
Food	Process
Movie studio	Job Order
Soap and cosmetics	Process
Web designing	Job order

PTS: 1   DIF: Easy   OBJ: LO: 20-01   NAT: BUSPROG: Analytic
KEY: Bloom's: Knowledge

2. The Mountain Springs Water Company has two departments. Purifying and Bottling. The Bottling Department received 67,000 liters from the Purifying Department. During the period, the Bottling Department completed 65,000 liters, including 3,000 liters of work in process at the beginning of the period. The ending work in process was 5,000 liters. How many liters were started and completed during the period?

ANS:
62,000 liters started and completed (65,000 completed − 3,000 beginning WIP)

PTS: 1   DIF: Easy   OBJ: LO: 20-02   NAT: BUSPROG: Analytic
KEY: Bloom's: Application

3. The Mountain Springs Water Company has two departments. Purifying and Bottling. The Bottling Department received 58,000 liters from the Purifying Department. During the period, the Bottling Department completed 56,000 liters, including 4,000 liters of work in process at the beginning of the period. The ending work in process was 6,000 liters. How many liters were started and completed during the period?

ANS:
52,000 liters started and completed (56,000 completed − 4,000 beginning WIP)

PTS: 1   DIF: Easy   OBJ: LO: 20-02   NAT: BUSPROG: Analytic
KEY: Bloom's: Application

4. The Mountain Springs Water Company has two departments, Purifying and Bottling. The Bottling Department had 3,000 liters in beginning work in process inventory (30% complete). During the period 71,000 liters were completed. The ending work in process was 5,000 liters (70% completed). What are the total equivalent units for direct materials (using the FIFO method)   if materials were added at the beginning of the process?

ANS:

	Whole Units		Equivalent Units
Inventory in process, beginning of period	3,000	× 0%	0
Started and completed during the period	68,000	× 100%	68,000
Transferred out of Bottling (completed)	71,000		68,000
Inventory in process, end of period	5,000	× 100%	5,000
Total units to be assigned costs	76,000		73,000

PTS: 1   DIF: Moderate   OBJ: LO: 20-02   NAT: BUSPROG: Analytic
KEY: Bloom's: Application

5.   The Mountain Springs Water Company has two departments, Purifying and Bottling. The Bottling
      Department had 8,000 liters in beginning work in process inventory (60% complete). During the
      period 70,000 liters were completed. The ending work in process was 3,000 liters (60% completed).
      What are the total equivalent units for direct materials under the FIFO method if materials were
      added at the beginning of the process?

ANS:

	Whole Units		Equivalent Units
Inventory in process, beginning of period	8,000	× 0%	0
Started and completed during the period	62,000	× 100%	62,000
Transferred out of Bottling (completed)	70,000		62,000
Inventory in process, end of period	3,000	× 100%	3,000
Total units to be assigned costs	73,000		65,000

PTS: 1   DIF: Moderate   OBJ: LO: 20-02   NAT: BUSPROG: Analytic
KEY: Bloom's: Application

6.   The Bottling Department of Mountain Springs Water Company had 5,000 liters in beginning work
      in process inventory (20% complete). During the period, 58,000 liters were completed. The ending
      work in process inventory was 3,000 liters (90% complete). What are the equivalent units for
      conversion costs under the FIFO method?

ANS:

	Whole Units		Equivalent Units
Inventory in process, beginning of period	5,000	× 80%	4,000
Started and completed during the period	53,000	× 100%	53,000
Transferred out of Bottling (completed)	58,000		57,000
Inventory in process, end of period	3,000	× 90%	2,700
Total units to be assigned costs	61,000		59,700

PTS: 1   DIF: Moderate   OBJ: LO: 20-02   NAT: BUSPROG: Analytic
KEY: Bloom's: Application

7.   The Bottling Department of Mountain Springs Water Company had 4,000 liters in beginning work
      in process inventory (40% complete). During the period, 66,000 liters were completed. The ending
      work in process inventory was 3,000 liters (70% complete). What are the equivalent units for
      conversion costs, using the FIFO method?

ANS:

	Whole Units		Equivalent Units
Inventory in process, beginning of period	4,000	× 60%	2,400
Started and completed during the period	62,000	× 100%	62,000
Transferred out of Bottling (completed)	66,000		64,400
Inventory in process, end of period	3,000	× 70%	2,100
Total units to be assigned costs	69,000		66,500
Answer: 68,500 equivalent units			

PTS: 1   DIF: Moderate   OBJ: LO: 20-02   NAT: BUSPROG: Analytic
KEY: Bloom's: Application

8.   The cost of direct materials transferred into the Bottling Department of the Mountain Springs Water
     Company is $27,225. The conversion cost for the period in the Bottling Department is $7,596. The
     total equivalent units for direct materials and conversion are 60,500 and 63,300 respectively.
     Determine the direct materials and conversion cost per equivalent unit.
     Round answers to nearest cent.

     ANS:

     Equivalent units of materials : $\dfrac{\$27,225}{60,500 \text{ liters}} = \$0.45$

     Equivalent units of conversion : $\dfrac{\$7,596}{63,300 \text{ liters}} = \$0.12$

     PTS: 1   DIF: Moderate   OBJ: LO: 20-02   NAT: BUSPROG: Analytic
     KEY: Bloom's: Application

9.   The cost of direct materials transferred into the Bottling Department of the Mountain Springs Water
     Company is $28,072. The conversion cost for the period in the Bottling Department is $10,275. The
     total equivalent units for direct materials and conversion are 63,800 and 68,500 respectively.
     Determine the direct materials and conversion cost per equivalent unit.
     Round answers to nearest cent.

     ANS:

     Equivalent units of materials : $\dfrac{\$28,072}{63,800 \text{ liters}} = \$0.45$

     Equivalent units of conversion : $\dfrac{\$10,275}{68,500 \text{ liters}} = \$0.15$

     PTS: 1   DIF: Moderate   OBJ: LO: 20-02   NAT: BUSPROG: Analytic
     KEY: Bloom's: Application

10. The cost per equivalent units of direct materials and conversion in the Bottling Department of Mountain Springs Water Company is $.45 and $.12, respectively. The equivalent units to be assigned costs are as follows.

	Direct Materials	Conversion
Inventory in process, beginning of period	0	3,500
Started and completed during the period	57,000	57,000
Transferred out of Bottling (completed)	57,000	60,500
Inventory in process, end of period	3,500	1,800
Total units to be assigned costs	60,500	62,300

The beginning work in process inventory had a cost of $2,200. Determine the cost of completed and transferred out production, and the ending work in process inventory.

ANS:

	Direct Materials	Conversion	Total
Inventory in process, balance			$ 2,200
Inventory in process, beginning of period	0	+ 3,500 × $0.12	420
Started and completed during the period	57,000 × $.45	+ 57,000 × $0.12	32,490
Transferred out of Bottling (completed)			$35,110
Inventory in process, end of period	3,500 × $.45	+ 1,800 × $0.12	1,791
Total units to be assigned costs			$36,901

Completed and transferred out production: $35,110
Inventory in process, ending $1,791

PTS: 1 DIF: Challenging OBJ: LO: 20-02 NAT: BUSPROG: Analytic
KEY: Bloom's: Application

11. The cost per equivalent units of direct materials and conversion in the Bottling Department of Beverages on Jolt Company is $.47 and $.15, respectively. The equivalent units to be assigned costs are as follows.

	Direct Materials	Conversion
Inventory in process, beginning of period	0	3,000
Started and completed during the period	52,000	52,000
Transferred out of Bottling (completed)	52,000	55,000
Inventory in process, end of period	3,500	2,100
Total units to be assigned costs	55,500	57,100

The beginning work in process inventory had a cost of $3,500. Determine the cost of completed and transferred out production, and the ending work in process inventory.

ANS:

	Direct Materials	Conversion	Total
Inventory in process, balance			$ 3,500
Inventory in process, beginning of period	0	+ 3,000 × $0.15	450
Started and completed during the period	52,000 × $.47	+ 52,000 × $0.15	32,240
Transferred out of Bottling (completed)			$36,190
Inventory in process, end of period	3,500 × $.47	+ 2,100 × $0.15	1,960
Total units to be assigned costs			$38,150

Completed and transferred out production: $36,190
Inventory in process, ending $1,960

PTS: 1   DIF: Challenging   OBJ: LO: 20-02   NAT: BUSPROG: Analytic
KEY: Bloom's: Application

12. The cost of materials transferred into the Bottling Department of Mountain Springs Water Company is $32,400, with $26,000 from the Purifying Department, plus additional $6,400 from the materials storeroom. The conversion cost for the period in the Bottling Department is $8,750 ($3,750 factory applied and $5,000 direct labor.) The total costs transferred to finished goods for the period was $31,980. The Bottling Department had a beginning inventory of $1,860.

a. Journalize (1) the cost of transferred-in materials (2) conversion costs, and (3) the cost of transferred out to finished goods.

b. Determine the balance of Work in Process-Bottling at the end of the period.

ANS:
a. Work in Process-Bottling   32,400
        Work in Process-Purifying   26,000
        Materials   6,400

     Work in Process-Bottling   8,750
        Factory Overhead-Bottling   3,750
        Wages Payable   5,000

     Finished Goods   31,980
        Work in Process-Bottling   31,980

b. $11,030   ($1,860 + $32,400 + 8,750 − $31,980)

PTS: 1   DIF: Moderate   OBJ: LO: 20-03   NAT: BUSPROG: Analytic
KEY: Bloom's: Application

13. The cost of energy consumed in producing good units in the Bottling Department of Mountain Springs Water Company was $36,850 and $39,060 for June and July, respectively. The number of equivalent units produced in June and July was 55,000 and 62,000 liters respectively. Evaluate the change in the cost of energy between the two months.

ANS:

Energy costs per liter, June: $\dfrac{\$36{,}850}{55{,}000 \text{ liters}}$ = $0.67

Energy costs per liter, July: $\dfrac{\$39{,}060}{62{,}000 \text{ liters}}$ = $0.63

The cost of energy has decreased by $0.04 ($0.67 − $0.63).

PTS: 1   DIF: Easy   OBJ: LO: 20-04   NAT: BUSPROG: Analytic
KEY: Bloom's: Application

14.   Amos Company's molding department opened on October 1, 2012. During October, 35,000 units
were completed and transferred out to the next department. On October 31, 2012, the 9,000 units
which remained in inventory were 40% complete with respect to conversion costs and 100%
complete with respect to materials.

Required:

How many equivalent units of work did the molding department complete during October for
materials and conversion costs?

ANS:
Materials: 35,000 + (9,000 * 1.00) = 44,000
Conversion costs: 35,000 + (9,000 * .4) = 38,600

PTS: 1   DIF: Moderate   OBJ: LO: 20-02   NAT: BUSPROG: Analytic
KEY: Bloom's: Application

15.   Kamin Company's mixing department had a beginning inventory of 4,000 units which had
accumulated conversion costs of $55,000. During the period, the mixing department accumulated
conversion costs of $92,000 and started 8,000 new units. Ending inventory was 2,500 units which
were 40% complete with respect to conversion costs. Kamin uses the average cost method to cost
inventories.

Required:

Calculate the cost per equivalent unit for conversion costs in the mixing department.

ANS:
Units transferred out = 4,000 + 8,000 − 2,500 = 9,500 units
Equivalent units = 9,500 + (2,500 * 0.40) = 10,500
Cost per equivalent unit = ($55,000 + $92,000) / (10,500) = $14

PTS: 1   DIF: Moderate   OBJ: 20-APP   NAT: BUSPROG: Analytic
KEY: Bloom's: Application

16. Kramer Company started its production operations on August 1. During August, the printing department completed 17,600 units. There were 4,400 units in ending inventory which were 80% complete with respect to materials and 10% complete with respect to conversion costs. During August, the department accumulated materials costs of $45,408 and conversion costs of $76,670.

Required:

a. Calculate the cost of the goods transferred out.
b. What is the value of the ending inventory?
Round intermediate computation to nearest cent.

ANS:
Cost per equivalent unit for materials = $45,408 / (17,600 + (.80)*(4,400)) = $2.15
Cost per equivalent unit for conversion costs = $76,670 / (17,600 + (.10)*(4,400)) = $4.25
a. ($2.15 + $4.25) * 17,600 = $112,640
b. ($2.15 * .80 * 4,400) + ($4.25 * .10 * 4,400) = $9,438

PTS: 1   DIF: Moderate   OBJ: LO: 20-02   NAT: BUSPROG: Analytic
KEY: Bloom's: Application

17. On March 1, Upton Company's packaging department had Work in Process inventory of 8,820 units, which had been transferred in from the finishing department. These units had accumulated costs of $315,000 in previous departments and $16,000 for conversion costs in the packaging department.

During March, 30,000 units were transferred into the department. These units had accumulated costs of $770,000 in the previous departments. The packaging department incurred $54,000 in conversion costs during the month.

Seven hundred units remained in ending inventory on March 31. These units were 80% complete with respect to conversion costs.

Required:

Calculate the cost per equivalent unit for transferred-in costs and for conversion costs for the packaging department using the average cost method.

ANS:
Units transferred out = 8,820 + 30,000 − 700 = 38,120
Transferred in costs = ($315,000 + $770,000) / (38,120 + 700) = $27.95 per equivalent unit
Conversion costs = ($16,000 + $54,000) / (38,120 + 560) = $1.81 per equivalent unit

PTS: 1   DIF: Moderate   OBJ: 20-APP   NAT: BUSPROG: Analytic
KEY: Bloom's: Application

MATCHING

Match the industries who would typically use job order costing and those that would typically use process costing.
a.   Job order costing
b.   Process costing

1. Movie studio
2. Gasoline refinery
3. Home construction
4. Paper manufacturer
5. Flour mill

1. ANS: A   PTS: 1   DIF: Easy   OBJ: LO: 20-01
    NAT: BUSPROG: Analytic   KEY: Bloom's: Knowledge
2. ANS: B   PTS: 1   DIF: Easy   OBJ: LO: 20-01
    NAT: BUSPROG: Analytic   KEY: Bloom's: Knowledge
3. ANS: A   PTS: 1   DIF: Easy   OBJ: LO: 20-01
    NAT: BUSPROG: Analytic   KEY: Bloom's: Knowledge
4. ANS: B   PTS: 1   DIF: Easy   OBJ: LO: 20-01
    NAT: BUSPROG: Analytic   KEY: Bloom's: Knowledge
5. ANS: B   PTS: 1   DIF: Easy   OBJ: LO: 20-01
    NAT: BUSPROG: Analytic   KEY: Bloom's: Knowledge

Match the following terms with their definitions.
a. cost of production report   d. yield
b. equivalent units of production   e. just-in-time processing
c. manufacturing cells

6. Measures the quantity of output of production relative to the inputs.
7. Provides information for controlling and improving operations.
8. Focuses on reducing time, cost, and poor quality within the process
9. The portion of whole units that are complete with respect to materials or conversion costs.
10. Work centers for processing in a just in time system.

6. ANS: D   PTS: 1   DIF: Easy   OBJ: LO: 20-04
    NAT: BUSPROG: Analytic   KEY: Bloom's: Knowledge
7. ANS: A   PTS: 1   DIF: Easy   OBJ: LO: 20-02
    NAT: BUSPROG: Analytic   KEY: Bloom's: Knowledge
8. ANS: E   PTS: 1   DIF: Easy   OBJ: LO: 20-05
    NAT: BUSPROG: Analytic   KEY: Bloom's: Knowledge
9. ANS: B   PTS: 1   DIF: Easy   OBJ: LO: 20-02
    NAT: BUSPROG: Analytic   KEY: Bloom's: Knowledge
10. ANS: C   PTS: 1   DIF: Easy   OBJ: LO: 20-05
    NAT: BUSPROG: Analytic   KEY: Bloom's: Knowledge

Match the correct term with the statement that describes it.
a. direct labor and factory overhead
b. direct labor and direct materials
c. transferred-in costs
d. equivalent units
e. process costing
f. job costing
g. FIFO method
h. cost of production report

11. A process costing method that costs each period's equivalent units of work with that period's costs per equivalent unit

12. Measure of the work done during a production period, expressed in terms of fully complete units of output

13. Conversion costs

14. Summary of the activity in a processing department for a specific period

15. Costing system used by a company producing computer chips

16. Prime costs

17. Costs incurred in a previous process that are carried forward as part of the product's cost when it moves to the next department

18. Costing system used by a company producing by a company producing custom window treatments

11.	ANS: G	PTS: 1	DIF: Moderate	OBJ: LO: 20-02		
	NAT: BUSPROG: Analytic		KEY: Bloom's: Knowledge			
12.	ANS: D	PTS: 1	DIF: Moderate	OBJ: LO: 20-02		
	NAT: BUSPROG: Analytic		KEY: Bloom's: Knowledge			
13.	ANS: A	PTS: 1	DIF: Moderate	OBJ: LO: 20-02		
	NAT: BUSPROG: Analytic		KEY: Bloom's: Knowledge			
14.	ANS: H	PTS: 1	DIF: Moderate	OBJ: LO: 20-02		
	NAT: BUSPROG: Analytic		KEY: Bloom's: Knowledge			
15.	ANS: E	PTS: 1	DIF: Moderate	OBJ: LO: 20-02		
	NAT: BUSPROG: Analytic		KEY: Bloom's: Knowledge			
16.	ANS: B	PTS: 1	DIF: Moderate	OBJ: LO: 20-02		
	NAT: BUSPROG: Analytic		KEY: Bloom's: Knowledge			
17.	ANS: C	PTS: 1	DIF: Moderate	OBJ: LO: 20-02		
	NAT: BUSPROG: Analytic		KEY: Bloom's: Knowledge			
18.	ANS: F	PTS: 1	DIF: Moderate	OBJ: LO: 20-02		
	NAT: BUSPROG: Analytic		KEY: Bloom's: Knowledge			

PROBLEM

1. The inventory at June 1 and costs charged to Work in Process - Department 60 during June are as follows:

3,800 units, 60% completed	$60,400a
Direct materials, 32,000 units	378,000
Direct labor	274,000
Factory overhead	168,000
Total cost to be accounted for	$880,400

During June, 32,000 units were placed into production and 31,200 units were completed, including those in inventory on June 1. On June 30, the inventory of work in process consisted of 4,600 units which were 85% completed. Inventories are costed by the first-in, first-out method and all materials are added at the beginning of the process.

Determine the following, presenting your computations (Prepare your computations using unit cost data to four decimal places, i.e. $4.4444, to minimize rounding differences):

(a)   equivalent units of production for conversion cost
(b)   conversion cost per equivalent unit
(c)   total and unit cost of finished goods started in prior period and completed in the current period
(d)   total and unit cost of finished goods started and completed in the current period
(e)   total cost of work in process inventory at June 30

ANS:

(a)   Equivalent units of production:
      To process units in inventory on June 1:
      $3,800 \times 40\%$ 1,520
      To process units started and completed in June:
      $31,200 - 3,800$ 27,400
      To process units in inventory on June 30:
      $4,600 \times 85\%$ 3,910
      Equivalent units of production for conversion cost   32,830

(b)   Conversion cost per equivalent unit of production:
      Conversion costs:
      Direct labor $274,000
      Factory overhead   168,000
                                                                                                                 $442,000
      Unit conversion cost, $442,000 \div 32,830$ $13.4633

(c)   Cost of finished goods started in the prior period and completed in current period:

      Work in process inventory on June 1:
      $3,800 \times 60\%$ $ 60,400
      Conversion costs in current period,
      $3,800 \times 40\% = 1,520$ units at $13.4633   20,464
      Total cost $ 80,864
      Beginning inventory,
      Unit cost, $80,864 \div 3,800$ $21.2800

(d)   Cost of finished goods started and completed in current period:
      Direct materials, 27,400 units at $11.8125 $323,663
      Conversion costs, 27,400 units at $13.4633   368,894
      Total cost $692,557
      Unit cost, $692,557 \div 27,400$ $25.2758

(e)   Cost of work in process inventory at June 30:
      Direct materials, 4,600 units at $11.8125 $ 54,338
      Conversion costs, 3,910 units at $13.4633   52,642
      Total cost $ 106,980

      Total cost accounted for, $80,864 + $692,557 + $106,980 $880,401*
      * $1 rounding difference

PTS: 1   DIF: Challenging   OBJ: LO: 20-02   NAT: BUSPROG: Analytic
KEY: Bloom's: Application

2. The inventory at May 1 and the costs charged to Work in Process--Department B during May for Stella Company are as follows:

Beginning WIP, 12,000 units, 60% completed	$ 62,400
From Department A, 55,000 units started this period	
Direct materials added	
	115,500
Direct labor incurred	384,915
Factory overhead incurred	138,000

During May, all direct materials are transferred from Department A, the units in process at May 1 were completed, and of the 55,000 units entering the department, all were completed except 6,000 units which were 70% completed. Inventories are costed by the first-in, first-out method. Prepare a cost of production report for May. Round unit cost data to four decimal places and total cost to nearest cent.

ANS:

Stella Company
Cost of Production Report--Department B
For the Month Ended May 31, 20--

		Equivalent Units	
	Whole	Direct	
UNITS	Units	Materials	Conversion
Units charged to production:			
Inventory in process, May 1	12,000		
Received from Department A	55,000		
Total units accounted for by Dept. B	67,000		
Units to be assigned costs:			
Inventory in process, May 1			
(60% completed)	12,000	0	4,800
Started and completed in May	49,000	49,000	49,000
Transferred to finished goods in May	61,000	49,000	53,800
Inventory in process, May 31			
(70% complete)	6,000	6,000	4,200
Total units to be assigned costs	67,000	55,000	58,000

		Costs	
	Direct		
COSTS	Materials	Conversion	Total Costs
Units costs:			
Total costs for May in Dept. B	$ 115,500	$ 522,915	
Total equivalent units	÷ 55,000	÷ 58,000	
Cost per equivalent unit	$ 2.1000	$ 9.0158	
Costs charged to production:			
Inventory in process, May 1			$ 62,400
Costs incurred in May			638,415
Total costs accounted for by			
Department B			$700,815

Costs allocated to completed and
partially completed units:

Inventory in process, May 1, bal			$ 62,400
To complete inventory in process, May 1	$ 0	$ 43,276	43,276
Started and completed in May	102,900	441,774	544,674
Transferred to finished goods in May			650,350
Inventory in process, May 31	12,600	37,866	50,466
Total costs assigned by Dept. B			$700,816*

*$1 rounding error

PTS: 1   DIF: Challenging   OBJ: LO: 20-02   NAT: BUSPROG: Analytic
KEY: Bloom's: Application

3.   Zither Co. manufactures a product called Zens in a three-process series. All materials are introduced at the beginning of the first process. Zither uses the first-in, first-out method of inventory costing. Unit and cost data for the first process (Department A) for the month of October 2012 follow:

Conversion	Units	Completion	Cost
Work in process inventory:			
October 1	12,000	60%	$140,400
October 31	5,000	40%	?
Started in October	14,000		
Direct materials cost			106,400
Conversion cost			70,310
Completed in October	21,000		?

Prepare Zither's Department A cost of production report for October.

ANS:

Zither Company
Cost of Production Report—Department A
For the Month Ended October 31, 2012

	Equivalent Units		
UNITS	Whole Units	Direct Materials	Conversion
Units charged to production:			
Inventory in process, October 1	12,000		
Received from materials store area	14,000		
Total units accounted for by Department A	26,000		
Less completed and transferred	21,000		
Department A ending inventory	5,000		

Units to be assigned costs:

Inventory in process, October 1 (60% completed)	12,000	0	4,800
Started and completed in October	9,000	9,000	9,000
Transferred to Department B in October	21,000	9,000	13,800
Inventory in process, October 31 (40% complete)	5,000	5,000	2,000
Total units to be assigned costs	26,000	14,000	15,800

	Costs		
COSTS	Direct Materials	Conversion	Total Costs
Units costs:			
Total costs for October in Department A	$106,400	$70,310	
Total equivalent units	÷14,000	÷15,800	
Cost per equivalent unit	$ 7.60	$ 4.45	
Costs charged to production:			
Inventory in process, October 1			$140,400
Costs incurred in October			176,710
Total costs accounted for by Department A			$317,110
Costs allocated to completed and partially completed units:			
Inventory in process, October 1 balance			$140,400
To complete inventory in process, October 1	$ 0	$21,360	21,360
Started and completed in October	68,400	40,050	108,450
Transferred to finished goods in October			270,210
Inventory in process, October 31	38,000	8,900	46,900
Total costs assigned by Department A			$317,110

PTS: 1   DIF: Challenging   OBJ: LO: 20-02   NAT: BUSPROG: Analytic
KEY: Bloom's: Application

4. The inventory at April 1, 2012, and the costs charged to Work in Process--Department B during April for Zarley Company are as follows:

1,200 units, 40% completed	$ 47,800
From Department A, 26,000 units	845,000
Direct labor	312,000
Factory overhead	176,770

During April, all direct materials are transferred from Department A, the units in process at April 1 were completed, and of the 26,000 units entering the department, all were completed except 1,000 units which were 70% completed as to conversion costs. Inventories are costed by the first-in, first-out method.

Prepare a cost of production report for April.

ANS:

Zarley Company
Cost of Production Report--Department B
For the Month Ended April 30, 2012

	Whole Units	Equivalent Units — Direct Materials	Conversion
UNITS			
Units charged to production:			
Inventory in process, April 1	1,200		
Received from Department A	26,000		
Total units accounted for by Dept. B	27,200		
Units to be assigned costs:			
Inventory in process, April 1			
(40% completed)	1,200	0	720
Started and completed in April	25,000	25,000	25,000
Transferred to finished goods in April	26,200	25,000	25,720
Inventory in process, April 30			
(70% complete)	1,000	1,000	700
Total units to be assigned costs	27,200	26,000	26,420

	Direct Materials	Conversion	Total Costs
COSTS			
Units costs:			
Total costs for April in Dept. B	$845,000	$488,770	
Total equivalent units	÷ 26,000	÷ 26,420	
Cost per equivalent unit	$ 32.50	$ 18.50	
Costs charged to production:			
Inventory in process, April 1			$ 47,800
Costs incurred in April			1,333,770
Total costs accounted for by Department B			$1,381,570
Costs allocated to completed and partially completed units:			
Inventory in process, April 1, bal.			$ 47,800
To complete inventory in process, April 1	$ 0	$ 13,320	13,320
Started and completed in April	812,500	462,500	1,275,000
Transferred to finished goods in April			1,336,120
Inventory in process, April 30	32,500	12,950	45,450
Total costs assigned by Dept. B			$1,381,570

PTS: 1   DIF: Challenging   OBJ: LO: 20-02   NAT: BUSPROG: Analytic
KEY: Bloom's: Application

5.   The inventory at April 1, 2012, and the costs charged to Work in Process--Department B during
April for Hawk Company are as follows:

500 units, 60% completed	$ 3,460
From Department A, 10,000 units	36,300
Direct labor	7,960
Factory overhead	12,500

During April, all direct materials are transferred from Department A, the units in process at April 1
were completed, and of the 10,000 units entering the department, all were completed except 1,200
units which were 25% completed as to conversion costs. Inventories are costed by the first-in,
first-out method.

Prepare a cost of production report for April.

ANS:

Hawk Company
Cost of Production Report--Department B
For the Month Ended April 30, 2012

		Equivalent Units	
	Whole	Direct	
UNITS	Units	Materials	Conversion
Units charged to production:			
Inventory in process, April 1	500		
Received from Department A	10,000		
Total units accounted for by Dept. B	10,500		
Units to be assigned costs:			
Inventory in process, April 1			
(60% completed)	500	0	200
Started and completed in April	8,800	8,800	8,800
Transferred to finished goods in April	9,300	8,800	9,000
Inventory in process, April 30			
(25% complete)	1,200	1,200	300
Total units to be assigned costs	10,500	10,000	9,300

	Costs		
	Direct		
COSTS	Materials	Conversion	Total Costs
Units costs:			
Total costs for April in Dept. B	$ 36,300	$ 20,460	
Total equivalent units	÷ 10,000	÷ 9,300	
Cost per equivalent unit	$ 3.63	$ 2.20	
Costs charged to production:			
Inventory in process, April 1			$ 3,460
Costs incurred in April			56,760

Total costs accounted for by
  Department B $60,220
Costs allocated to completed and
partially completed units:
  Inventory in process, April 1, bal. $ 3,460
  To complete inventory in
    process, April 1 $ 0 $ 440   440
  Started and completed in April   31,944   19,360   51,304
  Transferred to finished
    goods in April   55,204
  Inventory in process, April 30   4,356   660   5,016
  Total costs assigned by Dept. B $60,220

PTS: 1   DIF: Challenging   OBJ: LO: 20-02   NAT: BUSPROG: Analytic
KEY: Bloom's: Application

6. Information for the Sandy Manufacturing Company for the month of July 2012 is as follows:

Beginning work in process: Cost of Inventory at process, July 1 $5,010
Units − 800
Direct materials = 100% complete
Conversion costs = 70% complete

Units started in July = 14,000   Costs charged to Work in Process during July:
Ending work in process inventory: Direct materials costs = $57,400
Units = 1,500   Direct labor costs   = 20,049
Direct materials = 100% complete   Factory overhead costs = 30,073
Conversion costs = 30% complete

Prepare a cost of production report for the month of July, using the FIFO method.

ANS:

Sandy Manufacturing Company
Cost of Production Report
For the Month Ended July 31, 2012

	Units	Material Equivalent Units	Conversion Equivalent Units
Beginning work in process (70% complete)	800	-0-	240
Units started & completed (14,000 started − 1,500 ending)	12,500	12,500	12,500
Ending work in process (30% complete)	1,500	1,500	450
	14,800	14,000	13,190

COSTS	Direct Materials	Conversion	Total Costs
Units costs;			
Total cost for July	$ 57,400	$50,122*	
Total Equivalent units (from above)	14,000	13,190	
Costs per equivalent unit	$ 4.10	$ 3.80	$ 7.90
Costs charged to production:			
Inventory in process, July 1			$ 5,010
Cost incurred in July			107,522
Total costs accounted for in July			$112,532

* ($20,049 + $30,073)

	Direct Materials	Conversion	Total Costs
Costs allocated to completed and partially completed units:			
Inventory in process, July 1 – balance			$ 5,010
To complete inventory in process, July 1	$ 0	$ 912	912
		(a)	
Started and completed in July	51,250 (b)	47,500 (c)	98,750
Transferred to finished goods in July			$104,672
Inventory in process July 31	6,150 (d)	1,710 (e)	7,860
Total costs accounted for in July			$112,532

(a) 240 × $3.80   (b) 12,500 × $4.10   (c) 12,500 × $3.80   (d) 1,500 × $4.10
(e) 450 × $3.80

PTS: 1   DIF: Challenging   OBJ: LO: 20-02   NAT: BUSPROG: Analytic
KEY: Bloom's: Application

7.   Eagle Co. manufactures bentwood chairs and tables.   Wood for both products is steam-bent in the
same process, but different types of wood are used for each product.   Thus, materials cost is
identified separately to each product.   One production cycle uses 20 board feet.   Labor cost is
identified to the process as a whole, as is overhead cost.   Data for the month of July follow:

	Chairs	Tables
Direct material cost per board foot	$ 3.60	$ 4.20
Number of parts formed per production cycle (20 board feet)	10	8
Actual operating hours in July	120	380
Parts produced during July	4,000	9,000

Budgeted annual conversion cost:	
Labor	$150,000
Utilities	125,000
Depreciation	65,000
Other overhead	50,000
Total	$390,000

Budgeted annual operating hours for steam-bending	5,200

(a)   Compute July's predetermined rate for the steam-bending process.
(b)   Compute July's direct material costs for chairs and tables.
(c)   Compute conversion costs to be applied to chairs and tables in July.
(d)   Journalize the following entries:
    (1)   Assignment of direct materials to chairs and tables.
    (2)   Application of conversion costs to chairs and tables.
    (3)   The transfer of completed chairs and tables to the Finishing Department. All of July's production was completed in July.

ANS:

(a)   Steam-bending conversion cost per hour = \$390,000/5,200 hrs.
$$= \$75 \text{ per hour}$$

(b)   Direct material cost per unit:

	Chairs	Tables
($3.60/ft. × 20 ft. per cycle) / 10 parts per cycle	$ 7.20	
($4.20/ft. × 20 ft. per cycle) / 8 parts per cycle		$ 10.50
Total direct materials cost:		
(4,000 units × $7.20/u.)	$28,800	
(9,000 units × $10.50/u.)		$94,500

(c)   Conversion cost per unit:

	Chairs	Tables
($75/hr. × 120 hrs./mo.) / 4,000 units	2.25	
($75/hr. × 380 hrs./mo.) / 9,000 units		3.17 (rounded)
Total conversion cost:		
(4,000 units × $2.25/u.)	$ 9,000	
(9,000 units × $3.17/u.)		$28,530

(d)   (1)

Work in Process--Chairs	28,800	
Work in Process--Tables	94,500	
Materials		123,300

(2)

Work in Process--Chairs	9,000	
Work in Process--Tables	28,530	
Conversion Costs Applied		37,530

(3)

Finished Goods--Chairs	37,800	
Finished Goods--Tables	123,030	
Work in Process--Chairs		37,800
Work in Process--Tables		123,030

PTS: 1   DIF: Moderate   OBJ: LO: 20-02| LO: 20-03
NAT: BUSPROG: Analytic   KEY: Bloom's: Application

8. Tough Hardware purchases raw materials and processes those purchases through a
    receiving/inspection process prior to stocking for production. Tough places 3 purchase orders for
    materials for production and receives the goods that day. The first PO is for 2,500 1/2"× 96" milling
    blanks at $2.75 each. The second is for 4,000 pieces of 48"× 96"× 1" sheet steel at $15.55 each. The
    third PO is for five 55 gallon drums of Milling Lubrication Oil at $475.00 per barrel.

    The receiving/inspection process is completed and the goods are transferred from Receiving
    Inventory to Raw Materials. The Receiving/Inspection Department assigns manufacturing overhead
    of $55.00 per purchase order as well as $2.75 per piece on metal goods and $35.00 per container on
    fluids. All labor is allocated through overhead.

    (a) Write the journal entry to purchase and receive these items to Receiving Inventory on account.

    (b) Assign overhead to the metal goods.

    (c) Assign overhead to the fluid goods.

    (d) Transfer all goods to Raw Materials Inventory.

    ANS:
    (a) Receiving Inventory   71,450
            Accounts Payable   71,450

        PO 1 – 2,500 pieces × $2.75 each = $ 6,875
        PO 2 – 4,000 pieces × $15.55 each =   62,200
        PO 3 – 5 pieces × $475.00 each =   2,375
                    Total $ 71,450

    (b) Assign overhead to the metal goods.
        Receiving Inventory   17,985
            Factory Overhead   17,985

        PO 1 – 2,500 pieces × $2.75 each = $ 6,875
        PO 1 – PO overhead   55
        PO 2 – 4,000 pieces × $2.75 each =   11,000
        PO 2 – PO overhead   55
                    Total $17,985

    (c) Assign overhead to the fluid goods.
        Receiving Inventory   230
            Factory Overhead   230

        PO 3 – 5 pieces × $35.00 each = $175
        PO 3 – PO overhead   55
                    Total $230

    (d) Transfer all goods to Raw Materials Inventory.
        Raw Material Inventory   89,665
            Receiving Inventory   89,665

    PTS: 1   DIF: Challenging   OBJ: LO: 20-02| LO: 20-03
    NAT: BUSPROG: Analytic   KEY: Bloom's: Application

9. The Brass Works is in the process of determining manufacturing overhead. Journalize events (a) -
    (d) to Factory Overhead, Miscellaneous Expense, or allocated between the two as appropriate. All
    items were paid in cash at the time of acquisition.   Next calculate the overhead application rate and
    apply overhead to Work-in-Process.

    (a) Brass Works purchases an insurance policy for $4,000. It is computed that 80% of the
         value of the policy protects production, the balance protects the administrative offices.

    (b) The electric bill is received showing an amount due of $1,200. This meter is utilized only
         by production as the office spaces have their own meter.

    (c) Payroll reports that the sales manager's salary for the period is $3,500 and that
         production supervisors wages for the period are $5,500.

    (d) The stockroom reports that $2,575 in materials were purchased for the production
         maintenance department.

    (e) If the driver for the application of overhead is drop-forge strokes and there are expected
         to be 1,000 strokes in this period, what is the rate per stroke? Do not round your answer.

    (f) Assuming that there are 1,150 drop-forge strokes in this period, apply factory overhead
         to Work In Process. Round your answers to nearest dollar.
    Round overhead rate to four decimal places and total cost to nearest dollar.

    ANS:
    (a) Factory Overhead ($4,000 × 80%)   3,200
          Miscellaneous Expense ($4,000 × 20%)   800
            Cash   4,000

    (b) Factory Overhead   1,200
            Cash   1,200

    (c) Miscellaneous Expense   3,500
          Factory Overhead   5,500
            Cash   9,000

    (d) Factory Overhead   2,575
            Cash   2,575

    (e) Factory Overhead $ 3,200
          Factory Overhead   1,200
          Factory Overhead   5,500
          Factory Overhead   2,575
                  Total $12,475

    Drop-forge stroke rate = $12,475 / 1,000 strokes = $12.475 per stroke.

    (f) Work In Process   14,346
                  Manufacturing Overhead   14,346

PTS: 1   DIF: Challenging   OBJ: LO: 20-03   NAT: BUSPROG: Analytic
KEY: Bloom's: Application

10. The estimated total factory overhead cost and total machine hours for Department 40 for the current year are $250,000 and 56,250 respectively. During January, the first month of the current year, actual machine hours used totaled 5,100 and factory overhead cost incurred totaled $22,000.

   (a) Determine the factory overhead rate based on machine hours.

   (b) Present the entry to apply factory overhead to production in Department 40 for January.

   (c) What is the balance of Factory Overhead − Department 40 at January 31?

   (d) Does the balance of Factory Overhead − Department 40 at January 31 represent overapplied or underapplied factory overhead?
   Round total cost to nearest dollar value.

   ANS:
   (a) $250,000/56,250 = $4.44 per machine hour

   (b) Work in Process--Department 40
       (5,100 × $4.44)   22,644
          Factory Overhead--Department 40   22,644

   (c) $644 credit

   (d) overapplied factory overhead

   PTS: 1   DIF: Moderate   OBJ: LO: 20-03   NAT: BUSPROG: Analytic
   KEY: Bloom's: Application

11. A firm produces its products by a continuous process involving three production departments, 1 through 3. Present entries to record the following selected transactions related to production during August:

   (a) Materials purchased on account, $120,000.
   (b) Material requisitioned for use in Department 1, $125,700, of which $124,200 entered directly into the product.
   (c) Labor cost incurred in Department 1, $195,400, of which $174,000 was used directly in the manufacture of the product.
   (d) Factory overhead costs for Department 1 incurred on account, $54,700.
   (e) Depreciation on machinery in Department 1, $29,200.
   (f) Expiration of prepaid insurance chargeable to Department 1, $7,000.
   (g) Factory overhead applied to production, $106,300.
   (h) Output of Department 1 transferred to Department 2, $362,700.

   ANS:
   (a) Materials   120,000
          Accounts Payable   120,000

   (b) Factory Overhead--Department 1   1,500
       Work in Process--Department 1   124,200
          Materials   125,700

(c)	Factory Overhead--Department 1	21,400	
	Work in Process--Department 1	174,000	
	Wages Payable		195,400

| (d) | Factory Overhead--Department 1 | 54,700 | |
| | Accounts Payable | | 54,700 |

| (e) | Factory Overhead--Department 1 | 29,200 | |
| | Accumulated Depreciation--Machinery | | 29,200 |

| (f) | Factory Overhead--Department 1 | 7,000 | |
| | Prepaid Insurance | | 7,000 |

| (g) | Work in Process--Department 1 | 106,300 | |
| | Factory Overhead | | 106,300 |

| (h) | Work in Process--Department 2 | 362,700 | |
| | Work in Process--Department 1 | | 362,700 |

PTS: 1 DIF: Moderate OBJ: LO: 20-03 NAT: BUSPROG: Analytic
KEY: Bloom's: Application

12. Fast-Flow Paints produces mixer base paint through a two stage process, Mixing and Packaging. The following events depict the movement of value into and out of production. Journalize each event if appropriate, if not, provide a short narrative reason as to why you choose not to journalize that action. Bob, the Production Manager, accepts an order to continue processing the current run of mixer base paint.

(a) $27,000.00 worth of materials are withdrawn from Raw Materials inventory. Of this amount, $25,500.00 will be issued to the Mixing Department and the balance will be issued to the Maintenance Department to be used on production line machines.

(b) Bob calculates that labor for the period is $12,500.00. Of this value $1,750.00 is for maintenance and indirect labor. The remainder is directly associated with mixing.

(c) Bob, who is paid a salary but earns about $35.00 / hour, spends 1 hour inspecting the production line.

(d) The manufacturing overhead drivers for Mixing are (1) hours of mixer time at $575.00 per hour, and material movements from Raw Materials at $125.00 per movement. An inspection of the machine timers reveals that a total of 8 hours has been consumed in making this product. An inspection of "Stocking Orders" indicates that only one material movement was utilized to "load" the raw materials. (Note: All values have been journalized to Factory Overhead, you need only apply it to the production run.)

(e) Within Fast-Flow items are transferred between departments at a standard cost or value. This production run has created 4,015 gallons of mixer base paint. This paint is transferred to Packaging at a standard cost of $10.05 per gallon.

(f) Packaging draws $755.00 in raw materials for packaging of this production run.

(g)   Packaging documents that 12 hours of direct labor at $10.25 per hour were consumed in the packaging of this production run.

(h)   Packaging uses a driver of direct labor hours to allocate manufacturing overhead at the rate of $25.00 per hour.

(i)   Packaging transfers these 4,015 gallons of packaged goods to Finished Goods Inventory at a standard cost of $10.34 per gallon.

Round total cost to nearest dollar value.

ANS:

(a) Work In Process - Mixing	25,500	
Factory Overhead	1,500	
Raw Materials		27,000

(b) Work In Process - Mixing	10,750	
Factory Overhead	1,750	
Wages Payable		12,500

(c) Bob's inspection of the assembly line is not directly chargeable to production. As a manager of a production unit it will be incorporated in the cost of production through the allocation of overhead.

(d) Work In Process - Mixing	4,725	
Factory Overhead		4,725

(e) Work In Process - Packaging	40,351	
Work In Process - Mixing		40,351

(f) Work In Process - Packaging	755	
Raw Materials		755

(g) Work In Process - Packaging	123	
Wages Payable		123

(h) Work In Process - Packaging	300	
Factory Overhead		300

(i) Finished Goods Inventory	41,515	
Work In Process - Packaging		41,515

PTS: 1   DIF: Challenging   OBJ: LO: 20-03   NAT: BUSPROG: Analytic
KEY: Bloom's: Application

13.   Zang Co. manufacturers its products in a continuous process involving two departments, Machining and Assembly.   Present entries to record the following selected transactions related to production during June:

(a)   Materials purchased on account, $180,000.
(b)   Materials requisitioned by: Machining, $73,000 direct and $9,000 indirect materials; Assembly, $4,900 indirect materials.
(c)   Direct labor used by Machining, $23,000, Assembly, $47,000.

(d) Depreciation expenses: Machining, $4,500; Assembly, $7,800.
(e) Factory overhead applied: Machining, $9,700; Assembly, $11,300.
(f) Machining Department transferred $98,300 to Assembly Department; Assembly Department transferred $83,400 to finished goods.
(g) Sold goods on account, $100,000.   Cost of goods sold, $68,000.

ANS:

(a)	Materials	180,000	
	Accounts Payable		180,000
(b)	Work in Process--Machining	73,000	
	Factory Overhead--Machining	9,000	
	Factory Overhead--Assembly	4,900	
	Materials		86,900
(c)	Work in Process--Machining	23,000	
	Work in Process--Assembly	47,000	
	Wages Payable		70,000
(d)	Factory Overhead--Machining	4,500	
	Factory Overhead--Assembly	7,800	
	Accumulated Depreciation		12,300
(e)	Work in Process--Machining	9,700	
	Work in Process--Assembly	11,300	
	Factory Overhead--Machining		9,700
	Factory Overhead-Assembly		11,300
(f)	Work in Process--Assembly	98,300	
	Work in Process--Machining		98,300
	Finished Goods	83,400	
	Work in Process--Assembly		83,400
(g)	Accounts Receivable	100,000	
	Sales		100,000
	Cost of Goods Sold	68,000	
	Finished Goods		68,000

PTS: 1   DIF: Moderate   OBJ: LO: 20-04   NAT: BUSPROG: Analytic
KEY: Bloom's: Application

14. The inventory at June 1 and costs charged to Work in Process - Department 60 during June are as follows:

3,800 units, 80% completed ($25,000 Materials, $35,400 conversion)	$ 60,400
Direct materials, 32,000 units	368,000
Direct labor	244,000
Factory overhead	188,000
Total cost to be accounted for	$860,400

During June, 32,000 units were placed into production and 31,200 units were completed, including those in inventory on June 1. On June 30, the inventory of work in process consisted of 4,600 units which were 40% completed. Inventories are costed by the average cost method and all materials are added at the beginning of the process.

Determine the following, presenting your computations:

(a) equivalent units of production for conversion cost
(b) conversion cost per equivalent unit and material cost per equivalent unit.
(c) total and unit cost of finished goods completed in the current period
(d) total cost of work in process inventory at June 30

ANS:
(a) Equivalent units of production:

Transferred out	31,200
To process units in inventory on June 30:	
4,600 × 40% =	1,840
Equivalent units of production for conversion cost	33,040

(b) Conversion cost per equivalent unit of production:

Conversion costs: from beginning inventory	$ 35,400
Direct labor	$244,000
Factory overhead	188,000
	$467,400
Unit conversion cost, $467,400 ÷ 33,040	$ 14.15

Material cost per equivalent unit:	
From beginning inventory	$25,000
Added during the period	368,000
Total	393,000
Units (3,800+32,000)	35,800
Material cost per unit	$ 10.98

(c) Total and unit cost of finished goods completed in the current period

Unit cost of finished goods completed:	
Material costs per unit	$ 10.98
Conversion costs per unit	14.15
Total cost per unit	$ 25.13

Total costs of goods completed during the period:	
31,200 × $25.13	784,056

(d) Cost of work in process inventory at June 30:

Direct materials, 4,600 units at $10.98	$50,508
Conversion costs, 1,840 units at $14.15	26,036
Total cost	$76,544

PTS: 1   DIF: Challenging   OBJ: 20-APP   NAT: BUSPROG: Analytic
KEY: Bloom's: Application

15. On August 1, Jones Corporation's packaging department had Work in Process inventory of 8,000 units that were 75% complete with respect to materials and 30% complete with respect to conversion costs. The cost of these units was $99,525 ($62,000 transferred-in from previous departments, $28,775 in materials, and $8,750 in labor and overhead). During August, 125,000 units were transferred into the department. These units had accumulated costs in previous departments of $1,418,560. The packaging department incurred costs of $799,225 for materials and $498,010 for conversion costs in August and transferred 131,000 units out of the department. The 2,000 units remaining in ending inventory are 50% complete with respect to materials and 20% complete with respect to conversion costs. Jones Corporation uses the average cost method to cost its inventories.

Required

a. Calculate the cost per equivalent unit for transferred-in costs, materials, and conversion costs.

b. Calculate the cost of the units transferred out of the department.

c. Calculate the cost of the ending inventory.

ANS:
a. Cost per equivalent unit:
   Transferred-in costs = ($62,000 + $1,418,560) / 133,000 = $11.13
   Materials = ($28,775 + $799,225) / (131,000 + 1,000) = $6.27
   Conversion costs = ($8,750 + $498,010) / (131,000 + 400) = $3.86

b. Units transferred out = ($11.13 + $6.27 + $3.86) * 131,000 = $2,785,060

c. Ending inventory = (2,000 * $11.13) + (2,000 * .50 * $6.27) + (2,000 * .20 * $3.86)
                    = $30,074

PTS: 1   DIF: Challenging   OBJ: 20-APP   NAT: BUSPROG: Analytic
KEY: Bloom's: Application

16. Explain the concept of equivalent units. Give an example to validate your explanation.

ANS:
Equivalent units are a measure of the amount of work done during a production period, expressed in terms of fully completed units of output. If 40,000 units were started and completed, then the equivalent units would equal 40,000 units. However, if those same 40,000 units were started and only 50% complete, then the equivalent units would be $40,000 \times 50\% = 20,000$ units.

PTS: 1   DIF: Moderate   OBJ: LO: 20-01   NAT: BUSPROG: Analytic
KEY: Bloom's: Knowledge

17. Discuss how equivalent units are computed under the average cost method.

ANS:
Under average costing, equivalent units equal:
a) all work done to date on units transferred out irregardless of whether work was completed in prior period or current period and
b) work done to start ending inventory

PTS: 1   DIF: Moderate   OBJ: 20-APP   NAT: BUSPROG: Analytic
KEY: Bloom's: Knowledge

18. Job order manufacturing and process manufacturing are two major costing systems used in manufacturing.   Briefly contrast the characteristics of these two systems.

ANS:

Job Order System	Process System
Custom orders	Repetitive production
Heterogeneous product	Homogeneous product
Low production volume	High production volume
Low to medium standardization	High standardization

PTS: 1   DIF: Moderate   OBJ: LO: 20-01   NAT: BUSPROG: Analytic
KEY: Bloom's: Knowledge

19.   Describe the flow of materials in a process cost accounting system.

ANS:
When raw materials are purchased they are debited to the Materials account.   When direct materials are needed in a production department, a materials requisition report is used to move the materials from the storeroom to the production department.   Direct materials used are recorded with a debit to Work in Process Inventory for that department and a credit to Materials.   Indirect materials used in a department are recorded with a debit to Factory Overhead and a credit to Materials.

PTS: 1   DIF: Moderate   OBJ: LO: 20-03   NAT: BUSPROG: Analytic
KEY: Bloom's: Knowledge

TRUE/FALSE

1. Cost behavior refers to the methods used to estimate costs for use in managerial decision making.

   ANS: F   PTS: 1   DIF: Easy   OBJ: LO: 21-01
   NAT: BUSPROG: Analytic   KEY: Bloom's: Knowledge

2. Cost behavior refers to the manner in which a cost changes as the related activity changes.

   ANS: T   PTS: 1   DIF: Easy   OBJ: LO: 21-01
   NAT: BUSPROG: Analytic   KEY: Bloom's: Knowledge

3. The fixed cost per unit varies with changes in the level of activity.

   ANS: T   PTS: 1   DIF: Easy   OBJ: LO: 21-01
   NAT: BUSPROG: Analytic   KEY: Bloom's: Knowledge

4. A production supervisor's salary that does not vary with the number of units produced is an example of a fixed cost.

   ANS: T   PTS: 1   DIF: Easy   OBJ: LO: 21-01
   NAT: BUSPROG: Analytic   KEY: Bloom's: Knowledge

5. Direct materials cost that varies with the number of units produced is an example of a fixed cost of production.

   ANS: F   PTS: 1   DIF: Easy   OBJ: LO: 21-01
   NAT: BUSPROG: Analytic   KEY: Bloom's: Knowledge

6. In order to choose the proper activity base for a cost, managerial accountants must be familiar with the operations of the entity.

   ANS: T   PTS: 1   DIF: Easy   OBJ: LO: 21-01
   NAT: BUSPROG: Analytic   KEY: Bloom's: Knowledge

7. The relevant range is useful for analyzing cost behavior for management decision-making purposes.

   ANS: T   PTS: 1   DIF: Easy   OBJ: LO: 21-01
   NAT: BUSPROG: Analytic   KEY: Bloom's: Knowledge

8. The relevant activity base for a cost depends upon which base is most closely associated with the cost and the decision-making needs of management.

   ANS: T   PTS: 1   DIF: Easy   OBJ: LO: 21-01
   NAT: BUSPROG: Analytic   KEY: Bloom's: Knowledge

9. The range of activity over which changes in cost are of interest to management is called the relevant range.

ANS: T   PTS: 1   DIF: Easy   OBJ: LO: 21-01
NAT: BUSPROG: Analytic   KEY: Bloom's: Knowledge

10. Total fixed costs change as the level of activity changes.

ANS: F   PTS: 1   DIF: Easy   OBJ: LO: 21-01
NAT: BUSPROG: Analytic   KEY: Bloom's: Knowledge

11. Because variable costs are assumed to change in direct proportion to changes in the activity level, the graph of the variable costs when plotted against the activity level appears as a circle.

ANS: F   PTS: 1   DIF: Easy   OBJ: LO: 21-01
NAT: BUSPROG: Analytic   KEY: Bloom's: Knowledge

12. Variable costs are costs that remain constant in total dollar amount as the level of activity changes.

ANS: F   PTS: 1   DIF: Easy   OBJ: LO: 21-01
NAT: BUSPROG: Analytic   KEY: Bloom's: Knowledge

13. Variable costs are costs that remain constant on a per-unit basis as the level of activity changes.

ANS: T   PTS: 1   DIF: Easy   OBJ: LO: 21-01
NAT: BUSPROG: Analytic   KEY: Bloom's: Knowledge

14. Variable costs are costs that vary in total in direct proportion to changes in the activity level.

ANS: T   PTS: 1   DIF: Easy   OBJ: LO: 21-01
NAT: BUSPROG: Analytic   KEY: Bloom's: Knowledge

15. Variable costs are costs that vary on a per-unit basis with changes in the activity level.

ANS: F   PTS: 1   DIF: Easy   OBJ: LO: 21-01
NAT: BUSPROG: Analytic   KEY: Bloom's: Knowledge

16. Direct materials and direct labor costs are examples of variable costs of production.

ANS: T   PTS: 1   DIF: Easy   OBJ: LO: 21-01
NAT: BUSPROG: Analytic

17. Total variable costs change as the level of activity changes.

ANS: T   PTS: 1   DIF: Easy   OBJ: LO: 21-01
NAT: BUSPROG: Analytic   KEY: Bloom's: Knowledge

18. Unit variable cost does not change as the number of units of activity changes.

ANS: T   PTS: 1   DIF: Easy   OBJ: LO: 21-01
NAT: BUSPROG: Analytic   KEY: Bloom's: Knowledge

19. A mixed cost has characteristics of both a variable and a fixed cost.

ANS: T   PTS: 1   DIF: Easy   OBJ: LO: 21-01
NAT: BUSPROG: Analytic   KEY: Bloom's: Knowledge

20. Rental charges of $40,000 per year plus $3 for each machine hour over 18,000 hours is an example of a fixed cost.

ANS: F   PTS: 1   DIF: Easy   OBJ: LO: 21-01
NAT: BUSPROG: Analytic   KEY: Bloom's: Comprehension

21. A rental cost of $20,000 plus $.70 per machine hour of use is an example of a mixed cost.

ANS: T   PTS: 1   DIF: Easy   OBJ: LO: 21-01
NAT: BUSPROG: Analytic   KEY: Bloom's: Comprehension

22. For purposes of analysis, mixed costs can generally be separated into their variable and fixed components.

ANS: T   PTS: 1   DIF: Easy   OBJ: LO: 21-01
NAT: BUSPROG: Analytic   KEY: Bloom's: Knowledge

23. The contribution margin ratio is the same as the profit-volume ratio.

ANS: T   PTS: 1   DIF: Easy   OBJ: LO: 21-02
NAT: BUSPROG: Analytic   KEY: Bloom's: Knowledge

24. Variable costs as a percentage of sales are equal to 100% minus the contribution margin ratio.

ANS: T   PTS: 1   DIF: Easy   OBJ: LO: 21-02
NAT: BUSPROG: Analytic   KEY: Bloom's: Knowledge

25. The dollars available from each unit of sales to cover fixed cost and profit is the unit variable cost.

ANS: F   PTS: 1   DIF: Easy   OBJ: LO: 21-02
NAT: BUSPROG: Analytic   KEY: Bloom's: Knowledge

26. The ratio that indicates the percentage of each sales dollar available to cover the fixed costs and to provide operating income is termed the contribution margin ratio.

ANS: T   PTS: 1   DIF: Easy   OBJ: LO: 21-02
NAT: BUSPROG: Analytic   KEY: Bloom's: Knowledge

27. If sales total $2,000,000, fixed costs total $800,000, and variable costs are 60% of sales, the contribution margin ratio is 60%.

ANS: F   PTS: 1   DIF: Moderate   OBJ: LO: 21-02
NAT: BUSPROG: Analytic   KEY: Bloom's: Application

28. If sales total $2,000,000, fixed costs total $800,000, and variable costs are 60% of sales, the contribution margin ratio is 40%.

ANS: T   PTS: 1   DIF: Moderate   OBJ: LO: 21-02
NAT: BUSPROG: Analytic   KEY: Bloom's: Application

29. The data required for determining the break-even point for a business are the total estimated fixed costs for a period, stated as a percentage of net sales.

ANS: F   PTS: 1   DIF: Moderate   OBJ: LO: 21-03
NAT: BUSPROG: Analytic   KEY: Bloom's: Knowledge

30. If fixed costs are $500,000 and variable costs are 60% of break-even sales, profit is zero when sales revenue is $930,000.

ANS: F   PTS: 1   DIF: Moderate   OBJ: LO: 21-03
NAT: BUSPROG: Analytic   KEY: Bloom's: Application

31. If fixed costs are $850,000 and the unit contribution margin is $50, profit is zero when 15,000 units are sold.

ANS: F   PTS: 1   DIF: Moderate   OBJ: LO: 21-03
NAT: BUSPROG: Analytic   KEY: Bloom's: Application

32. The point in operations at which revenues and expired costs are exactly equal is called the break-even point.

ANS: T   PTS: 1   DIF: Easy   OBJ: LO: 21-03
NAT: BUSPROG: Analytic   KEY: Bloom's: Knowledge

33. Break-even analysis is one type of cost-volume-profit analysis.

ANS: T   PTS: 1   DIF: Easy   OBJ: LO: 21-03
NAT: BUSPROG: Analytic   KEY: Bloom's: Knowledge

34. If the property tax rates are increased, this change in fixed costs will result in a decrease in the break-even point.

ANS: F   PTS: 1   DIF: Moderate   OBJ: LO: 21-03
NAT: BUSPROG: Analytic   KEY: Bloom's: Knowledge

35. If yearly insurance premiums are increased, this change in fixed costs will result in an increase in the break-even point.

ANS: T   PTS: 1   DIF: Moderate   OBJ: LO: 21-03
NAT: BUSPROG: Analytic   KEY: Bloom's: Knowledge

36. If employees accept a wage contract that increases the unit contribution margin, the break-even point will decrease.

ANS: T   PTS: 1   DIF: Moderate   OBJ: LO: 21-03
NAT: BUSPROG: Analytic   KEY: Bloom's: Knowledge

37.   If employees accept a wage contract that decreases the unit contribution margin, the break-even point will decrease.

ANS: F   PTS: 1   DIF: Moderate   OBJ: LO: 21-03
NAT: BUSPROG: Analytic   KEY: Bloom's: Knowledge

38.   If direct materials cost per unit increases, the break-even point will decrease.

ANS: F   PTS: 1   DIF: Moderate   OBJ: LO: 21-03
NAT: BUSPROG: Analytic   KEY: Bloom's: Knowledge

39.   If direct materials cost per unit increases, the break-even point will increase.

ANS: T   PTS: 1   DIF: Moderate   OBJ: LO: 21-03
NAT: BUSPROG: Analytic   KEY: Bloom's: Knowledge

40.   If direct materials cost per unit decreases, the amount of sales necessary to earn a desired amount of profit will decrease.

ANS: T   PTS: 1   DIF: Moderate   OBJ: LO: 21-03
NAT: BUSPROG: Analytic   KEY: Bloom's: Knowledge

41.   If fixed costs are $450,000 and the unit contribution margin is $50, the sales necessary to earn an operating income of $50,000 are 10,000 units.

ANS: T   PTS: 1   DIF: Moderate   OBJ: LO: 21-03
NAT: BUSPROG: Analytic   KEY: Bloom's: Application

42.   If fixed costs are $650,000 and the unit contribution margin is $30, the sales necessary to earn an operating income of $30,000 are 14,000 units.

ANS: F   PTS: 1   DIF: Moderate   OBJ: LO: 21-03
NAT: BUSPROG: Analytic   KEY: Bloom's: Application

43.   Only a single line, which represents the difference between total sales revenues and total costs, is plotted on the profit-volume chart.

ANS: T   PTS: 1   DIF: Easy   OBJ: LO: 21-04
NAT: BUSPROG: Analytic   KEY: Bloom's: Knowledge

44.   Only a single line, which represents the difference between total sales revenues and total costs, is plotted on the cost-volume-profit chart.

ANS: F   PTS: 1   DIF: Easy   OBJ: LO: 21-04
NAT: BUSPROG: Analytic   KEY: Bloom's: Knowledge

45.   Cost-volume-profit analysis can be presented in both equation form and graphic form.

ANS: T   PTS: 1   DIF: Easy   OBJ: LO: 21-04
NAT: BUSPROG: Analytic   KEY: Bloom's: Knowledge

46. If a business sells two products, it is not possible to estimate the break-even point.

    ANS: F   PTS: 1   DIF: Challenging   OBJ: LO: 21-05
    NAT: BUSPROG: Analytic   KEY: Bloom's: Knowledge

47. If a business sells four products, it is not possible to estimate the break-even point.

    ANS: F   PTS: 1   DIF: Challenging   OBJ: LO: 21-05
    NAT: BUSPROG: Analytic   KEY: Bloom's: Knowledge

48. Even if a business sells six products, it is possible to estimate the break-even point.

    ANS: T   PTS: 1   DIF: Moderate   OBJ: LO: 21-05
    NAT: BUSPROG: Analytic   KEY: Bloom's: Knowledge

49. If the unit selling price is $40, the volume of sales is $3,000,000, sales at the break-even point amount to $2,500,000, and the maximum possible sales are $3,300,000, the margin of safety is 11,500 units.

    ANS: F   PTS: 1   DIF: Challenging   OBJ: LO: 21-05
    NAT: BUSPROG: Analytic   KEY: Bloom's: Application

50. If the unit selling price is $40, the volume of sales is $3,000,000, sales at the break-even point amount to $2,500,000, and the maximum possible sales are $3,300,000, the margin of safety is 14,500 units.

    ANS: F   PTS: 1   DIF: Challenging   OBJ: LO: 21-05
    NAT: BUSPROG: Analytic   KEY: Bloom's: Application

51. If the volume of sales is $6,000,000 and sales at the break-even point amount to $4,800,000, the margin of safety is 25%.

    ANS: F   PTS: 1   DIF: Moderate   OBJ: LO: 21-05
    NAT: BUSPROG: Analytic   KEY: Bloom's: Application

52. If the volume of sales is $7,000,000 and sales at the break-even point amount to $4,800,000, the margin of safety is 45.8%.

    ANS: F   PTS: 1   DIF: Moderate   OBJ: LO: 21-05
    NAT: BUSPROG: Analytic   KEY: Bloom's: Application

53. Companies with large amounts of fixed costs will generally have a high operating leverage.

    ANS: T   PTS: 1   DIF: Easy   OBJ: LO: 21-05
    NAT: BUSPROG: Analytic   KEY: Bloom's: Knowledge

54. A low operating leverage is normal for highly automated industries.

    ANS: F   PTS: 1   DIF: Challenging   OBJ: LO: 21-05
    NAT: BUSPROG: Analytic   KEY: Bloom's: Knowledge

55.   Garmo Co. has an operating leverage of 5. Next year's sales are expected to increase by 10%. The company's operating income will increase by 50%.

      ANS: T   PTS: 1   DIF: Challenging   OBJ: LO: 21-05
      NAT: BUSPROG: Analytic   KEY: Bloom's: Application

56.   The reliability of cost-volume-profit analysis does NOT depend on the assumption that costs can be accurately divided into fixed and variable components.

      ANS: F   PTS: 1   DIF: Challenging   OBJ: LO: 21-05
      NAT: BUSPROG: Analytic   KEY: Bloom's: Knowledge

57.   Absorption costing is required for financial reporting under generally accepted accounting principles.

      ANS: T   PTS: 1   DIF: Easy   OBJ: 21-APP
      NAT: BUSPROG: Analytic   KEY: Bloom's: Knowledge

58.   The adoption of variable costing for managerial decision making is based on the premise that fixed factory overhead costs are related to productive capacity of the manufacturing plant and are normally not affected by the number of units produced.

      ANS: T   PTS: 1   DIF: Challenging   OBJ: 21-APP
      NAT: BUSPROG: Analytic   KEY: Bloom's: Knowledge

59.   In an absorption costing income statement, the manufacturing margin is the excess of sales over the variable cost of goods sold.

      ANS: F   PTS: 1   DIF: Challenging   OBJ: 21-APP
      NAT: BUSPROG: Analytic   KEY: Bloom's: Knowledge

60.   Assuming no other changes, operating income will be the same under both the variable and absorption costing methods when the number of units manufactured equals the number of units sold.

      ANS: T   PTS: 1   DIF: Challenging   OBJ: 21-APP
      NAT: BUSPROG: Analytic   KEY: Bloom's: Knowledge

MULTIPLE CHOICE

1.   Cost behavior refers to the manner in which:
      a.   a cost changes as the related activity changes
      b.   a cost is allocated to products
      c.   a cost is used in setting selling prices
      d.   a cost is estimated

      ANS: A   PTS: 1   DIF: Easy   OBJ: LO: 21-01
      NAT: BUSPROG: Analytic   KEY: Bloom's: Knowledge

2.   The three most common cost behavior classifications are:
      a.   variable costs, product costs, and sunk costs
      b.   fixed costs, variable costs, and mixed costs

    c. variable costs, period costs, and differential costs
    d. variable costs, sunk costs, and opportunity costs

ANS: B   PTS: 1   DIF: Easy   OBJ: LO: 21-01
NAT: BUSPROG: Analytic   KEY: Bloom's: Knowledge

3. Costs that remain constant in total dollar amount as the level of activity changes are called:
    a. fixed costs
    b. mixed costs
    c. product costs
    d. variable costs

ANS: A   PTS: 1   DIF: Easy   OBJ: LO: 21-01
NAT: BUSPROG: Analytic   KEY: Bloom's: Knowledge

Graph 1

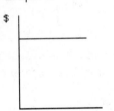

Total units produced

Graph 2

Total units produced

Graph 3

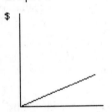

Total units produced

Graph 4

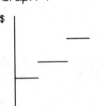

Total units produced

FIGURE 20.1

4. Which of the graphs in Figure 20-1 illustrates the behavior of a total fixed cost?
    a. Graph 2
    b. Graph 3
    c. Graph 4
    d. Graph 1

ANS: D   PTS: 1   DIF: Easy   OBJ: LO: 21-01
NAT: BUSPROG: Analytic   KEY: Bloom's: Application

5. Which of the graphs in Figure 20-1 illustrates the behavior of a total variable cost?
    a. Graph 2
    b. Graph 3
    c. Graph 4
    d. Graph 1

ANS: B   PTS: 1   DIF: Easy   OBJ: LO: 21-01
NAT: BUSPROG: Analytic   KEY: Bloom's: Application

6. Which of the graphs in Figure 20-1 illustrates the nature of a mixed cost?
   a. Graph 2
   b. Graph 3
   c. Graph 4
   d. Graph 1

ANS: A   PTS: 1   DIF: Easy   OBJ: LO: 21-01
NAT: BUSPROG: Analytic   KEY: Bloom's: Application

7. Which of the following costs is an example of a cost that remains the same in total as the number of units produced changes?
   a. Direct labor
   b. Salary of a factory supervisor
   c. Units of production depreciation on factory equipment
   d. Direct materials

ANS: B   PTS: 1   DIF: Easy   OBJ: LO: 21-01
NAT: BUSPROG: Analytic   KEY: Bloom's: Knowledge

8. Which of the following describes the behavior of the fixed cost per unit?
   a. Decreases with increasing production
   b. Decreases with decreasing production
   c. Remains constant with changes in production
   d. Increases with increasing production

ANS: A   PTS: 1   DIF: Easy   OBJ: LO: 21-01
NAT: BUSPROG: Analytic   KEY: Bloom's: Knowledge

9. Which of the following activity bases would be the most appropriate for food costs of a hospital?
   a. Number of cooks scheduled to work
   b. Number of x-rays taken
   c. Number of patients who stay in the hospital
   d. Number of scheduled surgeries

ANS: C   PTS: 1   DIF: Easy   OBJ: LO: 21-01
NAT: BUSPROG: Analytic   KEY: Bloom's: Knowledge

10. Which of the following activity bases would be the most appropriate for gasoline costs of a delivery service, such as United Postal Service?
    a. Number of trucks employed
    b. Number of miles driven
    c. Number of trucks in service
    d. Number of packages delivered

ANS: B   PTS: 1   DIF: Easy   OBJ: LO: 21-01
NAT: BUSPROG: Analytic   KEY: Bloom's: Knowledge

11. Most operating decisions of management focus on a narrow range of activity called the:
    a. relevant range of production
    b. strategic level of production

c. optimal level of production
d. tactical operating level of production

ANS: A   PTS: 1   DIF: Easy   OBJ: LO: 21-01
NAT: BUSPROG: Analytic   KEY: Bloom's: Knowledge

12. Costs that vary in total in direct proportion to changes in an activity level are called:
a. fixed costs
b. sunk costs
c. variable costs
d. differential costs

ANS: C   PTS: 1   DIF: Easy   OBJ: LO: 21-01
NAT: BUSPROG: Analytic   KEY: Bloom's: Knowledge

13. Which of the following is an example of a cost that varies in total as the number of units produced changes?
a. Salary of a production supervisor
b. Direct materials cost
c. Property taxes on factory buildings
d. Straight-line depreciation on factory equipment

ANS: B   PTS: 1   DIF: Easy   OBJ: LO: 21-01
NAT: BUSPROG: Analytic   KEY: Bloom's: Knowledge

14. Which of the following is NOT an example of a cost that varies in total as the number of units produced changes?
a. Electricity per KWH to operate factory equipment
b. Direct materials cost
c. Straight-line depreciation on factory equipment
d. Wages of assembly worker

ANS: C   PTS: 1   DIF: Easy   OBJ: LO: 21-01
NAT: BUSPROG: Analytic   KEY: Bloom's: Knowledge

15. Which of the following is NOT an example of a cost that varies in total as the number of units produced changes?
a. Electricity per KWH to operate factory equipment
b. Direct materials cost
c. Insurance premiums on factory building
d. Wages of assembly worker

ANS: C   PTS: 1   DIF: Easy   OBJ: LO: 21-01
NAT: BUSPROG: Analytic   KEY: Bloom's: Knowledge

16. Which of the following describes the behavior of the variable cost per unit?
a. Varies in increasing proportion with changes in the activity level
b. Varies in decreasing proportion with changes in the activity level
c. Remains constant with changes in the activity level
d. Varies in direct proportion with the activity level

ANS: C   PTS: 1   DIF: Easy   OBJ: LO: 21-01
NAT: BUSPROG: Analytic   KEY: Bloom's: Knowledge

17. The graph of a variable cost when plotted against its related activity base appears as a:
    a. circle
    b. rectangle
    c. straight line
    d. curved line

    ANS: C   PTS: 1   DIF: Easy   OBJ: LO: 21-01
    NAT: BUSPROG: Analytic   KEY: Bloom's: Knowledge

18. A cost that has characteristics of both a variable cost and a fixed cost is called a:
    a. variable/fixed cost
    b. mixed cost
    c. discretionary cost
    d. sunk cost

    ANS: B   PTS: 1   DIF: Easy   OBJ: LO: 21-01
    NAT: BUSPROG: Analytic   KEY: Bloom's: Knowledge

19. Which of the following costs is a mixed cost?
    a. Salary of a factory supervisor
    b. Electricity costs of $3 per kilowatt-hour
    c. Rental costs of $10,000 per month plus $.30 per machine hour of use
    d. Straight-line depreciation on factory equipment

    ANS: C   PTS: 1   DIF: Easy   OBJ: LO: 21-01
    NAT: BUSPROG: Analytic   KEY: Bloom's: Comprehension

20. For purposes of analysis, mixed costs are generally:
    a. classified as fixed costs
    b. classified as variable costs
    c. classified as period costs
    d. separated into their variable and fixed cost components

    ANS: D   PTS: 1   DIF: Easy   OBJ: LO: 21-01
    NAT: BUSPROG: Analytic   KEY: Bloom's: Knowledge

21. Marcye Co. manufactures office furniture. During the most productive month of the year, 3,500 desks were manufactured at a total cost of $84,400. In its slowest month, the company made 1,100 desks at a cost of $46,000. Using the high-low method of cost estimation, total fixed costs are:
    a. $56,000
    b. $28,400
    c. $17,600
    d. cannot be determined from the data given

    ANS: B   PTS: 1   DIF: Moderate   OBJ: LO: 21-01
    NAT: BUSPROG: Analytic   KEY: Bloom's: Application

22. Given the following cost and activity observations for Bounty Company's utilities, use the high-low method to calculate Bounty' variable utilities costs per machine hour.

	Cost	Machine Hours
March	$3,100	15,000
April	2,700	10,000
May	2,900	12,000
June	3,600	18,000

a. $10.00
b. $.67
c. $.63
d. $.11

ANS: D   PTS: 1   DIF: Moderate   OBJ: LO: 21-01
NAT: BUSPROG: Analytic   KEY: Bloom's: Application

23. Given the following cost and activity observations for Smithson Company's utilities, use the high-low method to calculate Smithson's fixed costs per month. Do not round your intermediate calculations.

	Cost	Machine Hours
January	$52,200	20,000
February	75,000	29,000
March	57,000	22,000
April	64,000	24,500

a. $1,533
b. $2,530
c. $22,800
d. $50,600

ANS: A   PTS: 1   DIF: Moderate   OBJ: LO: 21-01
NAT: BUSPROG: Analytic   KEY: Bloom's: Application

24. Given the following cost and activity observations for Taco Company's utilities, use the high-low method to calculate Taco's variable utilities costs per machine hour.

	Cost	Machine Hours
May	$ 8,300	15,000
June	10,400	20,000
July	7,200	12,000
August	9,500	18,000

a. $10.00
b. $.60
c. $.40
d. $.52

ANS: C   PTS: 1   DIF: Moderate   OBJ: LO: 21-01
NAT: BUSPROG: Analytic   KEY: Bloom's: Application

25. Manley Co. manufactures office furniture. During the most productive month of the year, 4,500 desks were manufactured at a total cost of $86,625. In its slowest month, the company made 1,800 desks at a cost of $49,500. Using the high-low method of cost estimation, total fixed costs are:
a. $61,875
b. $33,875
c. $24,750
d. cannot be determined from the data given

ANS: C   PTS: 1   DIF: Moderate   OBJ: LO: 21-01
NAT: BUSPROG: Analytic   KEY: Bloom's: Application

26. Which of the following statements is true regarding fixed and variable costs?
    a. Both costs are constant when considered on a per unit basis.
    b. Both costs are constant when considered on a total basis.
    c. Fixed costs are constant in total, and variable costs are constant per unit.
    d. Variable costs are constant in total, and fixed costs vary in total.

    ANS: C   PTS: 1   DIF: Moderate   OBJ: LO: 21-01
    NAT: BUSPROG: Analytic   KEY: Bloom's: Knowledge

27. As production increases, what would you expect to happen to fixed cost per unit?
    a. Increase
    b. Decrease
    c. Remain the same
    d. Either increase or decrease, depending on the variable costs

    ANS: B   PTS: 1   DIF: Easy   OBJ: LO: 21-01
    NAT: BUSPROG: Analytic   KEY: Bloom's: Knowledge

28. Knowing how costs behave is useful to management for all the following reasons except for
    a. predicting customer demand.
    b. predicting profits as sales and production volumes change.
    c. estimating costs.
    d. changing an existing product production.

    ANS: A   PTS: 1   DIF: Easy   OBJ: LO: 21-01
    NAT: BUSPROG: Analytic   KEY: Bloom's: Knowledge

29. The manufacturing cost of Prancer Industries for three months of the year are provided below:

	Total Cost	Production
April	$ 60,700	1,200 Units
May	80,920	1,800
June	100,300	2,400

    Using the high-low method, the variable cost per unit, and the total fixed costs are:
    a. $32.30 per unit and $77,520 respectively.
    b. $33 per unit and $21,100 respectively.
    c. $32 per unit and $76,800 respectively.
    d. $32.30 per unit and $22,780 respectively.

    ANS: B   PTS: 1   DIF: Moderate   OBJ: LO: 21-01
    NAT: BUSPROG: Analytic   KEY: Bloom's: Knowledge

30. As production increases, what should happen to the variable costs per unit?
    a. Stay the same.
    b. Increase.
    c. Decrease.
    d. Either increase or decrease, depending on the fixed costs.

    ANS: A   PTS: 1   DIF: Moderate   OBJ: LO: 21-01
    NAT: BUSPROG: Analytic   KEY: Bloom's: Knowledge

31. Cool-It Company manufactures and sells commercial air conditioners. Because of current trends, it expects to increase sales by 10 percent next year. If this expected level of production and sales occurs and plant expansion is not needed, how should this increase affect next year's total amounts for the following costs.

	Variable Costs	Fixed Costs	Mixed Costs
a.	increase	increase	increase
b.	increase	no change	increase
c.	no change	no change	increase
d.	decrease	increase	increase

ANS: B   PTS: 1   DIF: Moderate   OBJ: LO: 21-01
NAT: BUSPROG: Analytic   KEY: Bloom's: Application

32. Given the following costs and activities for Downing Company electrical costs, use the high-low method to calculate Downing's variable electrical costs per machine hour.

	Costs	Machine Hours
April	$11,700	15,000
May	$13,200	17,500
June	$11,400	14,500

   a. $2.08
   b. $6.00
   c. $0.60
   d. $1.20

ANS: C   PTS: 1   DIF: Moderate   OBJ: LO: 21-01
NAT: BUSPROG: Analytic   KEY: Bloom's: Application

33. The systematic examination of the relationships among selling prices, volume of sales and production, costs, and profits is termed:
   a. contribution margin analysis
   b. cost-volume-profit analysis
   c. budgetary analysis
   d. gross profit analysis

ANS: B   PTS: 1   DIF: Easy   OBJ: LO: 21-02
NAT: BUSPROG: Analytic   KEY: Bloom's: Knowledge

34. In cost-volume-profit analysis, all costs are classified into the following two categories:
   a. mixed costs and variable costs
   b. sunk costs and fixed costs
   c. discretionary costs and sunk costs
   d. variable costs and fixed costs

ANS: D   PTS: 1   DIF: Easy   OBJ: LO: 21-02
NAT: BUSPROG: Analytic   KEY: Bloom's: Knowledge

35. Contribution margin is:
   a. the excess of sales revenue over variable cost
   b. another term for volume in the "cost-volume-profit" analysis

c. profit
d. the same as sales revenue

ANS: A   PTS: 1   DIF: Easy   OBJ: LO: 21-02
NAT: BUSPROG: Analytic   KEY: Bloom's: Knowledge

36. The contribution margin ratio is:
a. the same as the variable cost ratio
b. the same as profit
c. the portion of equity contributed by the stockholders
d. the same as the profit-volume ratio

ANS: D   PTS: 1   DIF: Easy   OBJ: LO: 21-02
NAT: BUSPROG: Analytic   KEY: Bloom's: Knowledge

37. If sales are $820,000, variable costs are 45% of sales, and operating income is $260,000, what is the contribution margin ratio?
a. 45%
b. 55%
c. 62%
d. 32%

ANS: B   PTS: 1   DIF: Moderate   OBJ: LO: 21-02
NAT: BUSPROG: Analytic   KEY: Bloom's: Application

38. What ratio indicates the percentage of each sales dollar that is available to cover fixed costs and to provide a profit?
a. Margin of safety ratio
b. Contribution margin ratio
c. Costs and expenses ratio
d. Profit ratio

ANS: B   PTS: 1   DIF: Easy   OBJ: LO: 21-02
NAT: BUSPROG: Analytic   KEY: Bloom's: Knowledge

39. A firm operated at 80% of capacity for the past year, during which fixed costs were $210,000, variable costs were 70% of sales, and sales were $1,000,000. Operating profit was:
a. $90,000
b. $210,000
c. $590,000
d. $490,000

ANS: A   PTS: 1   DIF: Moderate   OBJ: LO: 21-02
NAT: BUSPROG: Analytic   KEY: Bloom's: Application

40. If sales are $425,000, variable costs are 62% of sales, and operating income is $50,000, what is the contribution margin ratio?
a. 38%
b. 26.8%
c. 11.8%
d. 62%

ANS: A   PTS: 1   DIF: Moderate   OBJ: LO: 21-02
NAT: BUSPROG: Analytic   KEY: Bloom's: Application

41.   Variable costs as a percentage of sales for Lemon Inc. are 80%, current sales are $600,000, and fixed costs are $130,000. How much will operating income change if sales increase by $40,000?
      a. $8,000 increase
      b. $8,000 decrease
      c. $30,000 decrease
      d. $30,000 increase

      ANS: A   PTS: 1   DIF: Moderate   OBJ: LO: 21-02
      NAT: BUSPROG: Analytic   KEY: Bloom's: Application

42.   Spice Inc.'s unit selling price is $60, the unit variable costs are $35, fixed costs are $125,000, and current sales are 10,000 units. How much will operating income change if sales increase by 8,000 units?
      a. $150,000 decrease
      b. $175,000 increase
      c. $200,000 increase
      d. $150,000 increase

      ANS: C   PTS: 1   DIF: Challenging   OBJ: LO: 21-02
      NAT: BUSPROG: Analytic   KEY: Bloom's: Application

43.   If sales are $914,000, variable costs are $498,130, and operating income is $260,000, what is the contribution margin ratio?
      a.   52.2%
      b.   28.4%
      c.   54.5%
      d.   45.5%

      ANS: D   PTS: 1   DIF: Moderate   OBJ: LO: 21-02
      NAT: BUSPROG: Analytic   KEY: Bloom's: Application

44.   A firm operated at 80% of capacity for the past year, during which fixed costs were $330,000, variable costs were 70% of sales, and sales were $1,000,000. Operating profit was:
      a. $140,000
      b.   ($30,000)
      c. $370,000
      d. $670,000

      ANS: B   PTS: 1   DIF: Moderate   OBJ: LO: 21-02
      NAT: BUSPROG: Analytic   KEY: Bloom's: Application

45.   If sales are $525,000, variable costs are 53% of sales, and operating income is $50,000, what is the contribution margin ratio?
      a.   47%
      b.   26.5%
      c.   9.5%
      d.   53%

      ANS: A   PTS: 1   DIF: Moderate   OBJ: LO: 21-02
      NAT: BUSPROG: Analytic   KEY: Bloom's: Application

46. Zipee Inc.'s unit selling price is $90, the unit variable costs are $40.50, fixed costs are $170,000, and current sales are 12,000 units. How much will operating income change if sales increase by 5,000 units?
    a. $125,000 decrease
    b. $175,000 increase
    c. $75,000 increase
    d. $247,500 increase

    ANS: D   PTS: 1   DIF: Challenging   OBJ: LO: 21-02
    NAT: BUSPROG: Analytic   KEY: Bloom's: Application

47. Zeke Company sells 25,000 units at $21 per unit. Variable costs are $10 per unit, and fixed costs are $75,000. The contribution margin ratio and the unit contribution margin are:
    a. 47% and $11 per unit
    b. 53% and $7 per unit
    c. 47% and $8 per unit
    d. 52% and $11 per unit

    ANS: D   PTS: 1   DIF: Moderate   OBJ: LO: 21-02
    NAT: BUSPROG: Analytic   KEY: Bloom's: Application

48. If the contribution margin ratio for France Company is 45%, sales were $425,000. and fixed costs were $100,000, what was the income from operations?
    a. $233,750
    b. $91,250
    c. $191,250
    d. $133,750

    ANS: B   PTS: 1   DIF: Moderate   OBJ: LO: 21-02
    NAT: BUSPROG: Analytic   KEY: Bloom's: Application

49. If fixed costs are $250,000, the unit selling price is $125, and the unit variable costs are $73, what is the break-even sales (units)?
    a. 3,425 units
    b. 2,381 units
    c. 2,000 units
    d. 4,808 units

    ANS: D   PTS: 1   DIF: Easy   OBJ: LO: 21-03
    NAT: BUSPROG: Analytic   KEY: Bloom's: Application

50. If fixed costs are $750,000 and variable costs are 60% of sales, what is the break-even point in sales dollars?
    a. $1,250,000
    b. $450,000
    c. $1,875,000
    d. $300,000

    ANS: C   PTS: 1   DIF: Easy   OBJ: LO: 21-03
    NAT: BUSPROG: Analytic   KEY: Bloom's: Application

51.   If fixed costs are $1,200,000, the unit selling price is $240, and the unit variable costs are $110, what
      is the amount of sales required to realize an operating income of $200,000?
      a.   9,231 units
      b.   12,000 units
      c.   10,769 units
      d.   5,833 units

      ANS: C   PTS: 1   DIF: Easy   OBJ: LO: 21-03
      NAT: BUSPROG: Analytic   KEY: Bloom's: Application

52.   If fixed costs are $300,000, the unit selling price is $31, and the unit variable costs are $22, what is
      the break-even sales (units) if fixed costs are reduced by $30,000?
      a.   30,000 units
      b.   8,710 units
      c.   12,273 units
      d.   20,000 units

      ANS: A   PTS: 1   DIF: Easy   OBJ: LO: 21-03
      NAT: BUSPROG: Analytic   KEY: Bloom's: Application

53.   If fixed costs are $500,000, the unit selling price is $55, and the unit variable costs are $30, what is
      the break-even sales (units) if fixed costs are increased by $80,000?
      a.   10,545 units
      b.   19,333 units
      c.   23,200 units
      d.   25,000 units

      ANS: C   PTS: 1   DIF: Easy   OBJ: LO: 21-03
      NAT: BUSPROG: Analytic   KEY: Bloom's: Application

54.   If fixed costs are $350,000, the unit selling price is $29, and the unit variable costs are $20, what is
      the break-even sales (units) if the variable costs are decreased by $4?
      a.   26,924 units
      b.   12,069 units
      c.   21,875 units
      d.   38,889 units

      ANS: A   PTS: 1   DIF: Easy   OBJ: LO: 21-03
      NAT: BUSPROG: Analytic   KEY: Bloom's: Application

55.   If fixed costs are $450,000, the unit selling price is $75, and the unit variable costs are $50, what are
      the old and new break-even sales (units) if the unit selling price increases by $10?
      a.   6,000 units and 5,294 units
      b.   18,000 units and 6,000 units
      c.   18,000 units and 12,858 units
      d.   9,000 units and 15,000 units

      ANS: C   PTS: 1   DIF: Easy   OBJ: LO: 21-03
      NAT: BUSPROG: Analytic   KEY: Bloom's: Application

56.   If fixed costs are $400,000 and the unit contribution margin is $20, what amount of units must be
      sold in order to have a zero profit?
      a.   25,000 units
      b.   10,000 units

c. 400,000 units
d. 20,000 units

ANS: D   PTS: 1   DIF: Easy   OBJ: LO: 21-03
NAT: BUSPROG: Analytic   KEY: Bloom's: Application

57. If fixed costs are $700,000 and the unit contribution margin is $17, what amount of units must be sold in order to realize an operating income of $100,000?
   a. 5,000
   b. 41,176
   c. 47,059
   d. 58,882

ANS: C   PTS: 1   DIF: Moderate   OBJ: LO: 21-03
NAT: BUSPROG: Analytic   KEY: Bloom's: Application

58. If fixed costs are $500,000 and the unit contribution margin is $20, what is the break-even point in units if fixed costs are reduced by $80,000?
   a. 25,000
   b. 29,000
   c. 4,000
   d. 21,000

ANS: D   PTS: 1   DIF: Moderate   OBJ: LO: 21-03
NAT: BUSPROG: Analytic   KEY: Bloom's: Application

59. If fixed costs are $600,000 and the unit contribution margin is $40, what is the break-even point if fixed costs are increased by $90,000?
   a. 17,250
   b. 15,000
   c. 8,333
   d. 9,667

ANS: A   PTS: 1   DIF: Moderate   OBJ: LO: 21-03
NAT: BUSPROG: Analytic   KEY: Bloom's: Application

60. If fixed costs are $561,000 and the unit contribution margin is $8.00, what is the break-even point in units if variable costs are decreased by $.50 a unit?
   a. 66,000
   b. 70,125
   c. 74,800
   d. 60,000

ANS: A   PTS: 1   DIF: Moderate   OBJ: LO: 21-03
NAT: BUSPROG: Analytic   KEY: Bloom's: Application

61. If variable costs per unit increased because of an increase in hourly wage rates, the break-even point would:
   a. decrease
   b. increase
   c. remain the same
   d. increase or decrease, depending upon the percentage increase in wage rates

ANS: B   PTS: 1   DIF: Moderate   OBJ: LO: 21-03
NAT: BUSPROG: Analytic   KEY: Bloom's: Knowledge

62. If variable costs per unit decreased because of a decrease in utility rates, the break-even point would:
    a. decrease
    b. increase
    c. remain the same
    d. increase or decrease, depending upon the percentage increase in utility rates

ANS: A   PTS: 1   DIF: Moderate   OBJ: LO: 21-03
NAT: BUSPROG: Analytic   KEY: Bloom's: Knowledge

63. If fixed costs increased and variable costs per unit decreased, the break-even point would:
    a. increase
    b. decrease
    c. remain the same
    d. cannot be determined from the data provided

ANS: D   PTS: 1   DIF: Easy   OBJ: LO: 21-03
NAT: BUSPROG: Analytic   KEY: Bloom's: Knowledge

64. Which of the following conditions would cause the break-even point to decrease?
    a. Total fixed costs increase
    b. Unit selling price decreases
    c. Unit variable cost decreases
    d. Unit variable cost increases

ANS: C   PTS: 1   DIF: Moderate   OBJ: LO: 21-03
NAT: BUSPROG: Analytic   KEY: Bloom's: Knowledge

65. Which of the following conditions would cause the break-even point to increase?
    a. Total fixed costs decrease
    b. Unit selling price increases
    c. Unit variable cost decreases
    d. Unit variable cost increases

ANS: D   PTS: 1   DIF: Moderate   OBJ: LO: 21-03
NAT: BUSPROG: Analytic   KEY: Bloom's: Knowledge

66. Which of the following conditions would cause the break-even point to increase?
    a. Total fixed costs increase
    b. Unit selling price increases
    c. Unit variable cost decreases
    d. Total fixed costs decrease

ANS: A   PTS: 1   DIF: Moderate   OBJ: LO: 21-03
NAT: BUSPROG: Analytic   KEY: Bloom's: Knowledge

67. Calzone Co. has budgeted salary increases to factory supervisors totaling 8%. If selling prices and all other cost relationships are held constant, next year's break-even point:
    a. will decrease by 8%
    b. will increase by 8%
    c. cannot be determined from the data given
    d. will increase at a rate greater than 8%

ANS: C   PTS: 1   DIF: Moderate   OBJ: LO: 21-03
NAT: BUSPROG: Analytic   KEY: Bloom's: Application

68. Flying Cloud Co. has the following operating data for its manufacturing operations:

Unit selling price $ 250
Unit variable cost   100
Total fixed costs $840,000

The company has decided to increase the wages of hourly workers which will increase the unit
variable cost by 10%. Increases in the salaries of factory supervisors and property taxes for the
factory will increase fixed costs by 4%. If sales prices are held constant, the next break-even point
for Flying Cloud Co. will be:
a.   increased by 640 units
b.   increased by 400 units
c.   decreased by 640 units
d.   increased by 800 units

ANS: A   PTS: 1   DIF: Moderate   OBJ: LO: 21-03
NAT: BUSPROG: Analytic   KEY: Bloom's: Application

69. If fixed costs are $850,000 and variable costs are 60% of sales, what is the break-even point
(dollars)?
a. $2,125,000
b. $ 340,000
c. $3,400,000
d. $1,416,666

ANS: A   PTS: 1   DIF: Easy   OBJ: LO: 21-03
NAT: BUSPROG: Analytic   KEY: Bloom's: Application

70. If fixed costs are $256,000, the unit selling price is $36, and the unit variable costs are $20, what is
the break-even sales (units)?
a.   12,800 units
b.   4,571 units
c.   16,000 units
d.   7,111 units

ANS: C   PTS: 1   DIF: Easy   OBJ: LO: 21-03
NAT: BUSPROG: Analytic   KEY: Bloom's: Application

71. If fixed costs are $1,500,000, the unit selling price is $250, and the unit variable costs are $130, what
is the amount of sales required to realize an operating income of $200,000?
a.   14,166 units
b.   12,500 units
c.   16,000 units
d.   11,538 units

ANS: A   PTS: 1   DIF: Easy   OBJ: LO: 21-03
NAT: BUSPROG: Analytic   KEY: Bloom's: Application

72. If fixed costs are $490,000, the unit selling price is $35, and the unit variable costs are $20, what is the break-even sales (units) if fixed costs are reduced by $40,000?
    a. 32,667 units
    b. 14,000 units
    c. 30,000 units
    d. 24,500 units

    ANS: C   PTS: 1   DIF: Easy   OBJ: LO: 21-03
    NAT: BUSPROG: Analytic   KEY: Bloom's: Application

73. If fixed costs are $400,000, the unit selling price is $25, and the unit variable costs are $15, what is the break-even sales (units) if the variable costs are increased by $2?
    a. 50,000 units
    b. 30,770 units
    c. 40,000 units
    d. 26,667 units

    ANS: A   PTS: 1   DIF: Easy   OBJ: LO: 21-03
    NAT: BUSPROG: Analytic   KEY: Bloom's: Application

74. If fixed costs are $240,000, the unit selling price is $32, and the unit variable costs are $20, what are the old and new break-even sales (units) if the unit selling price increases by $4?
    a. 7,500 units and 6,667 units
    b. 20,000 units and 30,000 units
    c. 20,000 units and 15,000 units
    d. 12,000 units and 15,000 units

    ANS: C   PTS: 1   DIF: Easy   OBJ: LO: 21-03
    NAT: BUSPROG: Analytic   KEY: Bloom's: Application

75. When the fixed costs are $120,000 and the contribution margin is $30, the break-even point is
    a. 16,000 units
    b. 8,000 units
    c. 6,000 units
    d. 4,000 units

    ANS: D   PTS: 1   DIF: Easy   OBJ: LO: 21-03
    NAT: BUSPROG: Analytic   KEY: Bloom's: Application

76. If fixed costs are $46,800, the unit selling price is $42, and the unit variable costs are $24, what is the break-even sales (units)?
    a. 2,400
    b. 1,950
    c. 1,114
    d. 2,600

    ANS: D   PTS: 1   DIF: Moderate   OBJ: LO: 21-03
    NAT: BUSPROG: Analytic   KEY: Bloom's: Application

77. If fixed costs are $46,800, the unit selling price is $42, and the unit variable costs are $24, what is the break-even sales (unit) if the variable costs are decreased by $2?
    a. 2,127
    b. 1,114

c. 2,340
d. 1,950

ANS: C   PTS: 1   DIF: Moderate   OBJ: LO: 21-03
NAT: BUSPROG: Analytic   KEY: Bloom's: Application

78. The point where the sales line and the total costs line intersect on the cost-volume-profit chart represents:
   a. the maximum possible operating loss
   b. the maximum possible operating income
   c. the total fixed costs
   d. the break-even point

ANS: D   PTS: 1   DIF: Easy   OBJ: LO: 21-04
NAT: BUSPROG: Analytic   KEY: Bloom's: Knowledge

79. The point where the profit line intersects the horizontal axis on the profit-volume chart represents:
   a. the maximum possible operating loss
   b. the maximum possible operating income
   c. the total fixed costs
   d. the break-even point

ANS: D   PTS: 1   DIF: Moderate   OBJ: LO: 21-04
NAT: BUSPROG: Analytic   KEY: Bloom's: Knowledge

80. With the aid of computer software, managers can vary assumptions regarding selling prices, costs, and volume and can immediately see the effects of each change on the break-even point and profit. This is called:
   a. "What if" or sensitivity analysis
   b. vary the data analysis
   c. computer aided analysis
   d. data gathering

ANS: A   PTS: 1   DIF: Easy   OBJ: LO: 21-04
NAT: BUSPROG: Analytic   KEY: Bloom's: Knowledge

81. In a cost-volume-profit chart, the
   a. total cost line begins at zero.
   b. slope of the total cost line is dependent on the fixed cost per unit.
   c. total cost line begins at the total fixed cost value on the vertical axis.
   d. total cost line normally ends at the highest sales value.

ANS: C   PTS: 1   DIF: Moderate   OBJ: LO: 21-04
NAT: BUSPROG: Analytic   KEY: Bloom's: Knowledge

82. The relative distribution of sales among the various products sold by a business is termed the:
   a. business's basket of goods
   b. contribution margin mix
   c. sales mix
   d. product portfolio

ANS: C   PTS: 1   DIF: Easy   OBJ: LO: 21-05
NAT: BUSPROG: Analytic   KEY: Bloom's: Knowledge

83. When a business sells more than one product at varying selling prices, the business's break-even point can be determined as long as the number of products does not exceed:
    a. two
    b. three
    c. fifteen
    d. there is no limit

    ANS: D   PTS: 1   DIF: Moderate   OBJ: LO: 21-05
    NAT: BUSPROG: Analytic   KEY: Bloom's: Knowledge

Carter Co. sells two products, Arks and Bins. Last year Carter sold 14,000 units of Arks and 56,000 units of Bins. Related data are:

Product	Unit Selling Price	Unit Variable Cost	Unit Contribution Margin
Arks	$120	$80	$40
Bins	80	60	20

84. What was Carter Co.'s sales mix last year?
    a. 20% Arks, 80% Bins
    b. 12% Arks, 28% Bins
    c. 70% Arks, 30% Bins
    d. 40% Arks, 20% Bins

    ANS: A   PTS: 1   DIF: Easy   OBJ: LO: 21-05
    NAT: BUSPROG: Analytic   KEY: Bloom's: Application

85. What was Carter Co.'s weighted average unit selling price?
    a. $200
    b. $100
    c. $ 80
    d. $ 88

    ANS: D   PTS: 1   DIF: Easy   OBJ: LO: 21-05
    NAT: BUSPROG: Analytic   KEY: Bloom's: Application

86. What was Carter Co.'s weighted average variable cost?
    a. $140
    b. $ 70
    c. $ 64
    d. $ 60

    ANS: C   PTS: 1   DIF: Easy   OBJ: LO: 21-05
    NAT: BUSPROG: Analytic   KEY: Bloom's: Application

87. What was Carter Co.'s weighted average unit contribution margin?
    a. $24
    b. $60
    c. $92
    d. $20

    ANS: A   PTS: 1   DIF: Easy   OBJ: LO: 21-05
    NAT: BUSPROG: Analytic   KEY: Bloom's: Application

88. Assuming that last year's fixed costs totaled $960,000, what was Carter Co.'s break-even point in units?
    a. 40,000 units
    b. 12,000 units
    c. 35,000 units
    d. 28,000 units

    ANS: A   PTS: 1   DIF: Easy   OBJ: LO: 21-05
    NAT: BUSPROG: Analytic   KEY: Bloom's: Application

89. If a business had sales of $4,000,000 and a margin of safety of 25%, the break-even point was:
    a. $5,000,000
    b. $3,000,000
    c. $12,000,000
    d. $1,000,000

    ANS: B   PTS: 1   DIF: Moderate   OBJ: LO: 21-05
    NAT: BUSPROG: Analytic   KEY: Bloom's: Application

90. Forde Co. has an operating leverage of 4. Sales are expected to increase by 12% next year. Operating income is:
    a. unaffected
    b. expected to increase by 3%
    c. expected to increase by 48%
    d. expected to increase by 4 %

    ANS: C   PTS: 1   DIF: Moderate   OBJ: LO: 21-05
    NAT: BUSPROG: Analytic   KEY: Bloom's: Application

91. If sales are $400,000, variable costs are 80% of sales, and operating income is $40,000, what is the operating leverage?
    a. 0
    b. 7.500
    c. 2.0
    d. 1.333

    ANS: C   PTS: 1   DIF: Moderate   OBJ: LO: 21-05
    NAT: BUSPROG: Analytic   KEY: Bloom's: Application

92. The difference between the current sales revenue and the sales at the break-even point is called the:
    a. contribution margin
    b. margin of safety
    c. price factor
    d. operating leverage

    ANS: B   PTS: 1   DIF: Easy   OBJ: LO: 21-05
    NAT: BUSPROG: Analytic   KEY: Bloom's: Application

93. Cost-volume-profit analysis cannot be used if which of the following occurs?
    a. Costs cannot be properly classified into fixed and variable costs
    b. The total fixed costs change
    c. The per unit variable costs change
    d. Per unit sales prices change

ANS: A   PTS: 1   DIF: Moderate   OBJ: LO: 21-05
NAT: BUSPROG: Analytic   KEY: Bloom's: Application

94.   Assume that Corn Co. sold 8,000 units of Product A and 2,000 units of Product B during the past year. The unit contribution margins for Products A and B are $30 and $60 respectively. Corn has fixed costs of $378,000. The break-even point in units is:
    a.   8,000 units
    b.   6,300 units
    c.   12,600 units
    d.   10,500 units

ANS: D   PTS: 1   DIF: Moderate   OBJ: LO: 21-05
NAT: BUSPROG: Analytic   KEY: Bloom's: Application

95.   If sales are $500,000, variable costs are 75% of sales, and operating income is $40,000, what is the operating leverage?
    a.   0
    b.   1.25
    c.   1.3
    d.   3.1

ANS: D   PTS: 1   DIF: Moderate   OBJ: LO: 21-05
NAT: BUSPROG: Analytic   KEY: Bloom's: Application

96.   The Rocky Company reports the following data.

Sales	$800,000
Variable costs	$300,000
Fixed costs	$120,000

Rocky Company's operating leverage is:
    a.   6.7
    b.   2.7
    c.   1.0
    d.   1.3

ANS: D   PTS: 1   DIF: Moderate   OBJ: LO: 21-05
NAT: BUSPROG: Analytic   KEY: Bloom's: Application

Rusty Co. sells two products, X and Y. Last year Rusty sold 5,000 units of X's and 35,000 units of Y's. Related data are:

Product	Unit Selling Price Price	Unit Variable Cost	Unit contribution Margin
X	$110.00	$70.00	$40.00
Y	70.00	50.00	$20.00

97.   What was Rusty Co.'s sales mix last year?
    a.   58% X's, 42% Y's
    b.   60% X's, 40% Y's
    c.   30% X's, 70% Y's
    d.   12.5% X's, 87.5% Y's

ANS: D PTS: 1   DIF: Moderate OBJ: LO: 21-05
NAT: BUSPROG: Analytic   KEY: Bloom's: Application

98. What was Rusty Co.'s weighted average unit selling price?
  a. $180.00
  b. $75.00
  c. $100.00
  d. $110.00

ANS: B PTS: 1   DIF: Moderate OBJ: LO: 21-05
NAT: BUSPROG: Analytic   KEY: Bloom's: Application

99. What was Rusty Co.'s weighted average unit variable cost?
  a. $52.50
  b. $70.00
  c. $120.00
  d. $50.00

ANS: A PTS: 1   DIF: Moderate OBJ: LO: 21-05
NAT: BUSPROG: Analytic   KEY: Bloom's: Application

100. What was Rusty Co.'s weighted average unit contribution margin?
  a. $60.00
  b. $20.00
  c. $40.00
  d. $22.50

ANS: D PTS: 1   DIF: Moderate OBJ: LO: 21-05
NAT: BUSPROG: Analytic   KEY: Bloom's: Application

101. Assuming that last year's fixed costs totaled $675,000. What was Rusty Co.'s break-even point in units?
  a. 16,875 units
  b. 30,100 units
  c. 30,000 units
  d. 11,250 units

ANS: C PTS: 1   DIF: Moderate OBJ: LO: 21-05
NAT: BUSPROG: Analytic   KEY: Bloom's: Application

102. If sales are $400,000, variable costs are 75% of sales, and operating income is $50,000, what is the operating leverage?
  a. 2.5
  b. 7.5
  c. 2.0
  d. 0

ANS: C PTS: 1   DIF: Moderate OBJ: LO: 21-05
NAT: BUSPROG: Analytic   KEY: Bloom's: Application

103. Which of the following is *not* an assumption underlying cost-volume-profit analysis?
  a. The break-even point will be passed during the period.
  b. Total sales and total costs can be represented by straight lines.

c. Costs can be accurately divided into fixed and variable components.
d. The sales mix is constant.

ANS: A   PTS: 1   DIF: Moderate   OBJ: LO: 21-05
NAT: BUSPROG: Analytic   KEY: Bloom's: Knowledge

104. When units manufactured exceed units sold:
a. variable costing income equals absorption costing income
b. variable costing income is less than absorption costing income
c. variable costing income is greater than absorption costing income
d. variable costing income is greater by the number of units produced multiplied by the
     variable cost ratio.

ANS: B   PTS: 1   DIF: Easy   OBJ: 21-APP
NAT: BUSPROG: Analytic   KEY: Bloom's: Knowledge

Harold Corporation just started business in January 2012. They had no beginning inventories.
During 2012 they manufactured 12,000 units of product, and sold 10,000 units. The selling price of
each unit was $20. Variable manufacturing costs were $4 per unit, and variable selling and
administrative costs were $2 per unit. Fixed manufacturing costs were $24,000 and fixed selling and
administrative costs were $6,000.

105. What would be the Harold Corporations net income for 2012 using absorption costing?
a. $114,000
b. $110,000
c. $4,000
d. $106,000

ANS: A   PTS: 1   DIF: Moderate   OBJ: 21-APP
NAT: BUSPROG: Analytic   KEY: Bloom's: Application

106. What would be the Harold Corporations Net income for 2012 using variable costing?
a. $114,000
b. $110,000
c. $4,000
d. $106,000

ANS: B   PTS: 1   DIF: Moderate   OBJ: 21-APP
NAT: BUSPROG: Analytic   KEY: Bloom's: Application

107. What would be the difference in Harold Corporation's Net income for 2012 if they used variable
costing instead of absorption costing?
a. No difference
b. $2,000 greater
c. $4,000 less
d. $6,000 less

ANS: C   PTS: 1   DIF: Moderate   OBJ: 21-APP
NAT: BUSPROG: Analytic   KEY: Bloom's: Application

108. Given the following cost data, what type of cost is shown?

Total Cost	# of units
$500	1
$1,000	2
$1,500	3
$2,000	4

a. mixed cost
b. variable cost
c. fixed cost
d. none of the above

ANS: B PTS: 1 DIF: Moderate OBJ: LO: 21-01
NAT: BUSPROG: Analytic KEY: Bloom's: Application

109. Given the following cost data, what type of cost is shown?

Cost per unit	# of units
$5,000	1
$2,500	2
$1,667	3
$1,250	4

a. mixed cost
b. variable cost
c. fixed cost
d. none of the above

ANS: C PTS: 1 DIF: Moderate OBJ: LO: 21-01
NAT: BUSPROG: Analytic KEY: Bloom's: Application

110. Given the following cost data, what type of cost is shown?

Total Cost	# of units
$3,500	1
$4,000	2
$4,500	3
$5,000	4

a. mixed cost
b. variable cost
c. fixed cost
d. none of the above

ANS: A PTS: 1 DIF: Challenging OBJ: LO: 21-01
NAT: BUSPROG: Analytic KEY: Bloom's: Application

OTHER

1. The manufacturing cost of Mocha Industries for three months of the year are provided below:

	Total Cost	Production
April	$ 63,100	1,100 Units
May	80,920	1,800
June	100,900	2,600

    Using the high-low method, determine the (a) variable cost per unit, and (b) the total fixed costs.

    ANS:
    a. $25.20 per unit = ($100,900 − $63,100) / (2,600 − 1,100)

    b. $35,380 = $100,900 − ($25.20 × 2,600)

    PTS: 1   DIF: Moderate   OBJ: LO: 21-01   NAT: BUSPROG: Analytic
    KEY: Bloom's: Application

2. The manufacturing cost of Carrie Industries for the first three months of the year are provided below:

	Total Cost	Production
January	$ 93,300	2,300 Units
February	115,500	3,100
March	79,500	1,900

    Using the high-low method, determine the (a) variable cost per unit, and (b) the total fixed cost.

    ANS:
    a. $30 per unit = ($115,500 − $79,500) / (3,100 − 1,900)

    b. $22,500 = $115,500 − ($30 × 3,100)

    PTS: 1   DIF: Moderate   OBJ: LO: 21-01   NAT: BUSPROG: Analytic
    KEY: Bloom's: Application

3. Carmelita Company sells 40,000 units at $18 per unit. Fixed costs are $62,000 and income from operations is $258,000. Determine the (a) variable cost per unit, (b) unit contribution margin, and (c) contribution margin ratio.

    ANS:
    a.

Sales	$720,000	(40,000 units × $18)
Variable costs	400,000	(40,000 units × $10)
Contribution margin	320,000	(40,000 units × $8)
Fixed costs	62,000	
Income from operations	$258,000	

b. $8 per unit = $18 − $10

c. $8 / $18 = 44.44%

PTS: 1   DIF: Easy   OBJ: LO: 21-02   NAT: BUSPROG: Analytic
KEY: Bloom's: Application

4. Penny Company sells 25,000 units at $59 per unit. Variable costs are $29 per unit, and loss from operations is ($50,000). Determine the (a) unit contribution margin (b) contribution margin ratio, and (c) fixed costs per unit at production of 25,000 units.

ANS:
a. $30 per unit = $59 − $29

b. $30 /$59 = 50.8%

c.

Sales	$1,475,000	(25,000 units × $59)
Variable costs	725,000	(25,000 units × $29)
Contribution margin	750,000	(25,000 units × $30)
Fixed costs	800,000	
Income from operations	($ 50,000)	

$800,000/25,000 = $32

PTS: 1   DIF: Moderate   OBJ: LO: 21-02   NAT: BUSPROG: Analytic
KEY: Bloom's: Application

5. Gladstorm Enterprises sells a product for $60 per unit. The variable cost is $20 per unit, while fixed costs are $85,000. Determine the (a) break-even point in sales units, and (b) break-even point in sales units if the selling price increased to $80 per unit. Round your answer to the nearest whole number.

ANS:
a. SP $60 − VC $20 = CM $40
   $85,000 / $40 = 2,125 units

b. SP $80 − VC $20 = CM $60
   $85,000 / $60 = 1,417 units

PTS: 1   DIF: Easy   OBJ: LO: 21-03   NAT: BUSPROG: Analytic
KEY: Bloom's: Application

6. Mia Enterprises sells a product for $90 per unit. The variable cost is $40 per unit, while fixed costs are $75,000. Determine the (a) break-even point in sales units, and (b) break-even point in sales units if the selling price increased to $100 per unit.

ANS:
a. SP $90 − VC $40 = CM $50 per unit
$75,000 / $50 = 1,500 units

b. SP $100 − VC $40 = CM $60 per unit
$75,000 / $60 = 1,250 units

PTS: 1   DIF: Easy   OBJ: LO: 21-03   NAT: BUSPROG: Analytic
KEY: Bloom's: Application

7.   The Atlantic Company sells a product with a break-even point of 3,000 sales units. The variable cost
     is $60 per unit, and fixed costs are $270,000. Determine the (a) unit sales price, and (b) break-even
     points in sales units if the company desires a target profit of $36,000.

     ANS:
     a.   3,000 units = $270,000 / ($X − $60)
                X = $150

     b.   3,400 units = ($270,000 + $36,000) / ($150 − $60)

     PTS: 1   DIF: Easy   OBJ: LO: 21-03   NAT: BUSPROG: Analytic
     KEY: Bloom's: Application

8.   The Waterfall Company sells a product for $150 per unit. The variable cost is $80 per unit, and fixed
     costs are $270,000. Determine the (a) break-even point in sales units, and (b) break-even points in
     sales units if the company desires a target profit of $36,000. Round your answer to the nearest whole
     number.

     ANS:
     a.   SP $150 − VC $80 = CM $70
            $270,000 / $70 = 3,857 units

     b.   ($270,000 + $36,000) / $70 = 4,371 units

     PTS: 1   DIF: Easy   OBJ: LO: 21-03   NAT: BUSPROG: Analytic
     KEY: Bloom's: Application

9.   Bobby Company has fixed costs of $160,000. The unit selling price, variable cost per unit, and
     contribution margin per unit for the company's two products are provided below.

Product	Selling Price per unit	Variable Cost per unit	Contribution Margin per unit
X	$180	$100	$80
Y	$100	$ 60	$40

     The sales mix for product X and Y is 60% and 40% respectively. Determine the break-even point in
     units of X and Y.

     ANS:
     Unit selling price of sales mix = $148 ($180 × .60) + ($100 × .40)
     Unit variable cost of sales mix = $84 ($100 × .60) + ($60 × .40)
     Unit contribution margin of sales mix = $64 ($80 × .60) + ($40 × .40)

     Break-even sales (units) = 2,500 ($160,000 / $64)

PTS: 1   DIF: Moderate   OBJ: LO: 21-05   NAT: BUSPROG: Analytic
KEY: Bloom's: Application

10.   Steven Company has fixed costs of $160,000. The unit selling price, variable cost per unit, and
       contribution margin per unit for the company's two products are provided below.

Product	Selling Price per unit	Variable Cost per unit	Contribution Margin per unit
X	$180	$80	$100
Y	$100	$50	$ 50

The sales mix for product X and Y is 60% and 40% respectively. Determine the break-even point in
units of X and Y.

ANS:
Unit selling price of sales mix = $148 ($180 × .60) + ($100 × .40)
Unit variable cost of sales mix = $68 ($80 × .60) + ($50 × .40)
Unit contribution margin of sales mix = $80 ($100 × .60) + ($50 × .40)

Break-even sales (units) = 2,000 ($160,000 / $80)

PTS: 1   DIF: Moderate   OBJ: LO: 21-05   NAT: BUSPROG: Analytic
KEY: Bloom's: Application

11.   The Keith Company reports the following data.
                    Sales $900,000
                    Variable costs $500,000
                    Fixed costs $350,000

Determine Keith Company's operating leverage.

ANS:
8.0 = ($900,000 − $500,000) / ($900,000 − $500,000 − $350,000)

PTS: 1   DIF: Easy   OBJ: LO: 21-05   NAT: BUSPROG: Analytic
KEY: Bloom's: Application

12.   The Tom Company reports the following data.
                    Sales $600,000
                    Variable costs $400,000
                    Fixed costs $100,000

Determine Tom Company's operating leverage.

ANS:
2.0 = ($600,000 − $400,000) / ($600,000 − $400,000 − $100,000)

PTS: 1   DIF: Easy   OBJ: LO: 21-05   NAT: BUSPROG: Analytic
KEY: Bloom's: Application

13. The Dean Company has sales of $500,000, and the break-even point in sales dollars of $300,000. Determine the company's margin of safety percentage.

ANS:
40% = ($500,000 − $300,000)/$500,000

PTS: 1   DIF: Easy   OBJ: LO: 21-05   NAT: BUSPROG: Analytic
KEY: Bloom's: Application

14. The Grant Company has sales of $300,000, and the break-even point in sales dollars if $225,000. Determine the company's margin of safety percentage.

ANS:
25% = ($300,000 − $225,000)/$300,000

PTS: 1   DIF: Easy   OBJ: LO: 21-05   NAT: BUSPROG: Analytic
KEY: Bloom's: Application

15. Blane Company has the following data:

Total Sales	$800,000
Total Variable Costs	$300,000
Fixed Costs	$200,000
Units sold	50,000 units

What will operating income be if units sold double to 100,000 units?

ANS:

Total Sales	$1,600,000
Total Variable Costs	$ 600,000
Contribution Margin	$1,000,000
Fixed Costs	$ 200,000
Operating Income	$ 800,000

PTS: 1   DIF: Moderate   OBJ: LO: 21-01   NAT: BUSPROG: Analytic
KEY: Bloom's: Application

16. Douglas Company has a contribution margin ratio of 30%. If Douglas has $336,420 in fixed costs, what amount of sales will need to be generated in order for the company to break even?

ANS:

$336,420 / 0.30 = $1,121,400

PTS: 1   DIF: Easy   OBJ: LO: 21-03   NAT: BUSPROG: Analytic
KEY: Bloom's: Application

17. Racer Industries has fixed costs of $900,000. Selling price per unit is $250 and variable cost per unit is $130.

   Required:

   a. How many units must Racer sell in order to break even?
   b. How many units must Racer sell in order to earn a profit of $480,000?
   c. A new employee suggests that Racer Industries sponsor a company 10-K as a form of advertising. The cost to sponsor the event is $7,200. How many more units must be sold to cover this cost?

   ANS:

   a. $900,000 / ($250 – 130) = 7,500 units
   b. ($900,000 + 480,000) / ($250 – 130) = 11,500 units
   c. $7,200 / ($250 – 130) = 60 units

   PTS: 1   DIF: Moderate   OBJ: LO: 21-03   NAT: BUSPROG: Analytic
   KEY: Bloom's: Application

18. Global Publishers has collected the following data for recent months:

Month	Issues published	Total cost
March	20,500	$20,960
April	21,800	22,464
May	17,750	18,495
June	21,200	21,395

   Required:

   a. Using the high-low method, find variable cost per unit, total fixed costs, and the total cost equation.

   b. What is the estimated cost for a month in which 19,000 issues are published?

   ANS:

   a. Variable cost per unit = ($22,464 – $18,495) / (21,800 – 17,750) = $0.98 per unit

   Total fixed costs = $18,495 – (17,750 × $0.98) = $1,100

   Total cost = $1,100 + ($0.98 × number of issues published)

   b. Total cost = $1,100 + ($0.98 × 19,000) = $19,720

   PTS: 1   DIF: Moderate   OBJ: LO: 21-01   NAT: BUSPROG: Analytic
   KEY: Bloom's: Application

19. Trail Bikes, Inc. sells three Deluxe bikes for every seven Standard bikes.   The Deluxe bike sells for $1,800 and has variable costs of $1,200.   The Standard bike sells for $600 and has variable costs of $200.

Required:

A. If Trail Bikes has fixed costs that total $1,702,000, how many bikes must be sold in order   for the company to break even?

B. How many of these bikes will be Deluxe bikes and how many will be the Standard bikes?

ANS:

Weighted average contribution margin

$$= (3 \times (\$1,800 - \$1,200) + 7 \times (\$600 - \$200)) / 10 = \$460$$

Break even point = $1,702,000/460 = 3,700 bikes

$$30\% \text{ Deluxe}\quad = \quad 1,110$$
$$70\% \text{ Standard} = \quad 2,590$$

PTS: 1   DIF: Moderate   OBJ: LO: 21-02   NAT: BUSPROG: Analytic
KEY: Bloom's: Application

20. If a business had a capacity of $10,000,000 of sales, actual sales of $6,000,000, break-even sales of $4,200,000, fixed costs of $1,800,000, and variable costs of 60% of sales, what is the margin of safety expressed as a percentage of sales?

ANS:

Margin of Safety = (Sales − Sales at Breakeven) / Sales
$$(\$6,000,000 - \$4,200,000) / \$6,000,000 = 30\%$$

PTS: 1   DIF: Moderate   OBJ: LO: 21-05   NAT: BUSPROG: Analytic
KEY: Bloom's: Application

21. Safari Co. sells two products, Orks and Zins. Last year Safari sold 21,000 units of Orks and 14,000 units of Zins. Related data are:

Product	Unit Selling Price	Unit Variable Cost	Unit Contribution Margin
Orks	$120	$80	$40
Zins	80	60	20

Calculate the following:
a. Safari Co.'s sales mix
b. Safari Co.'s weighted average unit selling price
c. Safari Co's weighted average unit contribution margin
d. Safari Co's break-even point assuming that last year's fixed costs were $160,000.

ANS:

a. Orks: 21,000 / (21,000 + 14,000) = 60%
    Zins: 14,000 / (21,000 + 14,000) = 40%

b. $120 × 60% + $80 × 40% = $104

c. ($120 − $80) × 60% + ($80 − $60) × 40% = $32

d. $160,000 / $32 = 5,000 units

PTS: 1 DIF: Moderate OBJ: LO: 21-05 NAT: BUSPROG: Analytic
KEY: Bloom's: Application

22. Given the following information:

Variable cost per unit = $5.00
July fixed cost per unit = $7.00
Units sold and produced in July 25,000

What is total estimated cost for August if 30,000 units are projected to be produced and sold?

ANS:
Total Fixed costs = $7.00 × 25,000 = $175,000

Total cost at 30,000 units = $175,000 + ($5.00 × 30,000 units) = $325,000

PTS: 1 DIF: Challenging OBJ: LO: 21-01 NAT: BUSPROG: Analytic
KEY: Bloom's: Application

23. Carrolton, Inc. currently sells widgets for $80 per unit. The variable cost is $30 per unit and total fixed costs equal $240,000 per year. Sales are currently 20,000 units annually.

The company is considering a 20% drop in selling price that they believe will raise units sold by 20%. Assuming all costs stay the same, what is the impact on income if they make this change?

ANS:
Current Scenario:

SP $80
VC $30
CM $50 × 20,000 units = $1,000,000 total contribution margin

Proposed Change:

SP $80 × 80% = $64
VC $30
CM $34 × (20,000 × 1.2) = $816,000 total contribution margin

Total CM (and income) drops by $184,000 ($1,000,000 − $816,000)

PTS: 1 DIF: Moderate OBJ: LO: 21-03 NAT: BUSPROG: Analytic
KEY: Bloom's: Application

24. Given the following:

Variable cost as a percentage of sales = 60%
Unit Variable cost = $30
Fixed costs = $200,000

What is the break-even point in units?

ANS:
$30/60% = $50 selling price

If VC as a percentage of sales is 60%, then Contribution Margin ratio is 40%

Unit CM = 40% × $50 = $20

Breakeven in units = $200,000 / $20 = 10,000 units

PTS: 1   DIF: Challenging   OBJ: LO: 21-02 | LO: 21-03
NAT: BUSPROG: Analytic   KEY: Bloom's: Application

25. A business had a margin of safety ratio of 20%, variable costs of 75% of sales, fixed costs of $240,000, a break-even point of $960,000, and operating income of $60,000 for the current year. Calculate the current year's sales.

ANS:

$960,000/.8 = $1,200,000

PTS: 1   DIF: Moderate   OBJ: LO: 21-05   NAT: BUSPROG: Analytic
KEY: Bloom's: Application

26. For the current year ending January 31, Harp Company expects fixed costs of $188,500 and a unit variable cost of $51.50. For the coming year, a new wage contract will increase the unit variable cost to $55.50. The selling price of $70.00 per unit is expected to remain the same.

(a) Compute the break-even sales (units) for the current year.
(b) Compute the anticipated break-even sales (units) for the coming year, assuming the new wage contract is signed.

Round your answer to the nearest whole number.

ANS:
(a) $188,500/($70.00 − $51.50) = 10,189 units

(b) $188,500/($70.00 − $55.50) = 13,000 units

PTS: 1   DIF: Easy   OBJ: LO: 21-03   NAT: BUSPROG: Analytic
KEY: Bloom's: Application

27.

    (a)   If Swannanoa Company's budgeted sales are $1,000,000, fixed costs are $350,000, and variable costs are $600,000, what is the budgeted contribution margin ratio?

    (b)   If the contribution margin ratio is 30%, sales are $900,000 and fixed costs are $200,000, what is the operating profit?

ANS:

(a)   Contribution margin = $1,000,000 − $600,000 = $400,000
       $400,000 / $1,000,000 = 40%

(b) $900,000 × 30% = $270,000 total contribution margin
       $270,000 − $200,000 = $70,000 operating income

PTS: 1   DIF: Easy   OBJ: LO: 21-02   NAT: BUSPROG: Analytic
KEY: Bloom's: Application

28.   Louis Company sells a single product at a price of $65 per unit. Variable costs per unit are $45 and total fixed costs are $625,500. Louis is considering the purchase of a new piece of equipment that would increase the fixed costs to $800,000, but decrease the variable costs per unit to $42.

Required:

If Louis Company expects to sell 44,000 units next year, should they purchase this new equipment?

ANS:

Under the current system, Louis' profit when 44,000 units are sold is
    (($65 − $45) × 44,000) − $625,500 = $254,500

If the new equipment is purchased, Louis' profit when 44,000 units are sold is
    (($65 − $42) × 44,000) − $800,000 = $212,000

Louis is better off not buying the new equipment.

PTS: 1   DIF: Challenging   OBJ: LO: 21-03   NAT: BUSPROG: Analytic
KEY: Bloom's: Application

29.   Cordell, Inc. has an operating leverage of 3. Sales are expected to increase by 9% next year. What is the expected change in operating income next year?

ANS:
If sales increase 9% and the operating leverage is 3, operating income is expected to increase by 27% (9% × 3).

PTS: 1   DIF: Easy   OBJ: LO: 21-05   NAT: BUSPROG: Analytic
KEY: Bloom's: Application

30. Explain how variable costing net income will be different than absorption costing net income under the following situations:

(1) A company had no beginning or ending inventory. During the year they produced and sold 10,000 units.

(2) A company had no beginning inventory. During the year they produced 10,000 units and sold 8,000 units.

(3) A company had 2,000 units in beginning inventory. During the year they produced 10,000 units and sold 12,000 units.

ANS:
(1) When there are no inventories (everything that is produced is sold) then variable costing income = absorption costing income.

(2) When the units produced > units sold, variable costing income < absorption costing income.

(3) When the units produced < units sold, variable costing income > absorption costing income.

PTS: 1   DIF: Moderate   OBJ: 21-APP   NAT: BUSPROG: Analytic
KEY: Bloom's: Application

MATCHING

Match the following terms with their definitions.
a. Relevant range
b. Break-even point
c. Contribution margin
d. Fixed costs
e. Variable costs

1. Vary in proportion to changes in activity levels.
2. Remain the same in total dollar amount as the level of activity changes
3. Where a business's revenues exactly equal costs
4. A specific activity range over which the cost changes are of interest.
5. The excess of sales revenues over variable costs

1. ANS: E   PTS: 1   DIF: Easy   OBJ: LO: 21-01
   NAT: BUSPROG: Analytic   KEY: Bloom's: Knowledge
2. ANS: D   PTS: 1   DIF: Easy   OBJ: LO: 21-01
   NAT: BUSPROG: Analytic   KEY: Bloom's: Knowledge
3. ANS: B   PTS: 1   DIF: Easy   OBJ: LO: 21-03
   NAT: BUSPROG: Analytic   KEY: Bloom's: Knowledge
4. ANS: A   PTS: 1   DIF: Easy   OBJ: LO: 21-01
   NAT: BUSPROG: Analytic   KEY: Bloom's: Knowledge
5. ANS: C   PTS: 1   DIF: Easy   OBJ: LO: 21-02
   NAT: BUSPROG: Analytic   KEY: Bloom's: Knowledge

Match the following terms with their definitions.
a. Profit-volume chart
b. Cost-volume-profit chart
c. Sales mix
d. Operating leverage
e. Margin of safety

6. Indicates the possible decrease in sales that may occur before operating loss results.
7. Contribution margin divided by income from operations.
8. Focuses on costs, sales, and operating profit or loss.
9. Focuses on profits rather than on revenues or costs.
10. The relative distribution of sales among products sold by a company.

6. ANS: E   PTS: 1   DIF: Easy   OBJ: LO: 21-05
    NAT: BUSPROG: Analytic   KEY: Bloom's: Knowledge
7. ANS: D   PTS: 1   DIF: Easy   OBJ: LO: 21-05
    NAT: BUSPROG: Analytic   KEY: Bloom's: Knowledge
8. ANS: B   PTS: 1   DIF: Easy   OBJ: LO: 21-04
    NAT: BUSPROG: Analytic   KEY: Bloom's: Knowledge
9. ANS: A   PTS: 1   DIF: Easy   OBJ: LO: 21-04
    NAT: BUSPROG: Analytic   KEY: Bloom's: Knowledge
10. ANS: C   PTS: 1   DIF: Easy   OBJ: LO: 21-05
    NAT: BUSPROG: Analytic   KEY: Bloom's: Knowledge

PROBLEM

1. The following is a list of various costs of producing sweatshirts. Classify each cost as either a variable, fixed, or mixed cost for units produced and sold.

(a) Leather used to make a handbag.
(b) Warehouse rent of $8,000 per month plus $.50 per square foot of storage used.
(c) Thread.
(d) Electricity costs of $.038 per kilowatt-hour.
(e) Janitorial costs of $4,000 per month.
(f) Advertising costs of $12,000 per month.
(g) Accounting salaries.
(h) Color dyes for producing different colors of sweatshirts.
(i) Salary of the production supervisor.
(j) Straight-line depreciation on sewing machines.
(k) Patterns for different designs. Patterns typically last many years before being replaced.
(l) Hourly wages of sewing machine operators.
(m) Property taxes on factory, building, and equipment.
(n) Cotton and polyester cloth.
(o) Maintenance costs with sewing machine company. The cost is $2,000 per year plus $.001 for each machine hour of use.

ANS:

(a)	variable	(i)	fixed
(b)	mixed	(j)	fixed
(c)	variable	(k)	fixed
(d)	variable	(l)	variable
(e)	fixed	(m)	fixed
(f)	fixed	(n)	variable
(g)	fixed	(o)	mixed
(h)	variable		

PTS: 1   DIF: Moderate   OBJ: LO: 21-01   NAT: BUSPROG: Analytic
KEY: Bloom's: Knowledge

2.   The cost graphs in the illustration below shows various types of cost behaviors.

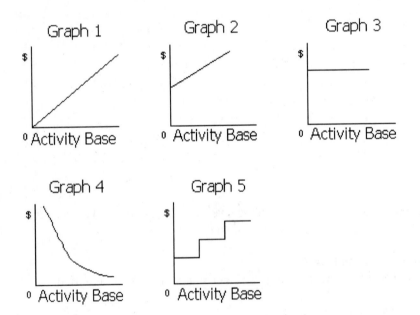

FIGURE 20.2

For each of the following costs, identify the cost graph that best describes its cost behavior as the number of units produced and sold increases:

(a)   Sales commissions of $6,000 plus $.05 for each item sold.
(b)   Rent on warehouse of $12,000 per month.
(c)   Insurance costs of $2,500 per month.
(d)   Per-unit cost of direct labor.
(e)   Total salaries of quality control supervisors. One supervisor must be added for each additional work shift.
(f)   Total employer pension costs of $.35 per direct labor hour.
(g)   Per-unit straight-line depreciation costs.
(h)   Per-unit cost of direct materials.
(i)   Total direct materials cost.
(j)   Electricity costs of $5,000 per month plus $.0004 per kilowatt-hour.
(k)   Per-unit cost of plant superintendent's salary.

(l) Salary of the night-time security guard of $3,800 per month.
(m) Repairs and maintenance costs of $3,000 for each 2,000 hours of factory machine usage.
(n) Total direct labor cost.
(o) Straight-line depreciation on factory equipment.

ANS:

	Graph		Graph
(a)	2	(i)	1
(b)	3	(j)	2
(c)	3	(k)	4
(d)	3	(l)	3
(e)	5	(m)	5
(f)	1	(n)	1
(g)	4	(o)	3
(h)	3		

PTS: 1   DIF: Moderate   OBJ: LO: 21-01   NAT: BUSPROG: Analytic
KEY: Bloom's: Application

3. Copper Hill Inc. manufactures laser printers within a relevant range of production of 70,000 to 100,000 printers per year. The following partially completed manufacturing cost schedule has been prepared:

	Number of Printers Produced		
	70,000	90,000	100,000
Total costs:			
Total variable costs	$350,000	(d)	(j)
Total fixed costs	630,000	(e)	(k)
Total costs	$980,000	(f)	(l)
Cost per unit:			
Variable cost per unit	(a)	(g)	(m)
Fixed cost per unit	(b)	(h)	(n)
Total cost per unit	(c)	(i)	(o)

Complete the preceding cost schedule, identifying each cost by the appropriate letter (a) through (o).

ANS:
(a) $5.00 ($350,000/70,000 printers)
(b) $9.00 ($630,000/70,000 printers)
(c) $14.00 ($980,000/70,000 printers)
(d) $450,000 ($5.00 × 90,000 printers)
(e) $630,000
(f) $1,080,000 ($450,000 + $630,000)
(g) $5.00
(h) $7.00 ($630,000/90,000 printers)
(i) $12.00 ($1,080,000/90,000 printers)
(j) $500,000 ($5.00 × 100,000 printers)
(k) $630,000
(l) $1,130,000 ($500,000 + $630,000)
(m) $5.00
(n) $6.30 ($630,000/100,000 units)
(o) $11.30 ($1,130,000/100,000 units)

PTS: 1   DIF: Easy   OBJ: LO: 21-02   NAT: BUSPROG: Analytic
KEY: Bloom's: Application

4.   For the current year ending April 30, Hal Company expects fixed costs of $60,000, a unit variable cost of $70, and anticipated break-even of 1,715 sales units.

(a)   Compute the unit sales price.
(b)   Compute the sales (units) required to realize an operating profit of $8,000.

Round your answer to the nearest whole number.

ANS:
(a) $60,000 / ($X − $70) = 1,715 units
         X = $105

(b)   ($60,000 + $8,000)/$35 = 1,943 units

PTS: 1   DIF: Easy   OBJ: LO: 21-03   NAT: BUSPROG: Analytic
KEY: Bloom's: Application

5.   Currently, the unit selling price is $50, the variable cost, $34, and the total fixed costs, $108,000. A proposal is being evaluated to increase the selling price to $54.

(a)   Compute the current break-even sales (units).
(b)   Compute the anticipated break-even sales (units), assuming that the unit selling price is increased and all costs remain constant.

ANS:
(a) $108,000/($50 − $34) = 6,750 units

(b) $108,000/($54 − $34) = 5,400 units

PTS: 1   DIF: Easy   OBJ: LO: 21-03   NAT: BUSPROG: Analytic
KEY: Bloom's: Application

6.   For the coming year, River Company estimates fixed costs at $109,000, the unit variable cost at $21, and the unit selling price at $85. Determine (a) the break-even point in units of sales, (b) the unit sales required to realize operating income of $150,000 and (c) the probable operating income if sales total $500,000.

Round units to the nearest whole number and percentage to one decimal place.

ANS:
(a) $109,000 / ($85 − $21) = 1,703 units

(b)   ($109,000 + $150,000) / $64 = 4,047 units

(c)   CM ratio = $64/$85 = 75.3%

         $500,000 × .753 = $376,500 contribution margin − $109,000 fixed costs =
         $267,500 operating income

7. For the past year, Pedi Company had fixed costs of $70,000, unit variable costs of $32, and a unit selling price of $40. For the coming year, no changes are expected in revenues and costs, except that property taxes are expected to increase by $10,000. Determine the break-even sales (units) for (a) the past year and (b) the coming year.

ANS:
(a)   S = $70,000/$8 = 8,750 units

(b)   S = $80,000/$8 = 10,000 units

8. For the past year, Hornbostel Company had fixed costs of $6,552,000, a unit variable cost of $444, and a unit selling price of $600. For the coming year, no changes are expected in revenues and costs, except that a new wage contract will increase variable costs by $6 per unit. Determine the break-even sales (units) for (a) the past year and (b) the coming year.

ANS:
(a)   S = $6,552,000 / $156 = 42,000 units

(b)   S = $6,552,000 / $150 = 43,680 units

9. Perfect Stampers makes and sells aftermarket hub caps. The variable cost for each hub cap is $4.75 and the hub cap sells for $9.95. Perfect Stampers has fixed costs per month of $3,120. Compute the contribution margin per unit and break-even sales in units and in dollars for the month.

ANS:
Contribution margin: $9.95 selling price − $4.75 variable cost = $5.20

Break even sales in units: $3,120 / $5.20 = 600 units.

Break even sales in dollars is $9.95 selling price × 600 units = $5,970.

10. A company with a break-even point at $900,000 in sales revenue had fixed costs of $225,000. When actual sales were $1,000,000 variable costs were $750,000. Determine (a) the margin of safety expressed in dollars, (b) the margin of safety expressed as a percentage of sales, (c) the contribution margin ratio, and (d) the operating income.

ANS:
(a) $1,000,000 − $900,000 = $100,000

(b) $100,000/$1,000,000 = 10%

(c)   Contribution margin ratio = $\dfrac{\$1,000,000 - \$750,000}{\$1,000,000}$ = 25.0%

(d) $1,000,000 − $225,000 − $750,000 = $25,000
     or
     $100,000 × 25.0% = $25,000

PTS: 1   DIF: Moderate   OBJ: LO: 21-03 | LO: 21-05
NAT: BUSPROG: Analytic   KEY: Bloom's: Application

11. A company has a margin of safety of 25%, a contribution margin ratio of 30%, and sales of $1,000,000.

(a)   What is the break-even point?

(b)   What is the operating income?

(c)   If neither the relationship between variable costs and sales nor the amount of fixed costs is expected to change in the next year, how much additional operating income can be earned by increasing sales by $110,000?

ANS:
(a)   Margin of safety = $1,000,000 × 25% = $250,000
     Break-even point = $1,000,000 − $250,000 = $750,000

(b) $250,000 (margin of safety) × 30% (contribution margin ratio) = $75,000

(c) $110,000 × 30% = $33,000

PTS: 1   DIF: Moderate   OBJ: LO: 21-03 | LO: 21-05
NAT: BUSPROG: Analytic   KEY: Bloom's: Application

12. Silver River Company sells Products S and T and has made the following estimates for the coming year:

Product	Unit Selling Price	Unit Variable Cost	Sales Mix
S	$30	$24	60%
T	70	56	40

Fixed costs are estimated at $202,400. Determine (a) the estimated sales in units of the overall product necessary to reach the break-even point for the coming year, (b) the estimated number of units of each product necessary to be sold to reach the break-even point for the coming year, and (c) the estimated sales in units of the overall product necessary to realize an operating income of $119,600 for the coming year.

ANS:
(a) Unit selling price = ($30 × 60%) + ($70 × 40%) = $46.00
     Unit variable cost = ($24 × 60%) + ($56 × 40%) = $36.80
     Unit contribution margin = $46.00 − $36.80 = $9.20
     $202,400/$9.20 = 22,000 overall units

(b) S: 13,200 units (22,000 units × 60%)
     T: 8,800 units (22,000 units × 40%)

(c) Sales = ($202,400 + $119,600)/$9.20 = 35,000 units

PTS: 1   DIF: Challenging   OBJ: LO: 21-05   NAT: BUSPROG: Analytic
KEY: Bloom's: Application

13. Define operating leverage. Explain the relationship between a company's operating leverage and how a change in sales is expected to impact profits.

ANS:
Operating leverage is the relationship between a company's contribution margin to income from operations. Companies with a high level of fixed costs have a high operating leverage and companies with low fixed costs have a low operating leverage.

To calculate how a change in sales will impact profits multiply the anticipated change in sales by the operating leverage. Thus, the higher a company's operating leverage, the larger the anticipated increase in profits from a change in sales.

PTS: 1   DIF: Moderate   OBJ: LO: 21-05   NAT: BUSPROG: Analytic
KEY: Bloom's: Knowledge

14. The following data are available from the accounting records of Suwanee Co. for the month ended May 31, 2012. 17,000 units were manufactured and sold during the accounting period at a price of $60 per unit. There was no beginning inventories and all units were completed (no work in process).

Cost	Total Cost	Number of Units	Unit Cost
Manufacturing costs:			
Variable	$442,000	17,000	$26
Fixed	170,000	17,000	10
Total	$612,000		$36
Selling and administrative expenses:			
Variable ($2 per unit sold)			$34,000
Fixed			32,000
Total			$66,000

(a) Prepare a variable costing income statement.
(b) Prepare an absorption costing income statement.

ANS:
(a)

Suwanee Co.
Variable Costing Income Statement
For the Month Ended May 31, 2012

Sales (17,000 × $60)		$1,020,000
Variable cost of goods sold (17,000 × $26)		442,000
Manufacturing margin		$ 578,000
Variable selling and administrative expenses		34,000
Contribution margin		$ 544,000
Fixed costs:		
Fixed manufacturing costs	$170,000	
Fixed selling and administrative expenses	32,000	202,000
Income from operations		$ 342,000

(b)

Suwanee Co.
Absorption Costing Income Statement
For the Month Ended May 31, 2012

Sales (17,000 × $60)	$1,020,000
Cost of goods sold	612,000
Gross profit	$ 408,000
Selling and administrative expenses	66,000
Income from operations	$ 342,000

PTS: 1   DIF: Moderate   OBJ: 21-APP   NAT: BUSPROG: Analytic
KEY: Bloom's: Knowledge

15. Kissimmee Paint Co. reported the following data for the month of July. There were no beginning inventories and all units were completed (no work in process).

	Total Cost	Number of Units	Unit Cost
Manufacturing costs:			
Variable	$465,000	30,000	$15.50
Fixed	210,000	30,000	7.00
Total	$675,000		$22.50

Selling and administrative expenses:
  Variable $2 per unit sold
  Fixed $39,000

In the month of July, 28,000 of the 30,000 units manufactured were sold at a price of $80 per unit.

(a) Prepare a variable costing income statement.
(b) Prepare an absorption costing income statement.
(c) Briefly explain why there is a difference in income from operations between the two methods.

ANS:
(a)

Kissimmee Co.
Variable Costing Income Statement
For the Month Ended July 31, 20--

Sales (28,000 × $80)		$2,240,000
Variable cost of goods sold:		
Variable cost of goods manufactured		
(30,000 × 15.50)	$465,000	
Less ending inventory (2,000 × $15.50)	31,000	
Variable cost of goods sold		434,000
Manufacturing margin		$1,806,000
Variable selling and administrative expenses		56,000
Contribution margin		$1,750,000
Fixed costs:		
Fixed manufacturing costs	$210,000	
Fixed selling and administrative expenses	39,000	249,000
Income from operations		$1,501,000

(b)

Kissimmee Co.
Absorption Costing Income Statement
For the Month Ended July 31, 20--

Sales (28,000 × $80)		$2,240,000
Cost of goods sold:		
Cost of goods manufactured (30,000 × $22.50)	$675,000	
Less ending inventory (2,000 × $22.50)	45,000	
Cost of goods sold		630,000
Gross profit		$1,610,000
Selling and administrative expenses		
(28,000 × $2 + $39,000)		95,000
Income from operations		$1,515,000

(c)
The difference of $14,000 in the amount of income from operations is due to the different treatment of fixed manufacturing expenses. The entire amount of the fixed manufacturing costs is included as an expense of the period in the variable costing statement. The ending inventory in the absorption costing statement includes $14,000 (2,000 × $7) of fixed manufacturing costs. This $14,000, by being included in inventory, is thus excluded from the current cost of goods sold and deferred to another period.

PTS: 1   DIF: Challenging   OBJ: 21-APP   NAT: BUSPROG: Analytic
KEY: Bloom's: Application

TRUE/FALSE

1. A formal written statement of management's plans for the future, expressed in financial terms, is called a budget.

    ANS: T   PTS: 1   DIF: Easy   OBJ: LO: 22-01
    NAT: BUSPROG: Analytic   KEY: Bloom's: Knowledge

2. Budgets are normally used only by profit-making businesses.

    ANS: F   PTS: 1   DIF: Easy   OBJ: LO: 22-01
    NAT: BUSPROG: Analytic   KEY: Bloom's: Knowledge

3. The objectives of budgeting are (1) establishing specific goals for future operations, (2) executing plans to achieve the goals, and (3) periodically comparing actual results with these goals.

    ANS: T   PTS: 1   DIF: Easy   OBJ: LO: 22-01
    NAT: BUSPROG: Analytic   KEY: Bloom's: Knowledge

4. When budget goals are set too tight, the budget becomes less effective as a tool for planning and controlling operations.

    ANS: T   PTS: 1   DIF: Easy   OBJ: LO: 22-01
    NAT: BUSPROG: Analytic   KEY: Bloom's: Knowledge

5. Employees view budgeting more positively when goals are established for them by senior management.

    ANS: F   PTS: 1   DIF: Easy   OBJ: LO: 22-01
    NAT: BUSPROG: Analytic   KEY: Bloom's: Knowledge

6. Budgetary slack can be avoided if lower and mid-level managers are requested to support all of their spending requirements with specific operational plans.

    ANS: T   PTS: 1   DIF: Easy   OBJ: LO: 22-01
    NAT: BUSPROG: Analytic   KEY: Bloom's: Knowledge

7. Goal conflict can be avoided if budget goals are carefully designed for consistency across all areas of the organization.

    ANS: T   PTS: 1   DIF: Easy   OBJ: LO: 22-01
    NAT: BUSPROG: Analytic   KEY: Bloom's: Knowledge

8. The budgeting process is used to effectively communicate planned expectations regarding profits and expenses to the entire organization.

    ANS: T   PTS: 1   DIF: Easy   OBJ: LO: 22-01
    NAT: BUSPROG: Analytic   KEY: Bloom's: Knowledge

9.   The budget procedures used by a large manufacturer of automobiles would probably not differ from those used by a small manufacturer of paper products.

     ANS: F   PTS: 1   DIF: Moderate   OBJ: LO: 22-02
     NAT: BUSPROG: Analytic   KEY: Bloom's: Knowledge

10. A budget procedure that provides for the maintenance at all times of a twelve-month projection into the future is called continuous budgeting.

     ANS: T   PTS: 1   DIF: Easy   OBJ: LO: 22-02
     NAT: BUSPROG: Analytic   KEY: Bloom's: Knowledge

11. A budget procedure that provides for the maintenance at all times of a twelve-month projection into the future is called master budgeting.

     ANS: F   PTS: 1   DIF: Easy   OBJ: LO: 22-02
     NAT: BUSPROG: Analytic   KEY: Bloom's: Knowledge

12. The budget procedure that requires all levels of management to start from zero in estimating sales, production, and other operating data is called zero-based budgeting.

     ANS: T   PTS: 1   DIF: Easy   OBJ: LO: 22-02
     NAT: BUSPROG: Analytic   KEY: Bloom's: Knowledge

13. The budget procedure that requires all levels of management to start from zero in estimating sales, production, and other operating data is called continuous budgeting.

     ANS: F   PTS: 1   DIF: Easy   OBJ: LO: 22-02
     NAT: BUSPROG: Analytic   KEY: Bloom's: Knowledge

14. Budgets are prepared in the Accounting Department and monitored by various department managers.

     ANS: F   PTS: 1   DIF: Easy   OBJ: LO: 22-02
     NAT: BUSPROG: Analytic   KEY: Bloom's: Knowledge

15. Once a static budget has been determined, it is changed regularly as the underlying activity changes.

     ANS: F   PTS: 1   DIF: Easy   OBJ: LO: 22-02
     NAT: BUSPROG: Analytic   KEY: Bloom's: Knowledge

16. The flexible budget is, in effect, a series of static budgets for different levels of activity.

     ANS: T   PTS: 1   DIF: Easy   OBJ: LO: 22-02
     NAT: BUSPROG: Analytic   KEY: Bloom's: Knowledge

17. Flexible budgeting requires all levels of management to start from zero and estimate sales, production, and other operating data as though operations were being started for the first time.

     ANS: F   PTS: 1   DIF: Easy   OBJ: LO: 22-02
     NAT: BUSPROG: Analytic   KEY: Bloom's: Knowledge

18. Flexible budgeting builds the effect of changes in level of activity into the budget system.

    ANS: T   PTS: 1   DIF: Easy   OBJ: LO: 22-02
    NAT: BUSPROG: Analytic   KEY: Bloom's: Knowledge

19. In preparing flexible budgets, the first step is to identify the fixed and variable components of the various costs and expenses being budgeted.

    ANS: T   PTS: 1   DIF: Easy   OBJ: LO: 22-02
    NAT: BUSPROG: Analytic   KEY: Bloom's: Knowledge

20. A process whereby the effect of fluctuations in the level of activity is built into the budgeting system is referred to as flexible budgeting.

    ANS: T   PTS: 1   DIF: Easy   OBJ: LO: 22-02
    NAT: BUSPROG: Analytic   KEY: Bloom's: Knowledge

21. The master budget of a small manufacturer would normally include all necessary component budgets except the capital expenditures budget.

    ANS: F   PTS: 1   DIF: Moderate   OBJ: LO: 22-03
    NAT: BUSPROG: Analytic   KEY: Bloom's: Knowledge

22. The master budget of a small manufacturer would normally include all necessary component budgets except the budgeted balance sheet.

    ANS: F   PTS: 1   DIF: Moderate   OBJ: LO: 22-03
    NAT: BUSPROG: Analytic   KEY: Bloom's: Knowledge

23. The master budget of a small manufacturer would normally include all component budgets that impact on the financial statements.

    ANS: T   PTS: 1   DIF: Moderate   OBJ: LO: 22-03
    NAT: BUSPROG: Analytic   KEY: Bloom's: Knowledge

24. The first budget to be prepared is usually the sales budget.

    ANS: T   PTS: 1   DIF: Easy   OBJ: LO: 22-03
    NAT: BUSPROG: Analytic   KEY: Bloom's: Knowledge

25. The first budget to be prepared is usually the production budget.

    ANS: F   PTS: 1   DIF: Easy   OBJ: LO: 22-03
    NAT: BUSPROG: Analytic   KEY: Bloom's: Knowledge

26. The first budget to be prepared is usually the cash budget.

    ANS: F   PTS: 1   DIF: Easy   OBJ: LO: 22-03
    NAT: BUSPROG: Analytic   KEY: Bloom's: Knowledge

27. After the sales budget is prepared, the production budget is normally prepared next.

    ANS: T   PTS: 1   DIF: Easy   OBJ: LO: 22-03
    NAT: BUSPROG: Analytic   KEY: Bloom's: Knowledge

28. After the sales budget is prepared, the capital expenditures budget is normally prepared next.

    ANS: F   PTS: 1   DIF: Easy   OBJ: LO: 22-03
    NAT: BUSPROG: Analytic   KEY: Bloom's: Knowledge

29. The budgeted volume of production is based on the sum of (1) the expected sales volume and (2) the desired ending inventory, less (3) the estimated beginning inventory.

    ANS: T   PTS: 1   DIF: Moderate   OBJ: LO: 22-04
    NAT: BUSPROG: Analytic   KEY: Bloom's: Knowledge

30. The budgeted volume of production is normally computed as the sum of (1) the expected sales volume and (2) the desired ending inventory.

    ANS: F   PTS: 1   DIF: Moderate   OBJ: LO: 22-04
    NAT: BUSPROG: Analytic   KEY: Bloom's: Knowledge

31. If Division Inc. expects to sell 200,000 units in 2012, desires ending inventory of 24,000 units, and has 22,000 units on hand as of the beginning of the year, the budgeted volume of production for 2012 is 202,000 units.

    ANS: T   PTS: 1   DIF: Moderate   OBJ: LO: 22-04
    NAT: BUSPROG: Analytic   KEY: Bloom's: Application

32. If Division Inc. expects to sell 200,000 units in 2012, desires ending inventory of 24,000 units, and has 22,000 units on hand as of the beginning of the year, the budgeted volume of production for 2012 is 198,000 units.

    ANS: F   PTS: 1   DIF: Moderate   OBJ: LO: 22-04
    NAT: BUSPROG: Analytic   KEY: Bloom's: Application

33. The budgeted direct materials purchases is based on the sum of (1) the materials needed for production and (2) the desired ending materials inventory, less (3) the estimated beginning materials inventory.

    ANS: T   PTS: 1   DIF: Moderate   OBJ: LO: 22-04
    NAT: BUSPROG: Analytic   KEY: Bloom's: Knowledge

34. The budgeted direct materials purchases is normally computed as the sum of (1) the materials for production and (2) the desired ending inventory.

    ANS: F   PTS: 1   DIF: Moderate   OBJ: LO: 22-04
    NAT: BUSPROG: Analytic   KEY: Bloom's: Knowledge

35. The production budget is the starting point for preparation of the direct labor cost budget.

ANS: T   PTS: 1   DIF: Easy   OBJ: LO: 22-04
NAT: BUSPROG: Analytic   KEY: Bloom's: Knowledge

36. The sales budget is the starting point for preparation of the direct labor cost budget.

ANS: F   PTS: 1   DIF: Easy   OBJ: LO: 22-04
NAT: BUSPROG: Analytic   KEY: Bloom's: Knowledge

37. Supervisor salaries, maintenance, and indirect factory wages would normally appear in the factory overhead cost budget.

ANS: T   PTS: 1   DIF: Easy   OBJ: LO: 22-04
NAT: BUSPROG: Analytic   KEY: Bloom's: Knowledge

38. Supervisor salaries, maintenance, and indirect factory wages would normally appear in the operating expenses budget.

ANS: F   PTS: 1   DIF: Moderate   OBJ: LO: 22-04
NAT: BUSPROG: Analytic   KEY: Bloom's: Knowledge

39. Supervisor salaries and indirect factory wages would normally appear in the direct labor cost budget.

ANS: F   PTS: 1   DIF: Moderate   OBJ: LO: 22-04
NAT: BUSPROG: Analytic   KEY: Bloom's: Knowledge

40. Detailed supplemental schedules based on department responsibility are often prepared for major items in the operating expenses budget.

ANS: T   PTS: 1   DIF: Easy   OBJ: LO: 22-04
NAT: BUSPROG: Analytic   KEY: Bloom's: Knowledge

41. The capital expenditures budget summarizes future plans for acquisition of fixed assets.

ANS: T   PTS: 1   DIF: Easy   OBJ: LO: 22-05
NAT: BUSPROG: Analytic   KEY: Bloom's: Knowledge

42. The cash budget summarizes future plans for acquisition of fixed assets.

ANS: F   PTS: 1   DIF: Easy   OBJ: LO: 22-05
NAT: BUSPROG: Analytic   KEY: Bloom's: Knowledge

43. The cash budget is affected by the sales budget, the various budgets for manufacturing costs and operating expenses, and the capital expenditures budget.

ANS: T   PTS: 1   DIF: Easy   OBJ: LO: 22-05
NAT: BUSPROG: Analytic   KEY: Bloom's: Knowledge

44. The cash budget presents the expected inflow and outflow of cash for a specified period of time.

     ANS: T   PTS: 1   DIF: Easy   OBJ: LO: 22-05
     NAT: BUSPROG: Analytic   KEY: Bloom's: Knowledge

45. The budgeted balance sheet assumes that all operating and financing plans are met.

     ANS: T   PTS: 1   DIF: Easy   OBJ: LO: 22-05
     NAT: BUSPROG: Analytic   KEY: Bloom's: Knowledge

46. The master budget is an integrated set of budgets that tie together a company's operating, financing
     and investing activities into an integrated plan for the coming year.

     ANS: T   PTS: 1   DIF: Easy   OBJ: LO: 22-03
     NAT: BUSPROG: Analytic   KEY: Bloom's: Knowledge

47. The capital expenditures budget is part of the planned investing activities of a company.

     ANS: T   PTS: 1   DIF: Easy   OBJ: LO: 22-05
     NAT: BUSPROG: Analytic   KEY: Bloom's: Knowledge

48. Consulting the persons affected by a budget when it is prepared can provide an effective means of
     motivation and cooperation.

     ANS: T   PTS: 1   DIF: Easy   OBJ: LO: 22-01
     NAT: BUSPROG: Analytic   KEY: Bloom's: Knowledge

49. A budget can be an effective means of communicating management's plans to the employees of a
     business.

     ANS: T   PTS: 1   DIF: Easy   OBJ: LO: 22-01
     NAT: BUSPROG: Analytic   KEY: Bloom's: Knowledge

50. Past performance is the best overall basis for evaluating current performance and assessing the need
     for corrective action.

     ANS: F   PTS: 1   DIF: Easy   OBJ: LO: 22-01
     NAT: BUSPROG: Analytic   KEY: Bloom's: Knowledge

51. Budget preparation is best determined in a top-down managerial approach.

     ANS: F   PTS: 1   DIF: Easy   OBJ: LO: 22-01
     NAT: BUSPROG: Analytic   KEY: Bloom's: Knowledge

52. The task of preparing a budget should be the sole task of the most important department in an
     organization.

     ANS: F   PTS: 1   DIF: Easy   OBJ: LO: 22-01
     NAT: BUSPROG: Analytic   KEY: Bloom's: Knowledge

53. The responsibility for coordinating the preparation of a master budget should be assigned to the CEO of a firm.

    ANS: F   PTS: 1   DIF: Easy   OBJ: LO: 22-01
    NAT: BUSPROG: Analytic   KEY: Bloom's: Knowledge

54. The financial budgets of a business include the cash budget, the budgeted income statement, and the budgeted balance sheet.

    ANS: T   PTS: 1   DIF: Moderate   OBJ: LO: 22-01
    NAT: BUSPROG: Analytic   KEY: Bloom's: Knowledge

55. The sales budget is derived from the production budget.

    ANS: F   PTS: 1   DIF: Easy   OBJ: LO: 22-01
    NAT: BUSPROG: Analytic   KEY: Bloom's: Knowledge

56. A capital expenditures budget is prepared before the operating budgets.

    ANS: F   PTS: 1   DIF: Easy   OBJ: LO: 22-01
    NAT: BUSPROG: Analytic   KEY: Bloom's: Knowledge

57. Part of the cash budget is based on information drawn from the capital expenditures budget.

    ANS: T   PTS: 1   DIF: Easy   OBJ: LO: 22-01
    NAT: BUSPROG: Analytic   KEY: Bloom's: Knowledge

MULTIPLE CHOICE

1. A formal written statement of management's plans for the future, expressed in financial terms, is a:
   a. gross profit report
   b. responsibility report
   c. budget
   d. performance report

    ANS: C   PTS: 1   DIF: Easy   OBJ: LO: 22-01
    NAT: BUSPROG: Analytic   KEY: Bloom's: Knowledge

2. The budget process involves doing all the following except:
   a. establishing specific goals
   b. executing plans to achieve the goals
   c. periodically comparing actual results with the goals
   d. dismissing all managers who fail to achieve operational goals specified in the budget

    ANS: D   PTS: 1   DIF: Easy   OBJ: LO: 22-01
    NAT: BUSPROG: Analytic   KEY: Bloom's: Knowledge

3. The budgetary unit of an organization which is led by a manager who has both the authority over and responsibility for the unit's performance is known as a:
   a. control center
   b. budgetary area

    c.   responsibility center
    d.   managerial department

ANS: C   PTS: 1   DIF: Easy   OBJ: LO: 22-01
NAT: BUSPROG: Analytic   KEY: Bloom's: Knowledge

4.   The benefits of comparing actual performance of the operations against planned goals include all of the following except:
    a.   providing prompt feedback to employees about their performance relative to the goal
    b.   preventing unplanned expenditures
    c.   helping to establish spending priorities
    d.   determining how managers are performing against prior years' actual operating results

ANS: D   PTS: 1   DIF: Easy   OBJ: LO: 22-01
NAT: BUSPROG: Analytic   KEY: Bloom's: Knowledge

5.   Budgeting supports the planning process by encouraging all of the following activities except:
    a.   requiring all organizational units to establish their goals for the upcoming period
    b.   increasing the motivation of managers and employees by providing agreed-upon expectations
    c.   directing and coordinating operations during the period
    d.   improving overall decision making by considering all viewpoints, options, and cost reduction possibilities

ANS: C   PTS: 1   DIF: Easy   OBJ: LO: 22-01
NAT: BUSPROG: Analytic   KEY: Bloom's: Knowledge

6.   When management seeks to achieve personal departmental objectives that may work to the detriment of the entire company, the manager is experiencing:
    a.   budgetary slack
    b.   padding
    c.   goal conflict
    d.   cushions

ANS: C   PTS: 1   DIF: Moderate   OBJ: LO: 22-01
NAT: BUSPROG: Analytic   KEY: Bloom's: Knowledge

7.   The budgeting process does not involve which of the following activities:
    a.   Specific goals are established
    b.   Periodic comparison of actual results to goals
    c.   Execution of plans to achieve goals
    d.   Increase in sales by increasing marketing efforts.

ANS: D   PTS: 1   DIF: Easy   OBJ: LO: 22-01
NAT: BUSPROG: Analytic   KEY: Bloom's: Knowledge

8.   Budgets need to be fair and attainable for employees to consider the budget important in their normal daily activities. Which of the following is not considered a human behavior problem?
    a.   Setting goals among managers that conflict with one another.
    b.   Setting goals too tightly making it difficult to meet performance expectation.
    c.   Allowing employees the opportunity to be a part of the budget process.
    d.   Allowing goals to be so low that employees develop a "spend it or lose it" attitude.

ANS: C   PTS: 1   DIF: Easy   OBJ: LO: 22-01
NAT: BUSPROG: Analytic   KEY: Bloom's: Knowledge

9. Which of the following budgets allow for adjustments in activity levels?
    a. Static Budget
    b. Continuous Budget
    c. Zero-Based Budget
    d. Flexible Budget

    ANS: D   PTS: 1   DIF: Easy   OBJ: LO: 22-02
    NAT: BUSPROG: Analytic   KEY: Bloom's: Knowledge

10. The process of developing budget estimates by requiring all levels of management to estimate sales, production, and other operating data as though operations were being initiated for the first time is referred to as:
    a. flexible budgeting
    b. continuous budgeting
    c. zero-based budgeting
    d. master budgeting

    ANS: C   PTS: 1   DIF: Easy   OBJ: LO: 22-02
    NAT: BUSPROG: Analytic   KEY: Bloom's: Knowledge

11. A variant of fiscal-year budgeting whereby a twelve-month projection into the future is maintained at all times is termed:
    a. flexible budgeting
    b. continuous budgeting
    c. zero-based budgeting
    d. master budgeting

    ANS: B   PTS: 1   DIF: Easy   OBJ: LO: 22-02
    NAT: BUSPROG: Analytic   KEY: Bloom's: Knowledge

12. Scott Manufacturing Co.'s static budget at 10,000 units of production includes $40,000 for direct labor and $4,000 for electric power. Total fixed costs are $25,000. At 12,000 units of production, a flexible budget would show:
    a. variable costs of $52,800 and $30,000 of fixed costs
    b. variable costs of $44,000 and $25,000 of fixed costs
    c. variable costs of $52,800 and $25,000 of fixed costs
    d. variable and fixed costs totaling $69,000

    ANS: C   PTS: 1   DIF: Moderate   OBJ: LO: 22-02
    NAT: BUSPROG: Analytic   KEY: Bloom's: Application

13. Bob and Sons' static budget for 10,000 units of production includes $50,000 for direct materials, $44,000 for direct labor, variable utilities of $5,000, and supervisor salaries of $25,000. A flexible budget for 12,000 units of production would show:
    a. the same cost structure in total
    b. direct materials of $60,000, direct labor of $52,800, utilities of $6,000, and supervisor salaries of $30,000
    c. total variable costs of $148,000
    d. direct materials of $60,000, direct labor of $52,800, utilities of $6,000, and supervisor salaries of $25,000

    ANS: D   PTS: 1   DIF: Moderate   OBJ: LO: 22-02
    NAT: BUSPROG: Analytic   KEY: Bloom's: Application

14. A disadvantage of static budgets is that they:
    a. are dependent on previous year's actual results
    b. cannot be used by service companies
    c. do not show possible changes in underlying activity levels
    d. show the expected results of a responsibility center for several levels of activity

    ANS: C   PTS: 1   DIF: Easy   OBJ: LO: 22-02
    NAT: BUSPROG: Analytic   KEY: Bloom's: Knowledge

15. A series of budgets for varying rates of activity is termed a(n):
    a. flexible budget
    b. variable budget
    c. master budget
    d. activity budget

    ANS: A   PTS: 1   DIF: Easy   OBJ: LO: 22-02
    NAT: BUSPROG: Analytic   KEY: Bloom's: Knowledge

16. For January, sales revenue is $700,000; sales commissions are 5% of sales; the sales manager's
    salary is $96,000; advertising expenses are $90,000; shipping expenses total 2% of sales; and
    miscellaneous selling expenses are $2,100 plus 1/2 of 1% of sales. Total selling expenses for the
    month of January are:
    a. $157,100
    b. $240,600
    c. $183,750
    d. $182,100

    ANS: B   PTS: 1   DIF: Moderate   OBJ: LO: 22-02
    NAT: BUSPROG: Analytic   KEY: Bloom's: Application

17. For February, sales revenue is $700,000; sales commissions are 5% of sales; the sales manager's
    salary is $96,000; advertising expenses are $80,000; shipping expenses total 2% of sales; and
    miscellaneous selling expenses are $2,500 plus 1/2 of 1% of sales. Total selling expenses for the
    month of February are:
    a. $151,000
    b. $227,500
    c. $225,000
    d. $231,000

    ANS: D   PTS: 1   DIF: Moderate   OBJ: LO: 22-02
    NAT: BUSPROG: Analytic   KEY: Bloom's: Application

18. For March, sales revenue is $1,000,000; sales commissions are 5% of sales; the sales manager's
    salary is $80,000; advertising expenses are $75,000; shipping expenses total 1% of sales; and
    miscellaneous selling expenses are $2,100 plus 1% of sales. Total selling expenses for the month of
    March are:
    a. $227,100
    b. $215,000
    c. $217,100
    d. $152,100

    ANS: A   PTS: 1   DIF: Moderate   OBJ: LO: 22-02
    NAT: BUSPROG: Analytic   KEY: Bloom's: Application

19. Cameron Manufacturing Co.'s static budget at 5,000 units of production includes $40,000 for direct labor and $5,000 for variable electric power. Total fixed costs are $20,000. At 8,000 units of production, a flexible budget would show:
    a. variable costs of $64,000 and $25,000 of fixed costs
    b. variable costs of $64,000 and $20,000 of fixed costs
    c. variable costs of $72,000 and $20,000 of fixed costs
    d. variable and fixed costs totaling $104,000

    ANS: C   PTS: 1   DIF: Moderate   OBJ: LO: 22-02
    NAT: BUSPROG: Analytic   KEY: Bloom's: Application

20. Tanya Inc.'s static budget for 10,000 units of production includes $60,000 for direct materials, $44,000 for direct labor, fixed utilities costs of $5,000, and supervisor salaries of $20,000. A flexible budget for 12,000 units of production would show:
    a. the same cost structure in total
    b. direct materials of $72,000, direct labor of $52,800, utilities of $5,000, and supervisor salaries of $20,000
    c. total variable costs of $154,800
    d. direct materials of $60,000, direct labor of $52,800, utilities of $6,000, and supervisor salaries of $20,000

    ANS: B   PTS: 1   DIF: Moderate   OBJ: LO: 22-02
    NAT: BUSPROG: Analytic   KEY: Bloom's: Application

21. The primary difference between a static budget and a flexible budget is that a static budget
    a. is suitable in volatile demand situation while flexible budget is suitable in a stable demand situation.
    b. is concerned only with future acquisitions of fixed assets, whereas a flexible budget is concerned with expenses that vary with sales.
    c. includes only fixed costs, whereas a flexible budget includes only variable costs.
    d. is a plan for a single level of production, whereas a flexible budget can be converted to any level of production.

    ANS: D   PTS: 1   DIF: Moderate   OBJ: LO: 22-02
    NAT: BUSPROG: Analytic   KEY: Bloom's: Knowledge

22. At the beginning of the period, the Cutting Department budgeted direct labor of $155,000, direct material of $165,000 and fixed factory overhead of $15,000 for 9,000 hours of production. The department actually completed 10,000 hours of production. What is the appropriate total budget for the department, assuming it uses flexible budgeting?
    a. $416,000
    b. $370,556
    c. $368,889
    d. $335,000

    ANS: B   PTS: 1   DIF: Moderate   OBJ: LO: 22-02
    NAT: BUSPROG: Analytic   KEY: Bloom's: Application

23. At the beginning of the period, the Assembly Department budgeted direct labor of $110,000, direct material of $170,000 and fixed factory overhead of $28,000 for 8,000 hours of production. The department actually completed 10,000 hours of production. What is the appropriate total budget for the department, assuming it uses flexible budgeting.
     a. $288,000
     b. $305,000
     c. $350,000
     d. $378,000

     ANS: D   PTS: 1   DIF: Moderate   OBJ: LO: 22-02
     NAT: BUSPROG: Analytic   KEY: Bloom's: Application

24. The production budgets are used to prepare which of the following budgets.
     a. Operating expenses
     b. Direct materials purchases, direct labor cost, factory overhead cost
     c. Sales in dollars
     d. Sales in units

     ANS: B   PTS: 1   DIF: Easy   OBJ: LO: 22-03
     NAT: BUSPROG: Analytic   KEY: Bloom's: Knowledge

25. Principal components of a master budget include which of the following?
     a. Production budget
     b. Sales budget
     c. Capital expenditures budget
     d. All of the above

     ANS: D   PTS: 1   DIF: Easy   OBJ: LO: 22-03
     NAT: BUSPROG: Analytic   KEY: Bloom's: Knowledge

26. The first budget customarily prepared as part of an entity's master budget is the:
     a. production budget
     b. cash budget
     c. sales budget
     d. direct materials purchases

     ANS: C   PTS: 1   DIF: Easy   OBJ: LO: 22-03
     NAT: BUSPROG: Analytic   KEY: Bloom's: Knowledge

27. Motorcycle Manufacturers, Inc. projected sales of 78,000 machines for 2012. The estimated January 1, 2012, inventory is 6,500 units, and the desired December 31, 2012, inventory is 7,000 units. What is the budgeted production (in units) for 2012?
     a. 77,500
     b. 71,000
     c. 78,500
     d. 71,500

     ANS: C   PTS: 1   DIF: Easy   OBJ: LO: 22-03
     NAT: BUSPROG: Analytic   KEY: Bloom's: Application

28. The budget that needs to be completed first when preparing the master budget is the:
     a. Production Budget
     b. Sales Budget

c. Cash Budget
d. Capital Expenditures Budget

ANS: B   PTS: 1   DIF: Easy   OBJ: LO: 22-03
NAT: BUSPROG: Analytic   KEY: Bloom's: Knowledge

29. Which of the following budgets is not directly associated with the production budget?
   a. Direct materials purchases budget
   b. Factory overhead cost budget
   c. Capital Expenditures budget
   d. Direct labor cost budget

ANS: C   PTS: 1   DIF: Easy   OBJ: LO: 22-03
NAT: BUSPROG: Analytic   KEY: Bloom's: Knowledge

Below is budgeted production and sales information for Flushing Company for the month of December:

	Product XXX	Product ZZZ
Estimated beginning inventory	32,000 units	20,000 units
Desired ending inventory	34,000 units	17,000 units
Region I, anticipated sales	320,000 units	260,000 units
Region II, anticipated sales	180,000 units	140,000 units

The unit selling price for product XXX is $5 and for product ZZZ is $15.

30. Budgeted sales for the month are:
   a. $3,180,000
   b. $5,820,000
   c. $1,800,000
   d. $8,500,000

ANS: D   PTS: 1   DIF: Moderate   OBJ: LO: 22-04
NAT: BUSPROG: Analytic   KEY: Bloom's: Application

31. Budgeted production for product XXX during the month is:
   a. 498,000 units
   b. 502,000 units
   c. 534,000 units
   d. 566,000 units

ANS: B   PTS: 1   DIF: Moderate   OBJ: LO: 22-04
NAT: BUSPROG: Analytic   KEY: Bloom's: Application

32. Budgeted production for product ZZZ during the month is:
   a. 403,000 units
   b. 380,000 units
   c. 397,000 units
   d. 417,000 units

ANS: C   PTS: 1   DIF: Moderate   OBJ: LO: 22-04
NAT: BUSPROG: Analytic   KEY: Bloom's: Application

33. Manicotti Corporation sells a single product. Budgeted sales for the year are anticipated to be 640,000 units, estimated beginning inventory is 108,000 units, and desired ending inventory is 90,000 units. The quantities of direct materials expected to be used for each unit of finished product are given below.

Material A .50 lb. per unit @ $ .60 per pound
Material B 1.00 lb. per unit @ $1.70 per pound
Material C 1.20 lb. per unit @ $1.00 per pound

The dollar amount of direct material A used in production during the year is:
a. $186,600
b. $181,200
c. $240,000
d. $210,600

ANS: A   PTS: 1   DIF: Moderate   OBJ: LO: 22-04
NAT: BUSPROG: Analytic   KEY: Bloom's: Application

Mandy Corporation sells a single product. Budgeted sales for the year are anticipated to be 640,000 units, estimated beginning inventory is 98,000 units, and desired ending inventory is 80,000 units. The quantities of direct materials expected to be used for each unit of finished product are given below.

Material A .50 lb. per unit @ $ .60 per pound
Material B 1.00 lb. per unit @ $1.70 per pound
Material C 1.20 lb. per unit @ $1.00 per pound

34. The dollar amount of direct material B used in production during the year is:
a. $1,057,400
b. $1,193,400
c. $1,026,800
d. $1,224,000

ANS: A   PTS: 1   DIF: Moderate   OBJ: LO: 22-04
NAT: BUSPROG: Analytic   KEY: Bloom's: Application

35. The dollar amount of direct material C used in production during the year is:
a. $746,400
b. $724,800
c. $824,400
d. $758,160

ANS: A   PTS: 1   DIF: Moderate   OBJ: LO: 22-04
NAT: BUSPROG: Analytic   KEY: Bloom's: Application

36. Production and sales estimates for March for the Robin Co. are as follows:

Estimated inventory (units), March 1	18,000
Desired inventory (unit), March 31	21,300
Expected sales volume (units):	
Area M	7,000
Area L	8,000
Area O	9,000
Unit sales price	$ 15

The number of units expected to be manufactured in March is:
a. 24,000
b. 27,000
c. 27,300
d. 21,300

ANS: C   PTS: 1   DIF: Moderate   OBJ: LO: 22-04
NAT: BUSPROG: Analytic   KEY: Bloom's: Application

37. Production and sales estimates for May for the Robin Co. are as follows:

Estimated inventory (units), May 1	19,500
Desired inventory (unit), May 31	19,300
Expected sales volume (units):	
Area W	6,000
Area X	7,000
Area Y	9,000
Unit sales price	$ 20

The number of units expected to be sold in May is:
a. 22,000
b. 2,700
c. 21,800
d. 19,300

ANS: A   PTS: 1   DIF: Moderate   OBJ: LO: 22-04
NAT: BUSPROG: Analytic   KEY: Bloom's: Application

38. Production and sales estimates for June are as follows:

Estimated inventory (units), June 1	21,000
Desired inventory (units), June 30	19,000
Expected sales volume (units):	
Area X	7,000
Area Y	4,000
Area Z	5,500
Unit sales price	$ 20

The number of units expected to be manufactured in June is:
a. 10,000
b. 11,500
c. 14,500
d. 12,500

ANS: C   PTS: 1   DIF: Moderate   OBJ: LO: 22-04
NAT: BUSPROG: Analytic   KEY: Bloom's: Application

39. Production and sales estimates for June are as follows:

Estimated inventory (units), June 1	8,000
Desired inventory (units), June 30	9,000
Expected sales volume (units):	
Area X	4,000
Area Y	10,000
Area Z	6,000
Unit sales price	$ 20

The budgeted total sales for June is:
a. $200,000
b. $400,000
c. $380,000
d. $250,000

ANS: B   PTS: 1   DIF: Moderate   OBJ: LO: 22-04
NAT: BUSPROG: Analytic   KEY: Bloom's: Application

40. If the expected sales volume for the current period is 8,000 units, the desired ending inventory is
     1,400 units, and the beginning inventory is 1,200 units, the number of units set forth in the
     production budget, representing total production for the current period, is:
     a. 10,600
     b. 8,200
     c. 66,000
     d. 6,800

ANS: B   PTS: 1   DIF: Moderate   OBJ: LO: 22-04
NAT: BUSPROG: Analytic   KEY: Bloom's: Application

Production estimates for August are as follows:

Estimated inventory (units), August 1	12,000
Desired inventory (units), August 31	9,000
Expected sales volume (units), August	75,000

For each unit produced, the direct materials requirements are as follows:

Direct material A ($5 per lb.)	3 lbs.
Direct material B ($18 per lb.)	1/2 lb.

41. The number of pounds of materials A and B required for August production is:
     a. 216,000 lbs. of A; 72,000 lbs. of B
     b. 216,000 lbs. of A; 36,000 lbs. of B
     c. 225,000 lbs. of A; 37,500 lbs. of B
     d. 234,000 lbs. of A; 39,000 lbs. of B

ANS: B   PTS: 1   DIF: Moderate   OBJ: LO: 22-04
NAT: BUSPROG: Analytic   KEY: Bloom's: Application

42. The total direct materials purchases (assuming no beginning or ending inventory of material) of
     materials A and B required for August production is:
     a. $1,080,000 for A; $1,296,000 for B
     b. $1,080,000 for A; $648,000 for B
     c. $1,125,000 for A; $675,000 for B
     d. $1,170,000 for A; $702,000 for B

ANS: B   PTS: 1   DIF: Moderate   OBJ: LO: 22-04
NAT: BUSPROG: Analytic   KEY: Bloom's: Application

43. Based on the following production and sales estimates for May, determine the number of units expected to be manufactured in May.

Estimated inventory (units), May 1	20,000
Desired inventory (units), May 31	25,000
Expected sales volume (units):	
South region	20,000
West region	40,000
North region	20,000
Unit sales price	$ 10

a. 75,000
b. 90,000
c. 85,000
d. 115,000

ANS: C   PTS: 1   DIF: Moderate   OBJ: LO: 22-04
NAT: BUSPROG: Analytic   KEY: Bloom's: Application

44. Which of the following budgets provides the starting point for the preparation of the direct labor cost budget?
a. Direct materials purchases budget
b. Cash budget
c. Production budget
d. Sales budget

ANS: C   PTS: 1   DIF: Easy   OBJ: LO: 22-04
NAT: BUSPROG: Analytic   KEY: Bloom's: Knowledge

45. Production and sales estimates for April are as follows:

Estimated inventory (units), April	19,000
Desired inventory (units), April 30	18,000
Expected sales volume (units):	
Area A	3,500
Area B	4,750
Area C	4,250
Unit sales price	$ 20

The number of units expected to be manufactured in April is:
a. 11,500
b. 10,000
c. 12,500
d. 13,500

ANS: A   PTS: 1   DIF: Moderate   OBJ: LO: 22-04
NAT: BUSPROG: Analytic   KEY: Bloom's: Application

46. Production and sales estimates for April are as follows:

Estimated inventory (units), April 1	9,000
Desired inventory (units), April 30	8,000
Expected sales volume (units):	
Area A	3,500
Area B	4,750
Area C	4,250
Unit sales price	$ 20

The budgeted total sales for April is:
a. $200,000
b. $230,000
c. $270,000
d. $250,000

ANS: D   PTS: 1   DIF: Moderate   OBJ: LO: 22-04
NAT: BUSPROG: Analytic   KEY: Bloom's: Application

47. If the expected sales volume for the current period is 7,000 units, the desired ending inventory is 400 units, and the beginning inventory is 300 units, the number of units set forth in the production budget, representing total production for the current period, is:
a. 6,900
b. 7,000
c. 7,200
d. 7,100

ANS: D   PTS: 1   DIF: Moderate   OBJ: LO: 22-04
NAT: BUSPROG: Analytic   KEY: Bloom's: Application

Production estimates for July are as follows:

Estimated inventory (units), July 1	8,500
Desired inventory (units), July 31	10,500
Expected sales volume (units), July	76,000

For each unit produced, the direct materials requirements are as follows:

Direct material A ($5 per lb.)	3 lbs.
Direct material B ($18 per lb.)	1/2 lb.

48. The number of pounds of materials A and B required for July production is:
a. 216,000 lbs. of A; 36,000 lbs. of B
b. 216,000 lbs. of A; 72,000 lbs. of B
c. 234,000 lbs. of A; 39,000 lbs. of B
d. 225,000 lbs. of A; 37,500 lbs. of B

ANS: C   PTS: 1   DIF: Moderate   OBJ: LO: 22-04
NAT: BUSPROG: Analytic   KEY: Bloom's: Application

49.   The total direct materials purchases of materials A and B (assuming no beginning or ending material
       inventory) required for July production is:
       a. $1,080,000 for A; $648,000 for B
       b. $1,080,000 for A; $1,296,000 for B
       c. $1,170,000 for A; $702,000 for B
       d. $1,125,000 for A; $675,000 for B

       ANS: C   PTS: 1   DIF: Moderate   OBJ: LO: 22-04
       NAT: BUSPROG: Analytic   KEY: Bloom's: Application

       The Cardinal Company had a finished goods inventory of 55,000 units on January 1. Its projected
       sales for the next four months were: January - 200,000 units; February - 180,000 units; March -
       210,000 units; and April - 230,000 units. The Cardinal Company wishes to maintain a desired
       ending finished goods inventory of 20% of the following months sales.

50.   What should the budgeted production be for January?
       a.   236,000
       b.   181,000
       c.   200,000
       d.   219,000

       ANS: B   PTS: 1   DIF: Moderate   OBJ: LO: 22-04
       NAT: BUSPROG: Analytic   KEY: Bloom's: Application

51.   What would be the budgeted production for February?
       a.   186,000
       b.   181,000
       c.   222,000
       d.   174,000

       ANS: A   PTS: 1   DIF: Moderate   OBJ: LO: 22-04
       NAT: BUSPROG: Analytic   KEY: Bloom's: Application

52.   What would be the budgeted production for March?
       a.   256,000
       b.   206,000
       c.   214,000
       d.   298,000

       ANS: C   PTS: 1   DIF: Moderate   OBJ: LO: 22-04
       NAT: BUSPROG: Analytic   KEY: Bloom's: Application

53.   What would be the budgeted inventory for March 31st?
       a.   46,000
       b.   36,000
       c.   Cannot be determined from the data given
       d.   42,000

       ANS: A   PTS: 1   DIF: Moderate   OBJ: LO: 22-04
       NAT: BUSPROG: Analytic   KEY: Bloom's: Application

54. The budget that summarizes future plans for the acquisition of fixed assets is the:
    a. direct materials purchases budget
    b. production budget
    c. sales budget
    d. capital expenditures budget

    ANS: D   PTS: 1   DIF: Easy   OBJ: LO: 22-04
    NAT: BUSPROG: Analytic   KEY: Bloom's: Knowledge

Below is budgeted production and sales information for Bluebird Company for the month of December:

	Product XXX	Product ZZZ
Estimated beginning inventory	30,000 units	18,000 units
Desired ending inventory	32,000 units	15,000 units
Anticipated sales	520,000 units	460,000 units

The unit selling price for product XXX is $5 and for product ZZZ is $14.

55. Budgeted production for product XXX during the month is:
    a. 522,000 units
    b. 552,000 units
    c. 518,000 units
    d. 520,000 units

    ANS: A   PTS: 1   DIF: Moderate   OBJ: LO: 22-04
    NAT: BUSPROG: Analytic   KEY: Bloom's: Application

56. Budgeted production for product ZZZ during the month is:
    a. 460,000 units
    b. 475,000 units
    c. 457,000 units
    d. 463,000 units

    ANS: C   PTS: 1   DIF: Moderate   OBJ: LO: 22-04
    NAT: BUSPROG: Analytic   KEY: Bloom's: Application

57. Production and sales estimates for June are as follows:

Estimated inventory (units), June 1	16,000
Desired inventory (units), June 30	18,000
Expected sales volume (units):	
Area X	4,000
Area Y	6,000
Area Z	5,500
Unit sales price	$ 20

The number of units expected to be manufactured in June is:
    a. 15,500
    b. 17,500
    c. 16,500
    d. 13,500

ANS: B   PTS: 1   DIF: Moderate   OBJ: LO: 22-04
NAT: BUSPROG: Analytic   KEY: Bloom's: Application

58. If the expected sales volume for the current period is 9,000 units, the desired ending inventory is 200 units, and the beginning inventory is 300 units, the number of units set forth in the production budget, representing total production for the current period, is:
a. 9,000
b. 8,900
c. 8,700
d. 9,100

ANS: B   PTS: 1   DIF: Moderate   OBJ: LO: 22-04
NAT: BUSPROG: Analytic   KEY: Bloom's: Application

59. Consider the following budget information: materials to be used totals $64,750; direct labor totals $198,400; factory overhead totals $394,800; work in process inventory January 1, 2012, was expected to be $189,100; and work in progress inventory on December 31, 2012, is expected to be $197,600. What is the budgeted cost of goods manufactured?
a. $649,450
b. $657,950
c. $197,600
d. $1,044,650

ANS: A   PTS: 1   DIF: Moderate   OBJ: LO: 22-04
NAT: BUSPROG: Analytic   KEY: Bloom's: Application

60. The budgeted finished goods inventory and cost of goods sold for a manufacturing company for the year 2012 are as follows: January 1 finished goods, $765,000; December 31 finished goods, $540,000; cost of goods sold for the year, $2,560,000. The budgeted costs of goods manufactured for the year is?
a. $1,255,000
b. $2,335,000
c. $2,785,000
d. $3100,000

ANS: B   PTS: 1   DIF: Easy   OBJ: LO: 22-04
NAT: BUSPROG: Analytic   KEY: Bloom's: Application

61. The budgeted finished goods inventory and cost of goods sold for a manufacturing company for the year 2012 are as follows: January 1 finished goods, $765,000; December 31 finished goods, $640,000; cost of goods sold for the year, $2,560,000. The budgeted costs of goods manufactured for the year is?
a. $1,405,000
b. $2,560,000
c. $2,435,000
d. $3,965,000

ANS: C   PTS: 1   DIF: Easy   OBJ: LO: 22-04
NAT: BUSPROG: Analytic   KEY: Bloom's: Application

The Warbler Jeans Company produces two different types of jeans. One is called the "Simple Life" and the other is called the "Fancy Life" The company's Production Budget requires 353,500 units of Simple jeans and 196,000 Fancy jeans to be manufactured. It is estimated that 2.5 direct labor hours will be needed to manufacture one pair of Simple Life jeans and 3.75 hours of direct labor hours for each pair of Fancy Life jeans.

62. What is the total number of direct labor hours needed for both lines of jeans?
     a. 883,750 direct labor hours
     b. 1,618,750 direct labor hours
     c. 735,000 direct labor hours
     d. 353,500 direct labor hours

ANS: B   PTS: 1   DIF: Easy   OBJ: LO: 22-04
NAT: BUSPROG: Analytic   KEY: Bloom's: Application

63. Woodpecker Co. has $296,000 in accounts receivable on January 1. Budgeted sales for January are
     $860,000. Woodpecker Co. expects to sell 20% of its merchandise for cash. Of the remaining 80%
     of sales on account, 75% are expected to be collected in the month of sale and the remainder the
     following month. The January cash collections from sales are:
     a. $812,000
     b. $688,000
     c. $468,000
     d. $984,000

ANS: D   PTS: 1   DIF: Moderate   OBJ: LO: 22-05
NAT: BUSPROG: Analytic   KEY: Bloom's: Application

64. Estimated cash payments are planned reductions in cash from all of the following except:
     a. manufacturing and operating expenses
     b. capital expenditures
     c. notes and accounts receivable collections
     d. payments for interest or dividends

ANS: C   PTS: 1   DIF: Easy   OBJ: LO: 22-05
NAT: BUSPROG: Analytic   KEY: Bloom's: Knowledge

65. Management accountants usually provide for a minimum cash balance in their cash budgets for
     which of the following reasons:
     a. stockholders demand a minimum cash balance
     b. to comply with U.S. GAAP
     c. it provides a safety buffer for variations in estimates
     d. to have funds available for major capital expenditures

ANS: C   PTS: 1   DIF: Easy   OBJ: LO: 22-05
NAT: BUSPROG: Analytic   KEY: Bloom's: Knowledge

Nuthatch Corporation began its operations on September 1 of the current year. Budgeted sales for
the first three months of business are $260,000, $375,000, and $400,000, respectively, for
September, October, and November. The company expects to sell 30% of its merchandise for cash.
Of sales on account, 80% are expected to be collected in the month of the sale and 20% in the month
following the sale.

66. The cash collections in September from accounts receivable are:
     a. $223,600
     b. $145,600
     c. $182,000
     d. $168,000

ANS: B   PTS: 1   DIF: Moderate   OBJ: LO: 22-05
NAT: BUSPROG: Analytic   KEY: Bloom's: Application

67. The cash collections in October from accounts receivable are:
    a. $246,400
    b. $262,500
    c. $210,000
    d. $294,500

ANS: A   PTS: 1   DIF: Moderate   OBJ: LO: 22-05
NAT: BUSPROG: Analytic   KEY: Bloom's: Application

68. The cash collections in November from accounts receivable are:
    a. $280,000
    b. $316,400
    c. $295,200
    d. $276,500

ANS: D   PTS: 1   DIF: Moderate   OBJ: LO: 22-05
NAT: BUSPROG: Analytic   KEY: Bloom's: Application

Finch Company began its operations on March 31 of the current year. Finch Co. has the following projected costs:

	April	May	June
Manufacturing costs(1)	$156,800	$195,200	$217,600
Insurance expense (2)	$ 1,000	$ 1,000	$ 1,000
Depreciation expense	$ 2,000	$ 2,000	$ 2,000
Property tax expense(3)	$ 500	$ 500	$ 500

(1) 3/4 of the manufacturing costs are paid for in the month they are incurred. 1/4 is paid in the following month.
(2) Insurance expense is $1,000 a month, however, the insurance is paid four times yearly in the first month of the quarter, i.e. January, April, July, and October.
(3) Property tax is paid once a year in November.

69. The cash payments for Finch Company in the month of April are:
    a. $122,600
    b. $120,600
    c. $123,100
    d. $121,100

ANS: B   PTS: 1   DIF: Moderate   OBJ: LO: 22-05
NAT: BUSPROG: Analytic   KEY: Bloom's: Application

70. The cash payments for Finch Company in the month of May are:
    a. $185,600
    b. $149,900
    c. $187,600
    d. $189,100

ANS: A   PTS: 1   DIF: Moderate   OBJ: LO: 22-05
NAT: BUSPROG: Analytic   KEY: Bloom's: Application

71. The cash payments for Finch Company in the month of June are:
    a. $215,500
    b. $188,800
    c. $214,000
    d. $212,000

    ANS: D   PTS: 1   DIF: Moderate   OBJ: LO: 22-05
    NAT: BUSPROG: Analytic   KEY: Bloom's: Application

72. Planning for capital expenditures is necessary for all of the following reasons except:
    a. machinery and other fixed assets wear out
    b. expansion may be necessary to meet increased demand
    c. amounts spent for office equipment may be immaterial
    d. fixed assets may fall below minimum standards of efficiency

    ANS: C   PTS: 1   DIF: Easy   OBJ: LO: 22-05
    NAT: BUSPROG: Analytic   KEY: Bloom's: Knowledge

73. As of January 1 of the current year, the Grackle Company had accounts receivables of $50,000.
    The sales for January, February, and March of 2012 were as follows: $120,000, $140,000 and
    $150,000. 20% of each month's sales are for cash. Of the remaining 80% (the credit sales), 60% are
    collected in the month of sale, with remaining 40% collected in the following month. What is the
    total cash collected (both from accounts receivable and for cash sales) in the month of January?
    a. $$74,000
    b. $110,000
    c. $71,600
    d. $131,600

    ANS: D   PTS: 1   DIF: Moderate   OBJ: LO: 22-05
    NAT: BUSPROG: Analytic   KEY: Bloom's: Application

74. As of January 1 of the current year, the Grackle Company had accounts receivables of $50,000. The
    sales for January, February, and March were as follows: $120,000, $140,000 and $150,000. 20% of
    each month's sales are for cash. Of the remaining 80% (the credit sales), 60% are collected in the
    month of sale, with remaining 40% collected in the following month. What is the total cash collected
    (both from accounts receivable and for cash sales) in the month of February?
    a. $129,600
    b. $62,400
    c. $133,600
    d. $91,200

    ANS: C   PTS: 1   DIF: Moderate   OBJ: LO: 22-05
    NAT: BUSPROG: Analytic   KEY: Bloom's: Application

75. As of January 1 of the current year, the Grackle Company had accounts receivables of $50,000. The
    sales for January, February, and March were as follows: $120,000, $140,000 and $150,000. 20% of
    each month's sales are for cash. Of the remaining 80% (the credit sales), 60% are collected in the
    month of sale, with remaining 40% collected in the following month. What is the total cash collected
    (both from accounts receivable and for cash sales) in the month of March?
    a. $74,800
    b. $146,800
    c. $102,000
    d. $116,800

ANS: B   PTS: 1   DIF: Moderate   OBJ: LO: 22-05
NAT: BUSPROG: Analytic   KEY: Bloom's: Application

76. As of January 1 of the current year, the Grackle Company had accounts receivables of $50,000. The sales for January, February, and March of 2012 were as follows: $120,000, $140,000 and $150,000. 20% of each month's sales are for cash. Of the remaining 80% (the credit sales), 60% are collected in the month of sale, with remaining 40% collected in the following month. What is the accounts receivable balance as of March 31?
   a. $72,000
   b. $48,000
   c. $58,720
   d. $$60,000

ANS: B   PTS: 1   DIF: Moderate   OBJ: LO: 22-05
NAT: BUSPROG: Analytic   KEY: Bloom's: Application

Dove Corporation began its operations on September 1 of the current year. Budgeted sales for the first three months of business are $250,000, $320,000, and $410,000, respectively, for September, October, and November. The company expects to sell 25% of its merchandise for cash. Of sales on account, 70% are expected to be collected in the month of the sale, 30% in the month following the sale.

77. The cash collections in October are:
   a. $320,000
   b. $248,000
   c. $304,250
   d. $382,500

ANS: C   PTS: 1   DIF: Moderate   OBJ: LO: 22-05
NAT: BUSPROG: Analytic   KEY: Bloom's: Application

78. The cash collections in November are:
   a. $317,750
   b. $389,750
   c. $490,000
   d. $410,000

ANS: B   PTS: 1   DIF: Moderate   OBJ: LO: 22-05
NAT: BUSPROG: Analytic   KEY: Bloom's: Application

79. Fashion Jeans, Inc. sells two lines of jeans; Simple Life and Fancy Life. Simple Life sells for $85.00 a pair and Fancy Life sells for $100.00 a pair. The company sells all of its jeans on credit and estimates that 60% is collected in the month of the sale, 35% is collected in the following month, and the rest is considered to be uncollectible. The estimated sales for Simple are as follows: January 20,000 jeans, February 27,500 jeans, and March 25,000 jeans. The estimated sales for Fancy are as follows: January 18,000 jeans, February 19,000, and March 20,500 jeans. What are the expected cash receipts for the month of March?
   a. $3,988,125
   b. $2,505,000
   c. $2,125,000
   d. $4,175,000

ANS: A   PTS: 1   DIF: Easy   OBJ: LO: 22-05
NAT: BUSPROG: Analytic   KEY: Bloom's: Application

80. The operating budgets of a company include:
    a. the cash budget
    b. the capital expenditures budget
    c. the financing budget
    d. the production budget

    ANS: D   PTS: 1   DIF: Moderate   OBJ: LO: 22-03
    NAT: BUSPROG: Analytic   KEY: Bloom's: Knowledge

A company is preparing its their Cash Budget. The following data has been provided for cash receipts and payments.

	January	February	March
Cash Receipts	$1,061,200	$1,182,400	$1,091,700
Cash Payments	$984,500	$1,210,000	$1,075,000

The company's cash balance at January 1st is $290,000. This company desires a minimum cash balance of $340,000.

81. What is the amount of excess cash or deficiency of cash (after considering the minimum cash balance required) for January?
    a. $26,700 excess
    b. $136,700 deficiency
    c. $356,700 excess
    d. $60,000 excess

    ANS: A   PTS: 1   DIF: Challenging   OBJ: LO: 22-05
    NAT: BUSPROG: Analytic   KEY: Bloom's: Application

82. What is the amount of excess cash or deficiency of cash (after considering the minimum cash balance required) for February?
    a. $109,100 deficiency
    b. $10,900 excess
    c. $900 deficiency
    d. $109,100 excess

    ANS: C   PTS: 1   DIF: Challenging   OBJ: LO: 22-05
    NAT: BUSPROG: Analytic   KEY: Bloom's: Application

83. What is the amount of excess cash or deficiency of cash (after considering the minimum cash balance required) for March?
    a. $214,200 excess
    b. $15,800 excess
    c. $60,000 deficiency
    d. $25,300 excess

    ANS: B   PTS: 1   DIF: Challenging   OBJ: LO: 22-05
    NAT: BUSPROG: Analytic   KEY: Bloom's: Application

84. An August sales forecast projects 6,000 units are going to be sold at a price of $11.50 per unit. The desired ending iventory in units is 15% higher than the beginning inventory of 1,000 units. Total August sales are anticipated to be:
   a. $80,500
   b. $69,000
   c. $60,000
   d. $57,500

   ANS: B   PTS: 1   DIF: Moderate   OBJ: LO: 22-04
   NAT: BUSPROG: Analytic   KEY: Bloom's: Application

85. A department store has budgeted sales of 12,000 men's suits in September. Management wants to have 6,000 suits in inventory at the end of the month to prepare for the winter season. Beginning inventory for September is expected to be 4,000 units.   What is the dollar amount of the purchase of suits? Each suit has a cost of $75.
   a. $900,000
   b. $1,050,000
   c. $1,350,000
   d. $1,200,000

   ANS: B   PTS: 1   DIF: Moderate   OBJ: LO: 22-04
   NAT: BUSPROG: Analytic   KEY: Bloom's: Application

86. A sporting goods store purchased $7,000 of ski boots in October.   The store had $3,000 of ski boots in inventory at the beginning of October, and expects to have $2,000 of ski boots in inventory at the end of October to cover part of anticipated November sales.   What is the budgeted cost of goods sold for October?
   a. $10,000
   b. $5,700
   c. $8,000
   d. $9,500

   ANS: C   PTS: 1   DIF: Moderate   OBJ: LO: 22-04
   NAT: BUSPROG: Analytic   KEY: Bloom's: Application

87. Truliant co. sells a product called Withall and has predicted the following sales for the first four months of the current year:

	January	February	March	April
Sales in units	1,700	1,900	2,100	1,600

   Ending inventory for each month should be 20% of next month's sales, and the December 31 inventory is consistent with that policy.   How many units should be purchased in February?

   a. 1,940
   b. 1,800
   c. 1,900
   d. 1,850

   ANS: A   PTS: 1   DIF: Moderate   OBJ: LO: 22-02
   NAT: BUSPROG: Analytic   KEY: Bloom's: Application

88. Yadkin Valley's April sales forecast projects that 6,000 units will sell at a price of $10.50 per unit. The desired ending inventory is 30% higher than the beginning inventory, which was 1,000 units. Budgeted purchases of units in April would be:
    a. 7,000 units
    b. 6,000 units
    c. 6,300 units
    d. 7,300 units

    ANS: C   PTS: 1   DIF: Moderate   OBJ: LO: 22-02
    NAT: BUSPROG: Analytic   KEY: Bloom's: Application

    Next year's sales forecast shows that 20,000 units of Product A and 22,000 units of Product B are going to be sold for prices of $10 and $12 per unit, respectively. The desired ending inventory of Product A is 20% higher than its beginning inventory of 2,000 units. The beginning inventory of Product B is 2,500 units. The desired ending inventory of B is 3,000 units.

89. Total budgeted sales of both products for the year would be:
    a. $42,000
    b. $200,000
    c. $264,000
    d. $464,000

    ANS: D   PTS: 1   DIF: Moderate   OBJ: LO: 22-02
    NAT: BUSPROG: Analytic   KEY: Bloom's: Application

90. Budgeted purchases of Product A for the year would be:
    a. 22,400 units
    b. 20,400 units
    c. 20,000 units
    d. 12,200 units

    ANS: B   PTS: 1   DIF: Moderate   OBJ: LO: 22-02
    NAT: BUSPROG: Analytic   KEY: Bloom's: Application

91. Budgeted purchases of Product B for the year would be:
    a. 24,500 units
    b. 22,500 units
    c. 26,500 units
    d. 23,200 units

    ANS: B   PTS: 1   DIF: Moderate   OBJ: LO: 22-02
    NAT: BUSPROG: Analytic   KEY: Bloom's: Application

92. Heedy Company is trying to decide how many units of merchandise to order each month. The company policy is to have 20% of the next month's sales in inventory at the end of each month. Projected sales for August, September, and October are 30,000 units, 20,000 units, and 40,000 units, respectively. How many units must be purchased in September?
    a. 24,000
    b. 18,000
    c. 28,000
    d. 22,000

    ANS: A   PTS: 1   DIF: Moderate   OBJ: LO: 22-02
    NAT: BUSPROG: Analytic   KEY: Bloom's: Application

93. If budgeted beginning inventory is $8,300, budgeted ending inventory is $9,400, and budgeted cost of goods sold is $10,260, budgeted purchases should be:
    a. $1,100
    b. $9,300
    c. $11,360
    d. $11,250

ANS: C PTS: 1   DIF: Moderate OBJ: LO: 22-02
NAT: BUSPROG: Analytic   KEY: Bloom's: Application

94. When preparing the cash budget, all the following should be considered except:
    a. Cash receipts from customers.
    b. Depreciation expense.
    c. Cash payments to suppliers.
    d. Cash payments for equipment.

ANS: B PTS: 1   DIF: Moderate OBJ: LO: 22-04
NAT: BUSPROG: Analytic   KEY: Bloom's: Knowledge

95. Which of the following would not be used in preparing a cash budget for October?
    a. Beginning cash balance on October 1.
    b. Budgeted salaries expense for October.
    c. Estimated depreciation expense for October.
    d. Budgeted sales and collections for October.

ANS: C PTS: 1   DIF: Moderate OBJ: LO: 22-04
NAT: BUSPROG: Analytic   KEY: Bloom's: Knowledge

96. Southern Company is preparing a cash budget for April. The company has $12,000 cash at the beginning of April and anticipates $30,000 in cash receipts and $34,500 in cash disbursements during April. Southern Company has an agreement with its bank to maintain a cash balance of at least $10,000. To maintain the $10,000 required balance, during April the company must:
    a. borrow $4,500.
    b. borrow $2,500.
    c. borrow $7,500.
    d. borrow $5,000.

ANS: B PTS: 1   DIF: Moderate OBJ: LO: 22-04
NAT: BUSPROG: Analytic   KEY: Bloom's: Application

97. Tara Company's budget includes the following credit sales for the current year: September, $25,000; October, $36,000; November, $30,000; December, $32,000. Experience has shown that payment for the credit sales is received as follows: 15% in the month of sale, 60% in the first month after sale, 20% in the second month after sale, and 5% is uncollectible. How much cash can Tara Company expect to collect in November as a result of current and past credit sales?
    a. $19,700
    b. $28,400
    c. $30,000
    d. $31,100

ANS: D PTS: 1   DIF: Moderate OBJ: LO: 22-04
NAT: BUSPROG: Analytic   KEY: Bloom's: Application

98. A company's history indicates that 20% of its sales are for cash and the rest are on credit. Collections on credit sales are 20% in the month of the sale, 50% in the next month, 25% the following month, and 5% is uncollectible. Projected sales for December, January, and February are $60,000, $85,000, and $95,000, respectively. The February expected cash receipts from all current and prior credit sales is:
   a. $61,200
   b. $57,000
   c. $66,400
   d. $90,250

   ANS: A   PTS: 1   DIF: Challenging   OBJ: LO: 22-04
   NAT: BUSPROG: Analytic   KEY: Bloom's: Application

99. Gilbert's expects its September sales to be 20% higher than its August sales of $150,000. Purchases were $100,000 in August and are expected to be $120,000 in September. All sales are on credit and are collected as follows: 30% in the month of the sale and 70% in the following month. Merchandise purchases are paid as follows: 25% in the month of purchase and 75% in the following month. The beginning cash balance on September 1 is $7,500. The ending balance on September 30 would be:
   a. $61,500
   b. $75,000
   c. $72,300
   d. $71,500

   ANS: A   PTS: 1   DIF: Challenging   OBJ: LO: 22-04
   NAT: BUSPROG: Analytic   KEY: Bloom's: Application

OTHER

1. At the beginning of the period, the Cutting Department budgeted direct labor of $30,000 and supervisor salaries of $20,000 for 3,000 hours of production. The department actually completed 5,000 hours of production. Determine the budget for the department assuming that it uses flexible budgeting?

   ANS:
   Variable cost:
       Direct labor (5,000 × $10.00* per hour) $50,000
   Fixed cost:
       Supervisor salaries $20,000
   Total department cost $70,000
   *$30,000 ÷ 3,000 hours

   PTS: 1   DIF: Easy   OBJ: LO: 22-02   NAT: BUSPROG: Analytic
   KEY: Bloom's: Application

2. Crow Manufacturers, Inc. projected sales of 75,000 bicycles for 2012. The estimated January 1, 2012, inventory is 5,000 units, and the desired December 31, 2012, inventory is 8,000 units. What is the budgeted production (in units) for 2012?

ANS:

Expected units to be sold	75,000
Plus: desired ending inventory, December 31, 2012	8,000
Total	83,000
Less estimated beginning inventory, January 1, 2012	5,000
Total units to be produced	78,000

PTS: 1 DIF: Easy OBJ: LO: 22-03 NAT: BUSPROG: Analytic
KEY: Bloom's: Application

3. To meet projected annual sales, Greenleaf Manufacturers, Inc. needs to produce 75,000 machines for 2012. The estimated January 1, 2012, inventory is 7,000 units, and the desired December 31, 2012, inventory is 12,000 units. What are projected sales units for 2012?

ANS:

Expected units to be sold	70,000
Plus: desired ending inventory, December 31, 2012	12,000
Total	82,000
Less estimated beginning inventory, January 1, 2012	7,000
Total units to be produced	75,000

PTS: 1 DIF: Easy OBJ: LO: 22-03 NAT: BUSPROG: Analytic
KEY: Bloom's: Application

4. Magnolia, Inc. manufactures bedding sets. The budgeted production is for 55,000 comforters in 2012. Each comforter requires 7 yards of material. The estimated January 1, 2012, beginning inventory is 31,000 yards. The desired ending balance is 30,000 yards of material. If the material costs $4.00 per yard, determine the materials budget for 2012.

ANS:

Yards of material required for production:	
Comforter material (55,000 × 7 yards)	385,000
Plus: desired ending inventory, December 31, 2012	30,000
Total	415,000
Less estimated beginning inventory, January 1, 2012	31,000
Total yards to purchase	384,000
Unit price (per yard)	$ 4.00
Total direct material to be purchased	$1,536,000

PTS: 1 DIF: Moderate OBJ: LO: 22-04 NAT: BUSPROG: Analytic
KEY: Bloom's: Application

5. Sweet Dreams, Inc. manufactures bedding sets. The budgeted production is for 52,000 comforters in 2012. Each comforter requires 1.5 hours to cut and sew the material. If cutting and sewing labor costs $11.00 per hour, determine the direct labor budget for 2012.

ANS:

Hours required for cutting and sewing:	
Comforters (52,000 × 1.5 hours)	78,000 hrs
Hourly rate	$ 11.00
Total direct labor cost	$ 858,000

PTS: 1 DIF: Easy OBJ: LO: 22-04 NAT: BUSPROG: Analytic
KEY: Bloom's: Application

6. Warmfeet manufactures comforters. Assume the estimated inventories on January 1, 2012, for finished goods, work in process, and materials were $51,000, $28,000 and $33,000 respectively. Also assume the desired inventories on December 31, 2012, for finished goods, work in process, and materials were $48,000, $35,000 and $29,000 respectively. Direct material purchases were $555,000. Direct labor was $252,000 for the year. Factory overhead was $176,000. Prepare a cost of goods sold budget for Warmfeet, Inc.

ANS:

Warmfeet, Inc. Cost of Goods Sold Budget For the Year Ending December 31, 2012			
Finished goods inventory, January 1, 2012			$ 51,000
Work in process inventory, January 1, 2012		$ 28,000	
Direct materials inventory, January 1, 2012	$ 33,000		
Direct materials purchases	555,000		
Cost of direct materials available for sale	$588,000		
Less direct materials inventory December 31, 2012	29,000		
Cost of direct materials placed in production	$559,000		
Direct labor	252,000		
Factory overhead	176,000		
Total manufacturing costs		987,000	
Total work in process during the period		$ 1,015,000	
Less work in process inventory, December 31, 2012		35,000	
Costs of good manufactured			980,000
Cost of finished goods available for sale			$ 1,031,000
Less finished goods inventory, December 31, 2012			48,000
Costs of goods sold			$ 983,000

PTS: 1 DIF: Challenging OBJ: LO: 22-04 NAT: BUSPROG: Analytic
KEY: Bloom's: Application

7. Warmfeet manufactures comforters. Assume the estimated inventories on January 1, 2012, for finished goods, work in process, and materials were $39,000, $33,000 and $27,000 respectively. Also assume the desired inventories on December 31, 2012, for finished goods, work in process, and materials were $42,000, $35,000 and $21,000 respectively. Direct material purchases were $575,000. Direct labor was $212,000 for the year. Factory overhead was $156,000. Prepare a cost of goods sold budget for Warmfeet, Inc.

ANS:

Warmfeet, Inc. Cost of Good Sold Budget For the Year Ending December 31, 2012			
Finished goods inventory, January 1, 2012			$ 39,000
Work in process inventory, January 1, 2012		$ 33,000	
Direct materials inventory, January 1, 2012	$ 27,000		
Direct materials purchases	575,000		
Cost of direct materials available for sale	$ 602,000		
Less direct materials inventory December 31, 2012	21,000		
Cost of direct materials placed in production	$ 581,000		
Direct labor	212,000		
Factory overhead	156,000		
Total manufacturing costs		949,000	
Total work in process during the period		$ 982,000	
Less work in process inventory, December 31, 2012		35,000	
Costs of good manufactured			947,000
Cost of finished goods available for sale			986,000
Less finished goods inventory, December 31, 2012			42,000
Costs of goods sold			$944,000

PTS: 1   DIF: Challenging   OBJ: LO: 22-04   NAT: BUSPROG: Analytic
KEY: Bloom's: Application

8. Big Wheel, Inc. collects 25% of its sales on account in the month of the sale and 75% in the month following the sale. If sales on account are budgeted to be $225,000 for March and $250,000 for April, what are the budgeted cash receipts from sales on account for April?

ANS:

	April
Collections from March sales (75% × $225,000)	$168,750
Collections from April (25% × $250,000)	62,500
Total receipts from sales on account	$231,250

PTS: 1   DIF: Moderate   OBJ: LO: 22-05   NAT: BUSPROG: Analytic
KEY: Bloom's: Application

9. Big Wheel, Inc. collects 25% of its sales on account in the month of the sale and 75% in the month
    following the sale. If sales on account are budgeted to be $150,000 for March and receipts from sales
    on account total $162,500 in April, what are budgeted sales on account for April?

    ANS:

	April
Collections from March sales (75% × $150,000)	$112,500
Collections from April (25% × X)	50,000
Total receipts from sales on account	$162,500

    X = $200,000

    PTS: 1   DIF: Moderate   OBJ: LO: 22-05   NAT: BUSPROG: Analytic
    KEY: Bloom's: Application

10. Flanders Industries collects 35% of its sales on account in the month of the sale and 65% in the
    month following the sale. If sales on account are budgeted to be $175,000 for May and $225,000 for
    June, what are the budgeted cash receipts from sales on account for June?

    ANS:

	June
Collections from May sales (65% × $175,000)	$113,750
Collections from June (35% × $225,000)	78,750
Total receipts from sales on account	$192,500

    PTS: 1   DIF: Moderate   OBJ: LO: 22-05   NAT: BUSPROG: Analytic
    KEY: Bloom's: Application

11. Cuisine Inc. manufactures flatware sets. The budgeted production is for 80,000 sets in 2012. Each
    set requires 2.5 hours to polish the material. If polishing labor costs $15.00 per hour, determine the
    direct labor budget for 2012.

    ANS:

Hours required for forming:	
Sets (80,000 × 2.5 hours)	200,000 hrs
Hourly rate	$ 15.00
Total direct labor cost	$ 3,000,000

    PTS: 1   DIF: Easy   OBJ: LO: 22-04   NAT: BUSPROG: Analytic
    KEY: Bloom's: Application

12. Callon Industries has projected sales of 67,000 machines for 2012. The estimated January 1, 2012,
    inventory is 6,000 units, and the desired December 31, 2012, inventory is 15,000 units. What is the
    budgeted production (in units) for 2012?

    ANS:

Expected units to be sold	67,000
Plus: desired ending inventory, December 31, 2012	15,000
Total	82,000
Less estimated beginning inventory, January 1, 2012	6,000
Total units to be produced	76,000

PTS: 1   DIF: Easy   OBJ: LO: 22-03   NAT: BUSPROG: Analytic
KEY: Bloom's: Application

13. At the beginning of the period, the Molding Department budgeted direct labor of $33,000 and supervisor salaries of $24,000 for 3,000 hours of production. The department actually completed 2,500 hours of production. Determine the budget for the department assuming that it uses flexible budgeting?

ANS:

Variable cost:	
Direct labor (2,500 × $11.00* per hour)	$27,500
Fixed cost:	
Supervisor salaries	$24,000
Total department cost	$51,500
*$33,000 ÷ 3,000 hours	

PTS: 1   DIF: Easy   OBJ: LO: 22-02   NAT: BUSPROG: Analytic
KEY: Bloom's: Application

14. Maxim Technologies projected sales of 35,000 computers for 2012. The estimated January 1, 2012, inventory is 3,000 units, and the desired December 31, 2012, inventory is 9,000 units. What is the budgeted production (in units) for 2012?

ANS:

Expected units to be sold	35,000
Plus: desired ending inventory, December 31, 2012	9,000
Total	44,000
Less estimated beginning inventory, January 1, 2012	3,000
Total units to be produced	41,000

PTS: 1   DIF: Easy   OBJ: LO: 22-03   NAT: BUSPROG: Analytic
KEY: Bloom's: Application

MATCHING

Match the following terms with the best definition given.
a. Planning
b. Directing
c. Controlling
d. Budget padding
e. Goal conflict

1. Actions to achieve budgeted goals.
2. Setting goals.
3. Occurs when budgets are too loose.
4. Occurs when employee self-interests are different from company goals.
5. Compare actual performance against budgeted goals.

1. ANS: B   PTS: 1   DIF: Easy   OBJ: LO: 22-01
   NAT: BUSPROG: Analytic   KEY: Bloom's: Knowledge
2. ANS: A   PTS: 1   DIF: Easy   OBJ: LO: 22-01
   NAT: BUSPROG: Analytic   KEY: Bloom's: Knowledge
3. ANS: D   PTS: 1   DIF: Easy   OBJ: LO: 22-01
   NAT: BUSPROG: Analytic   KEY: Bloom's: Knowledge
4. ANS: E   PTS: 1   DIF: Easy   OBJ: LO: 22-01
   NAT: BUSPROG: Analytic   KEY: Bloom's: Knowledge
5. ANS: C   PTS: 1   DIF: Easy   OBJ: LO: 22-01
   NAT: BUSPROG: Analytic   KEY: Bloom's: Knowledge

Match the following terms with the best definition given.
   a. Static budget
   b. Flexible budget
   c. Master budget
   d. Sales budget
   e. Production budget

6. Integrated set of operating, investing and financing budgets for a period of time.
7. Begins by estimating the quantity of sales.
8. Shows expected results at several activity levels.
9. Estimates the number of units to be manufactured to meet sales and inventory levels.
10. Shows expected results at only one activity level.

6. ANS: C   PTS: 1   DIF: Easy   OBJ: LO: 22-03
    NAT: BUSPROG: Analytic   KEY: Bloom's: Knowledge
7. ANS: D   PTS: 1   DIF: Easy   OBJ: LO: 22-04
    NAT: BUSPROG: Analytic   KEY: Bloom's: Knowledge
8. ANS: B   PTS: 1   DIF: Easy   OBJ: LO: 22-02
    NAT: BUSPROG: Analytic   KEY: Bloom's: Knowledge
9. ANS: E   PTS: 1   DIF: Easy   OBJ: LO: 22-04
    NAT: BUSPROG: Analytic   KEY: Bloom's: Knowledge
10. ANS: A   PTS: 1   DIF: Easy   OBJ: LO: 22-02
    NAT: BUSPROG: Analytic   KEY: Bloom's: Knowledge

Match the following terms with the best definition given.
   a. budget
   b. capital expenditure budget
   c. sales budget
   d. production budget
   e. cash budget
   f. budgeted balance sheet

11. An accounting report that presents predicted amounts of the company's assets, liabilities, and equity as of the end of the budget period.
12. A formal statement of future plans, usually expressed in monetary terms.
13. A plan showing the units of goods to be sold and the sales to be derived; usually the starting point in the budgeting process.
14. A plan that lists dollar amounts to be both received from disposing of plant assets and spent on purchasing additional pant assets to carry out the budgeted business activities.

15. A plan showing the number of units to be produced each month.
16. A plan that shows the expected cash inflows and outflows during the budget period, including receipts from loans needed to maintain a minimum cash balance and repayments of such loans.

11. ANS: F   PTS: 1   DIF: Moderate   OBJ: LO: 22-04
    NAT: BUSPROG: Analytic   KEY: Bloom's: Knowledge
12. ANS: A   PTS: 1   DIF: Moderate   OBJ: LO: 22-01
    NAT: BUSPROG: Analytic   KEY: Bloom's: Knowledge
13. ANS: C   PTS: 1   DIF: Moderate   OBJ: LO: 22-04
    NAT: BUSPROG: Analytic   KEY: Bloom's: Knowledge
14. ANS: B   PTS: 1   DIF: Moderate   OBJ: LO: 22-05
    NAT: BUSPROG: Analytic   KEY: Bloom's: Knowledge
15. ANS: D   PTS: 1   DIF: Moderate   OBJ: LO: 22-04
    NAT: BUSPROG: Analytic   KEY: Bloom's: Knowledge
16. ANS: E   PTS: 1   DIF: Moderate   OBJ: LO: 22-05
    NAT: BUSPROG: Analytic   KEY: Bloom's: Knowledge

PROBLEM

1. Finewood Cabinet Manufacturers uses flexible budgets that are based on the following manufacturing data for the month of July:

Direct materials	$8 per unit
Direct labor	$5 per unit
Electric power (variable)	$0.30 per unit
Electric power (fixed)	$4,000 per month
Supervisor salaries	$15,000 per month
Property taxes on factory	$4,000 per month
Straight-line depreciation	$2,900 per month

Prepare a flexible budget for Finewood based on production of 10,000, 15,000, and 20,000 units.

ANS:

Finewood Cabinet Manufacturers
Flexible Manufacturing Budget
For the Month Ended July 31, 20--

Units of production	10,000	15,000	20,000
Variable cost:			
Direct materials ($8 per unit)	$ 80,000	$120,000	$160,000
Direct labor ($5 per unit)	50,000	75,000	100,000
Electric power ($0.30 per unit)	3,000	4,500	6,000
Total variable cost	$133,000	$199,500	$266,000
Fixed cost:			
Electric power	$ 4,000	$ 4,000	$ 4,000
Supervisor salaries	15,000	15,000	15,000
Property taxes	4,000	4,000	4,000
Depreciation expense	2,900	2,900	2,900
Total fixed cost	$ 25,900	$ 25,900	$ 25,900
Total manufacturing costs	$158,900	$225,400	$291,900

PTS: 1   DIF: Moderate   OBJ: LO: 22-02   NAT: BUSPROG: Analytic
KEY: Bloom's: Application

2. Prepare a monthly flexible selling expense budget for PineTree Company for sales volumes of
    $300,000, $350,000, and $400,000, based on the following data:

Sales commissions	6% of sales
Sales manager's salary	$120,000 per month
Advertising expense	$ 90,000 per month
Shipping expense	1% of sales
Miscellaneous selling expense	$4,000 per month plus 1.5% of sales

ANS:

PineTree Company
Monthly Selling Expense Budget

	$300,000	$350,000	$400,000
Sales volume			
Variable expense:			
Sales commissions	$ 18,000	$ 21,000	$ 24,000
Shipping expense	3,000	3,500	4,000
Misc. selling expense	4,500	5,250	6,000
Total variable expense	$ 25,500	$ 29,750	$ 34,000
Fixed expense:			
Sales manager's salary	$120,000	$120,000	$120,000
Advertising expense	90,000	90,000	90,000
Misc. selling expense	4,000	4,000	4,000
Total fixed expense	$214,000	$214,000	$214,000
Total selling expense	$239,500	$243,750	$248,000

PTS: 1   DIF: Moderate   OBJ: LO: 22-02   NAT: BUSPROG: Analytic
KEY: Bloom's: Application

3. Prepare a flexible budget for Cedar Jeans Company using production levels of 16,000, 18,000, and
    20,000 units produced. The following is additional information necessary to complete the budget:

Variable costs:
Direct Labor ($6.00 per unit)
    Direct Materials ($8.00 per unit)
    Variable Manufacturing Costs ($2.50 per unit)

Fixed costs:
Supervisor's Salaries	$80,000
Rent	12,000
Depreciation On Equipment	24,000

ANS:

Cedar Jeans Company
Flexible Budget
For the Year Ended December 31, 20--

Units of production	16,000	18,000	20,000
Variable Costs:			
Direct Labor ($6.00 per unit)	$ 96,000	$108,000	$120,000
Direct Materials ($8.00 per unit)	128,000	144,000	160,000
Variable Costs ($2.50 per unit)	40,000	45,000	50,000
Total Variable Costs	$ 264,000	$297,000	$330,000
Fixed Costs:			
Supervisor's Salaries	$ 80,000	$ 80,000	$ 80,000
Rent	12,000	12,000	12,000
Depreciation on Equipment	24,000	24,000	24,000
Total Fixed Costs	$116,000	$116,000	$116,000
Total Manufacturing Budget	$ 380,000	$413,000	$446,000

PTS: 1   DIF: Moderate   OBJ: LO: 22-02   NAT: BUSPROG: Analytic
KEY: Bloom's: Application

4.   The Svelte Jeans Company produces two different types of jeans. One is called the "Simple Life" and the other is called the "Fancy Life". The company sales budget estimates that 400,000 of the Simple Life Jeans and 250,000 of the Fancy Life will be sold during 20--. The company begins with 8,000 Simple Life Jeans and 17,000 Fancy Life Jeans. The company desires ending inventory of 7,500 of Simple Life Jeans and 10,000 Fancy Life Jeans. Prepare a Production Budget for the 20--.

ANS:

Svelte Jeans Company
Production Budget
For the Year Ending December 31, 20--

	Simple	Fancy
Expected units to be sold (As Per Sales Budget)	400,000	250,000
Plus desired ending inventory	7,500	10,000
Total	407,500	260,000
Less estimated beginning inventory	8,000	17,000
Total Units to be Produced	399,500	243,000

PTS: 1   DIF: Easy   OBJ: LO: 22-04   NAT: BUSPROG: Analytic
KEY: Bloom's: Application

5. Based on the following production and sales data of Shingle Co. for March of the current year, prepare (a) a sales budget and (b) a production budget.

	Product T	Product X
Estimated inventory, March 1	28,000 units	20,000 units
Desired inventory, March 31	32,000 units	15,000 units
Expected sales volume:		
Area I	320,000 units	260,000 units
Area II	190,000 units	130,000 units
Unit sales price	$6	$14

ANS:

(a)

Shingle Co.
Sales Budget
For Month Ending March 31, 20--

Product and Area	Unit Sales Volume	Unit Selling Price	Total Sales
Product T:			
Area I	320,000	$ 6	$1,920,000
Area II	190,000	6	1,140,000
Total	510,000		$3,060,000
Product X:			
Area I	260,000	$14	$3,640,000
Area II	130,000	14	1,820,000
Total	390,000		$5,460,000
Total revenue from sales			$8,520,000

(b)

Shingle Co.
Production Budget
For Month Ending March 31, 20--

	Product T	Product X
Sales.	510,000 units	390,000 units
Plus desired inventory, March 31, 20--	32,000	15,000
Total	542,000 units	405,000 units
Less estimated inventory, March 1, 20--	28,000	20,000
Total production	514,000 units	385,000 units

PTS: 1   DIF: Moderate   OBJ: LO: 22-04   NAT: BUSPROG: Analytic
KEY: Bloom's: Application

6. Crystal Company manufactures two models of microcassette recorders, VCH and MTV. Based on the following production data for April of the current year, prepare a production budget for April.

	VCH	MTV
Estimated inventory (units), April 1	2,800	4,200
Desired inventory (units), April 30	6,900	5,250
Expected sales volume (units):		
Eastern zone	12,500	12,960
Midwest zone	19,000	19,800
Western zone	14,500	9,840

ANS:

Crystal Company
Production Budget
For Month Ending April 30, 20--

	VCH	MTV
Sales	46,000 units	42,600 units
Plus desired ending inventory, April 30, 20--	6,900	5,250
Total	52,900 units	47,850 units
Less estimated beginning inventory, April 1, 20--	2,800	4,200
Total production	50,100 units	43,650 units

PTS: 1   DIF: Moderate   OBJ: LO: 22-04   NAT: BUSPROG: Analytic
KEY: Bloom's: Application

7. Purple Inc. production budget for Product X for the year ended December 31 is as follows:

	Product X	
Sales	640,000	units
Plus desired ending inventory	85,000	
Total	725,000	
Less estimated beginning inventory, Jan. 1	90,000	
Total production	635,000	

In Purple's production operations, Materials A, B, and C are required to make Product X. The quantities of direct materials expected to be used for each unit of product are as follows:

Product X	
Material A	.50 pound per unit
Material B	1.00 pound per unit
Material C	1.20 pound per unit

The prices of direct materials are as follows:

Material A	$0.60 per pound
Material B	1.70 per pound
Material C	1.00 per pound

Prepare a direct materials purchases budget for Product X, assuming that there are no beginning or ending inventories for direct materials (all units purchased are used in production).

ANS:

| | Direct Materials | | | |
	A	B	C	Total
Units required for production of Product X (Note A)	317,500 lb.	635,000 lb.	762,000 lb.	
Unit price	× $.60	× $1.70	× $1.00	
Total direct materials purchases	$190,500	$1,079,500	$762,000	$2,032,000

Note A: Material A   635,000 ×   .50 lb. per unit = 317,500 lbs.
            Material B   635,000 × 1.00 lb. per unit = 635,000 lbs.
            Material C   635,000 × 1.20 lb. per unit = 762,000 lbs.

PTS: 1   DIF: Challenging   OBJ: LO: 22-04   NAT: BUSPROG: Analytic
KEY: Bloom's: Application

8.   The Svelte Jeans Company produces two different types of jeans. One is called the "Simple Life" and
     the other is called the "Fancy Life". The company sales budget estimates that 350,000 of the Simple
     Life Jeans and 200,000 of the Fancy Life will be sold during 20xx. The Production Budget requires
     353,500 units of Simple Life jeans and 196,000 Fancy Life jeans be manufactured. The Simple Life
     jeans require 3 yards of denim material, a zipper, and 25 yards of thread. The Fancy Life jeans require
     4.5 yards of denim material, a zipper, and 40 yards of thread. Each yard of denim material costs $3.25,
     the zipper costs $.75 each, and the thread is $.01 per yard. There is enough material to make 2,000 jeans
     of each type at the beginning of the year. The desired amount of materials left in ending inventory is to
     have enough to manufacture 3,500 jeans of each type. Prepare a Direct Materials Purchases Budget.

     ANS:

Svelte Jeans Company
Direct Materials Purchases Budget
For the Year ending December 31, 20--

	Denim Total (Yards)	Zippers (Each)	Thread (Yards)	
Units Required:				
Simple (353,500 Units *3 Yards)	1,060,500	353,500	8,837,500	
Fancy (196,000 Units *4.5 Yards)	882,000	196,000	7,840,000	
Desired Ending Inventory:				
Simple (3,500 Units * 3 Yards)	10,500	3,500	87,500	
Fancy (3,500 Units * 4.5 Yards)	15,750	3,500		
			140,000	
Total	1,968,750	556,500	16,905,000	
Less Beginning Inventory:				
Simple (2,000 Units * 3 Yards)	6,000	2,000	50,000	
Fancy (2,000 Units * 4.5 Yards)	9,000	2,000	80,000	
Total Amount to be Purchased	1,953,750	552,500	16,775,000	
Unit Price	× $3.25	× $.75	× $.01	
Total Direct Materials to be Purchased	$6,349,688	$414,375	$ 167,750	$6,931,813

PTS: 1   DIF: Challenging   OBJ: LO: 22-04   NAT: BUSPROG: Analytic
KEY: Bloom's: Application

9. The treasurer of Systems Company has accumulated the following budget information for the first two months of the coming year:

	March	April
Sales.	$450,000	$520,000
Manufacturing costs	290,000	350,000
Selling and administrative expenses	41,400	46,400
Capital additions	250,000	---

The company expects to sell about 35% of its merchandise for cash. Of sales on account, 80% are expected to be collected in full in the month of the sale and the remainder in the month following the sale. One-fourth of the manufacturing costs are expected to be paid in the month in which they are incurred and the other three-fourths in the following month. Depreciation, insurance, and property taxes represent $6,400 of the probable monthly selling and administrative expenses. Insurance is paid in February and a $40,000 installment on income taxes is expected to be paid in April. Of the remainder of the selling and administrative expenses, one-half are expected to be paid in the month in which they are incurred and the balance in the following month. Capital additions of $250,000 are expected to be paid in March.

Current assets as of March 1 are composed of cash of $45,000 and accounts receivable of $51,000. Current liabilities as of March 1 are composed of accounts payable of $121,500 ($102,000 for materials purchases and $19,500 for operating expenses). Management desires to maintain a minimum cash balance of $20,000.

Prepare a monthly cash budget for March and April.

ANS:

Systems Company
Cash Budget
For the Two Months Ending April 30, 20--

	March	April
Estimated cash receipts from:		
Cash sales*	$157,500	$182,000
Collections of accounts receivable**	285,000	328,900
Total cash receipts	$442,500	$510,900
Estimated cash payments for:		
Manufacturing costs	$174,500	$305,000
Selling and administrative expenses	37,000	37,500
Capital additions	250,000	---
Income taxes	---	40,000
Total cash payments	$461,500	$382,500
Cash increase (decrease)	$(19,000)	$128,400
Cash balance at beginning of month	45,000	26,000
Cash balance at end of month	$ 26,000	$154,400
Minimum cash balance	20,000	20,000
Excess (deficiency)	$ 6,000	$134,400

* $450,000 × .35 = $157,500; $520,000 × .35 = $182,000

** ($450,000 × .65 × .80) + $51,000 = $285,000

($520,000 × .65 × .80) + ($450,000 × .65 × .20) = $328,900

10. Door & Window Co. was organized on August 1 of the current year. Projected sales for the next three months are as follows:

August	$120,000
September	200,000
October	230,000

The company expects to sell 40% of its merchandise for cash. Of the sales on account, 25% are expected to be collected in the month of the sale and the remainder in the following month.

Prepare a schedule indicating total cash collections for August, September, and October.

ANS:

Door & Window Co.
Schedule of Collections of Accounts Receivable
For Three Months Ending October 31, 20--

	August	September	October
Total Sales	$120,000	$200,000	$230,000
Cash Sales	$ 48,000	$ 80,000	$ 92,000
Credit Sales	$ 72,000	$120,000	$138,000
Collections of Accounts Receivable:			
August Credit Sales	$ 18,000	$ 54,000	
September Credit Sales		$ 30,000	$ 90,000
October Credit Sales			$ 34,500
Cash Sales	$ 48,000	$ 80,000	$ 92,000
Total Cash Collected	$ 66,000	$164,000	$216,500

11. Star Co. was organized on August 1 of the current year. Projected sales for the next three months are as follows:

August	$250,000
September	200,000
October	275,000

The company expects to sell 50% of its merchandise for cash. Of the sales on account, 30% are expected to be collected in the month of the sale and the remainder in the following month.

Prepare a schedule indicating cash collections for August, September, and October.

ANS:

Star Co.
Schedule of Cash Collections
For Three Months Ending October 31, 20--

	August	September	October
Sales	$250,000	$200,000	$275,000
Cash Sales	$125,000	$100,000	$137,500
Credit Sales	$125,000	$100,000	$137,500
Collections of Accounts Receivable:			
August credit sales	$ 37,500	$ 87,500	
September		$ 30,000	$ 70,000
October			$ 41,250
Total Credit Collections	$ 37,500	$117,500	$111,250
Total Collections (cash + credit sales)	$162,500	$217,500	$248,750

PTS: 1 DIF: Moderate OBJ: LO: 22-05 NAT: BUSPROG: Analytic
KEY: Bloom's: Application

12. Doran Technologies produces a single product. Expected manufacturing costs are as follows:

Variable costs
Direct materials	$4.00 per unit
Direct labor	$1.20 per unit
Manufacturing overhead	$0.95 per unit

Fixed costs per month
Depreciation	$ 6,000
Supervisory salaries	$13,500
Other fixed costs	$ 3,850

Required:

Estimate manufacturing costs for production levels of 25,000 units, 30,000 units, and 35,000 units per month.

ANS:

At 25,000 units = 25,000 ($4.00 + $1.20 + $0.95) + ($6,000 + $13,500 + $3,850) = $177,100
At 30,000 units = 30,000 ($4.00 + $1.20 + $0.95) + ($6,000 + $13,500 + $3,850) = $207,850
At 35,000 units = 35,000 ($4.00 + $1.20 + $0.95) + ($6,000 + $13,500 + $3,850) = $238,600

PTS: 1 DIF: Moderate OBJ: LO: 22-02 NAT: BUSPROG: Analytic
KEY: Bloom's: Application

13. Describe at least five benefits of budgeting.

ANS:
Student answers should include the following benefits:
1) Budgeting promotes good decision-making processes, including analysis and research.
2) Budgeting focuses management's attention on the future.
3) Budgeting provides a basis for evaluating performance.
4) Budgeting can be used as a motivator.
5) Budgeting provides a means of coordinating business activities.

PTS: 1   DIF: Moderate   OBJ: LO: 22-01   NAT: BUSPROG: Analytic
KEY: Bloom's: Comprehension

14. Describe a master budget and the sequence in which the individual budgets within the master budget are prepared.

ANS:
The master budget is a comprehensive plan, expressed in monetary terms, for an entire organization for a given period. It is prepared from individual budgets of the various segments of the organization.

The master budget usually starts with predictions of sales. Using the sales projection, the remaining operating budgets are prepared. Then capital expenditures are budgeted. Using the information from the operating and the capital expenditures budgets, the financial budgets can then be prepared, including the cash budget, budgeted income statement, and budgeted balance sheet.

PTS: 1   DIF: Moderate   OBJ: LO: 22-01   NAT: BUSPROG: Analytic
KEY: Bloom's: Comprehension

15. Why is the sales budget usually prepared first?

ANS:
The sales budget is normally prepared first because the other operating budgets and financial budgets depend on information provided by the sales budget. The plans of most departments are related to sales units and dollars.

PTS: 1   DIF: Moderate   OBJ: LO: 22-01   NAT: BUSPROG: Analytic
KEY: Bloom's: Knowledge

16. What is a capital expenditures budget?

ANS:
The capital expenditures budget lists the amounts to be both received from plant asset disposals and spent to purchase additional plant assets to carry out the budgeted business activities.

PTS: 1   DIF: Moderate   OBJ: LO: 22-04   NAT: BUSPROG: Analytic
KEY: Bloom's: Knowledge

17. What is a cash budget? How does management use a cash budget?

ANS:
A cash budget shows expected cash inflows and outflows during the budget period. Management can arrange loans to cover anticipated cash shortages before they are needed. The cash budget also helps avoid a cash balance that is too large.

PTS: 1   DIF: Moderate   OBJ: LO: 22-04   NAT: BUSPROG: Analytic
KEY: Bloom's: Knowledge

TRUE/FALSE

1. A variable cost system is an accounting system where standards are set for each manufacturing cost element.

   ANS: F   PTS: 1   DIF: Easy   OBJ: LO: 23-01
   NAT: BUSPROG: Analytic   KEY: Bloom's: Knowledge

2. One reason not to depend solely on historical records to set standards is that there may be inefficiencies contained in past costs.

   ANS: T   PTS: 1   DIF: Easy   OBJ: LO: 23-01
   NAT: BUSPROG: Analytic   KEY: Bloom's: Knowledge

3. Standard costs serve as a device for measuring efficiency.

   ANS: T   PTS: 1   DIF: Easy   OBJ: LO: 23-01
   NAT: BUSPROG: Analytic   KEY: Bloom's: Knowledge

4. The standard cost is how much a product should cost to manufacture.

   ANS: T   PTS: 1   DIF: Easy   OBJ: LO: 23-01
   NAT: BUSPROG: Analytic   KEY: Bloom's: Knowledge

5. Standard costs can be used with both the process cost and job order cost systems.

   ANS: T   PTS: 1   DIF: Easy   OBJ: LO: 23-01
   NAT: BUSPROG: Analytic   KEY: Bloom's: Knowledge

6. Cost systems using detailed estimates of each element of manufacturing cost entering into the finished product are called standard cost systems.

   ANS: T   PTS: 1   DIF: Easy   OBJ: LO: 23-01
   NAT: BUSPROG: Analytic   KEY: Bloom's: Knowledge

7. Cost systems using detailed estimates of each element of manufacturing cost entering into the finished product are called budgeted cost systems.

   ANS: F   PTS: 1   DIF: Easy   OBJ: LO: 23-01
   NAT: BUSPROG: Analytic   KEY: Bloom's: Knowledge

8. Normally standard costs should be revised when labor rates change to incorporate new union contracts.

   ANS: T   PTS: 1   DIF: Easy   OBJ: LO: 23-01
   NAT: BUSPROG: Analytic   KEY: Bloom's: Knowledge

9.   Standard costs should always be revised when they differ from actual costs.

ANS: F   PTS: 1   DIF: Easy   OBJ: LO: 23-01
NAT: BUSPROG: Analytic   KEY: Bloom's: Knowledge

10. Financial reporting systems that are guided by the principle of exceptions concept focus attention on variances from standard costs.

ANS: T   PTS: 1   D   IF: Easy   OBJ: LO: 23-01
NAT: BUSPROG: Analytic   KEY: Bloom's: Knowledge

11. In most businesses, cost standards are established principally by accountants.

ANS: F   PTS: 1   DIF: Easy   OBJ: LO: 23-01
NAT: BUSPROG: Analytic   KEY: Bloom's: Knowledge

12. It is correct to rely exclusively on past cost data when establishing standards.

ANS: F   PTS: 1   DIF: Easy   OBJ: LO: 23-01
NAT: BUSPROG: Analytic   KEY: Bloom's: Knowledge

13. Ideal standards are developed under conditions that assume no idle time, no machine breakdowns, and no materials spoilage.

ANS: T   PTS: 1   DIF: Easy   OBJ: LO: 23-01
NAT: BUSPROG: Analytic   KEY: Bloom's: Knowledge

14. Currently attainable standards do not allow for reasonable production difficulties.

ANS: F   PTS: 1   DIF: Easy   OBJ: LO: 23-01
NAT: BUSPROG: Analytic   KEY: Bloom's: Knowledge

15. If employees are given bonuses for exceeding normal standards, the standards may be very effective in motivating employees.

ANS: T   PTS: 1   DIF: Easy   OBJ: LO: 23-01
NAT: BUSPROG: Analytic   KEY: Bloom's: Knowledge

16. The fact that workers are unable to meet a properly determined direct labor standard is sufficient cause to change the standard.

ANS: F   PTS: 1   DIF: Easy   OBJ: LO: 23-01
NAT: BUSPROG: Analytic   KEY: Bloom's: Knowledge

17. Changes in technology, machinery, or production methods may make past cost data irrelevant when setting standards.

ANS: T   PTS: 1   DIF: Easy   OBJ: LO: 23-01
NAT: BUSPROG: Analytic   KEY: Bloom's: Knowledge

18. The difference between the standard cost of a product and its actual cost is called a variance.

ANS: T   PTS: 1   DIF: Easy   OBJ: LO: 23-01
NAT: BUSPROG: Analytic   KEY: Bloom's: Knowledge

19. Standards are performance goals used to evaluate and control operations.

ANS: T   PTS: 1   DIF: Easy   OBJ: LO: 23-01
NAT: BUSPROG: Analytic   KEY: Bloom's: Knowledge

20. Standards are set for only direct labor and direct materials.

ANS: F   PTS: 1   DIF: Easy   OBJ: LO: 23-01
NAT: BUSPROG: Analytic   KEY: Bloom's: Knowledge

21. Principle of exceptions allows managers to focus on correcting variances between standard costs and actual costs.

ANS: T   PTS: 1   DIF: Easy   OBJ: LO: 23-01
NAT: BUSPROG: Analytic   KEY: Bloom's: Knowledge

22. Because accountants have financial expertise, they are the only ones that are able to set standard costs for the production area.

ANS: F   PTS: 1   DIF: Moderate   OBJ: LO: 23-01
NAT: BUSPROG: Analytic   KEY: Bloom's: Knowledge

23. While setting standards, the managers should never allow for spoilage or machine breakdowns in their calculations.

ANS: F   PTS: 1   DIF: Moderate   OBJ: LO: 23-01
NAT: BUSPROG: Analytic   KEY: Bloom's: Knowledge

24. A budget performance report compares actual results with the budgeted amounts and reports differences for possible investigation.

ANS: T   PTS: 1   DIF: Easy   OBJ: LO: 23-02
NAT: BUSPROG: Analytic   KEY: Bloom's: Knowledge

25. A favorable cost variance occurs when actual cost is less than budgeted cost at actual volumes.

ANS: T   PTS: 1   DIF: Easy   OBJ: LO: 23-02
NAT: BUSPROG: Analytic   KEY: Bloom's: Knowledge

26. An unfavorable cost variance occurs when budgeted cost at actual volumes exceeds actual cost.

ANS: F   PTS: 1   DIF: Easy   OBJ: LO: 23-02
NAT: BUSPROG: Analytic   KEY: Bloom's: Knowledge

27. Standards are designed to evaluate price and quantity variances separately.

ANS: T   PTS: 1   DIF: Easy   OBJ: LO: 23-02
NAT: BUSPROG: Analytic   KEY: Bloom's: Knowledge

28. If the standard to produce a given amount of product is 2,000 units of direct materials at $12 and the actual was 1,600 units at $13, the direct materials quantity variance was $5,200 favorable.

ANS: F   PTS: 1   DIF: Moderate   OBJ: LO: 23-03
NAT: BUSPROG: Analytic   KEY: Bloom's: Knowledge

29. If the standard to produce a given amount of product is 1,000 units of direct materials at $11 and the actual was 800 units at $12, the direct materials quantity variance was $2,200 unfavorable.

ANS: F   PTS: 1   DIF: Moderate   OBJ: LO: 23-03
NAT: BUSPROG: Analytic   KEY: Bloom's: Knowledge

30. If the standard to produce a given amount of product is 1,000 units of direct materials at $11 and the actual was 800 units at $12, the direct materials price variance was $800 unfavorable.

ANS: T   PTS: 1   DIF: Moderate   OBJ: LO: 23-03
NAT: BUSPROG: Analytic   KEY: Bloom's: Knowledge

31. If the standard to produce a given amount of product is 1,000 units of direct materials at $11 and the actual was 800 units at $12, the direct materials price variance was $800 favorable.

ANS: F   PTS: 1   DIF: Moderate   OBJ: LO: 23-03
NAT: BUSPROG: Analytic   KEY: Bloom's: Knowledge

32. If the standard to produce a given amount of product is 1,000 units of direct materials at $11 and the actual was 800 units at $12, the direct materials quantity variance was $1,000 unfavorable.

ANS: F   PTS: 1   DIF: Moderate   OBJ: LO: 23-03
NAT: BUSPROG: Analytic   KEY: Bloom's: Knowledge

33. If the standard to produce a given amount of product is 600 direct labor hours at $17 and the actual was 500 hours at $15, the time variance was $1,500 unfavorable.

ANS: F   PTS: 1   DIF: Moderate   OBJ: LO: 23-03
NAT: BUSPROG: Analytic   KEY: Bloom's: Knowledge

34. If the standard to produce a given amount of product is 600 direct labor hours at $15 and the actual was 500 hours at $17, the time variance was $1,700 unfavorable.

ANS: F   PTS: 1   DIF: Moderate   OBJ: LO: 23-03
NAT: BUSPROG: Analytic   KEY: Bloom's: Knowledge

35. If the standard to produce a given amount of product is 600 direct labor hours at $15 and the actual was 600 hours at $17, the rate variance was $1,200 unfavorable.

ANS: T   PTS: 1   DIF: Moderate   OBJ: LO: 23-03
NAT: BUSPROG: Analytic   KEY: Bloom's: Knowledge

36. If the standard to produce a given amount of product is 500 direct labor hours at $15 and the actual was 600 hours at $17, the rate variance was $1,200 favorable.

   ANS: F   PTS: 1   DIF: Moderate   OBJ: LO: 23-03
   NAT: BUSPROG: Analytic   KEY: Bloom's: Knowledge

37. Standard costs are determined by multiplying expected price by expected quantity.

   ANS: T   PTS: 1   DIF: Easy   OBJ: LO: 23-03
   NAT: BUSPROG: Analytic   KEY: Bloom's: Knowledge

38. The direct labor time variance measures the efficiency of the direct labor force.

   ANS: T   PTS: 1   DIF: Easy   OBJ: LO: 23-03
   NAT: BUSPROG: Analytic   KEY: Bloom's: Knowledge

39. The variance from standard for factory overhead cost resulting from operating at a level above or below 100% of normal capacity is termed volume variance.

   ANS: T   PTS: 1   DIF: Easy   OBJ: LO: 23-04
   NAT: BUSPROG: Analytic   KEY: Bloom's: Knowledge

40. The variance from standard for factory overhead resulting from incurring a total amount of factory overhead cost that is greater or less than the amount budgeted for the level of operations achieved is termed controllable variance.

   ANS: T   PTS: 1   DIF: Easy   OBJ: LO: 23-04
   NAT: BUSPROG: Analytic   KEY: Bloom's: Knowledge

41. The most effective means of presenting standard factory overhead cost variance data is through a factory overhead cost variance report.

   ANS: T   PTS: 1   DIF: Easy   OBJ: LO: 23-04
   NAT: BUSPROG: Analytic   KEY: Bloom's: Knowledge

42. Since the controllable variance measures the efficiency of using variable overhead resources, if budgeted variable overhead exceeds actual results, the variance is favorable.

   ANS: T   PTS: 1   DIF: Easy   OBJ: LO: 23-04
   NAT: BUSPROG: Analytic   KEY: Bloom's: Knowledge

43. An unfavorable volume variance may be due to a failure of supervisors to maintain an even flow of work.

   ANS: T   PTS: 1   DIF: Easy   OBJ: LO: 23-04
   NAT: BUSPROG: Analytic   KEY: Bloom's: Knowledge

44. Favorable volume variances are never harmful, since achieving them encourages managers to run the factory above normal capacity.

   ANS: F   PTS: 1   DIF: Easy   OBJ: LO: 23-04
   NAT: BUSPROG: Analytic   KEY: Bloom's: Knowledge

45. Volume variance measures fixed factory overhead.

    ANS: T   PTS: 1   DIF: Moderate   OBJ: LO: 23-04
    NAT: BUSPROG: Analytic   KEY: Bloom's: Knowledge

46. Though favorable volume variances are usually good news, if inventory levels are too high, additional production could be harmful.

    ANS: T   PTS: 1   DIF: Easy   OBJ: LO: 23-04
    NAT: BUSPROG: Analytic   KEY: Bloom's: Knowledge

47. Standard costs are a useful management tool that can be used solely as a statistical device apart from the ledger or they can be incorporated in the accounts.

    ANS: T   PTS: 1   DIF: Easy   OBJ: LO: 23-05
    NAT: BUSPROG: Analytic   KEY: Bloom's: Knowledge

48. At the end of the fiscal year, the variances from standard are usually transferred to the finished goods account.

    ANS: F   PTS: 1   DIF: Moderate   OBJ: LO: 23-05
    NAT: BUSPROG: Analytic   KEY: Bloom's: Knowledge

49. Standard cost variances are usually not reported in reports to stockholders.

    ANS: T   PTS: 1   DIF: Easy   OBJ: LO: 23-05
    NAT: BUSPROG: Analytic   KEY: Bloom's: Knowledge

50. Standards are more widely used for nonmanufacturing expenses than for manufacturing costs.

    ANS: F   PTS: 1   DIF: Easy   OBJ: LO: 23-06
    NAT: BUSPROG: Analytic   KEY: Bloom's: Knowledge

51. Non-financial measures are often lined to the inputs or outputs of an activity or process.

    ANS: T   PTS: 1   DIF: Easy   OBJ: LO: 23-06
    NAT: BUSPROG: Analytic   KEY: Bloom's: Knowledge

52. A company must choice either a standard system or nonfinancial performance measures to evaluate the performance of a company.

    ANS: F   PTS: 1   DIF: Easy   OBJ: LO: 23-06
    NAT: BUSPROG: Analytic   KEY: Bloom's: Knowledge

53. Nonfinancial performance output measures are used to improve the input measures.

    ANS: F   PTS: 1   DIF: Easy   OBJ: LO: 23-06
    NAT: BUSPROG: Analytic   KEY: Bloom's: Knowledge

54. An example of a nonfinancial measure is the number of customer complaints.

ANS: T   PTS: 1   DIF: Easy   OBJ: LO: 23-06
NAT: BUSPROG: Analytic   KEY: Bloom's: Knowledge

55. A company should only use nonfinancial performance measures when financial measures cannot be calculated.

ANS: F   PTS: 1   DIF: Easy   OBJ: LO: 23-06
NAT: BUSPROG: Analytic   KEY: Bloom's: Knowledge

MULTIPLE CHOICE

1. Which of the following conditions normally would not indicate that standard costs should be revised?
   a. The engineering department has revised product specifications in responding to customer suggestions.
   b. The company has signed a new union contract which increases the factory wages on average by $5.00 an hour.
   c. Actual costs differed from standard costs for the preceding week.
   d. The world price of raw materials increased.

   ANS: C   PTS: 1   DIF: Moderate   OBJ: LO: 23-01
   NAT: BUSPROG: Analytic   KEY: Bloom's: Knowledge

2. Standards that represent levels of operation that can be attained with reasonable effort are called:
   a. theoretical standards
   b. ideal standards
   c. variable standards
   d. normal standards

   ANS: D   PTS: 1   DIF: Moderate   OBJ: LO: 23-01
   NAT: BUSPROG: Analytic   KEY: Bloom's: Knowledge

3. Standard costs are used in companies for a variety of reasons. Which of the following is not one of the benefits for using standard costs?
   a. Used to indicate where changes in technology and machinery need to be made.
   b. Used to identify inventory
   c. Used to plan direct materials, direct labor, and factory factory overhead.
   d. Used to control costs.

   ANS: A   PTS: 1   DIF: Easy   OBJ: LO: 23-01
   NAT: BUSPROG: Analytic   KEY: Bloom's: Knowledge

4. The principle of exceptions allows managers to
   a. focus on correcting variances between standard costs and actual costs.
   b. focus on correcting variances between variable costs and actual costs.
   c. focus on correcting variances between competitor's costs and actual costs.
   d. focus on correcting variances between competitor's costs and standard costs.

   ANS: A   PTS: 1   DIF: Easy   OBJ: LO: 23-01
   NAT: BUSPROG: Analytic   KEY: Bloom's: Knowledge

5. Periodic comparisons between planned objectives and actual performance are reported in:
   a. zero-base reports
   b. budget performance reports
   c. master budgets
   d. budgets

   ANS: B   PTS: 1   DIF: Easy   OBJ: LO: 23-02
   NAT: BUSPROG: Analytic   KEY: Bloom's: Knowledge

6. The standard price and quantity of direct materials are separated because:
   a. GAAP reporting requires this separation
   b. direct materials prices are controlled by the purchasing department, and quantity used is controlled by the production department
   c. standard quantities are more difficult to estimate than standard prices
   d. standard prices change more frequently than standard quantities

   ANS: B   PTS: 1   DIF: Easy   OBJ: LO: 23-02
   NAT: BUSPROG: Analytic   KEY: Bloom's: Knowledge

7. Standard costs are divided into which of the following components?
   a. Variance Standard and Quantity Standard
   b. Materials Standard and Labor Standard
   c. Quality Standard and Quantity Standard
   d. Price Standard and Quantity Standard

   ANS: D   PTS: 1   DIF: Easy   OBJ: LO: 23-02
   NAT: BUSPROG: Analytic   KEY: Bloom's: Knowledge

8. A favorable cost variance occurs when
   a. Actual costs are more than standard costs.
   b. Standard costs are more than actual costs.
   c. Standard costs are less than actual costs.
   d. None of the above.

   ANS: B   PTS: 1   DIF: Easy   OBJ: LO: 23-02
   NAT: BUSPROG: Analytic   KEY: Bloom's: Knowledge

9. The total manufacturing cost variance consists of:
   a. Direct materials price variance, direct labor cost variance, and fixed factory overhead volume variance
   b. Direct materials cost variance, direct labor rate variance, and factory overhead cost variance
   c. Direct materials cost variance, direct labor cost variance, variable factory overhead controllable variance
   d. Direct materials cost variance, direct labor cost variance, factory overhead cost variance

   ANS: D   PTS: 1   DIF: Moderate   OBJ: LO: 23-02
   NAT: BUSPROG: Analytic   KEY: Bloom's: Knowledge

10. Which of the following is not a reason standard costs are separated in two components?
    a. the price and quantity variances need to be identified separately to correct the actual major differences.
    b. identifying variances determines which manager must find a solution to major discrepancies.

c. if a negative variance is over-shadowed by a favorable variance, managers may overlook potential corrections.
d. variances brings attention to discrepancies in the budget and requires managers to revise budgets closer to actual.

ANS: D   PTS: 1   DIF: Moderate   OBJ: LO: 23-02
NAT: BUSPROG: Analytic   KEY: Bloom's: Knowledge

11. The standard costs and actual costs for direct materials for the manufacture of 3,000 actual units of product are as follows:

Standard Costs
Direct materials (per completed unit)   1.04 kilograms @$8.75

Actual Costs
Direct materials   2,500 kilograms @ $8

The amount of direct materials price variance is:
a. $2,250 unfavorable
b. $1,950 favorable
c. $1,875 favorable
d. $1,950 unfavorable

ANS: C   PTS: 1   DIF: Moderate   OBJ: LO: 23-03
NAT: BUSPROG: Analytic   KEY: Bloom's: Application

12. The standard costs and actual costs for direct materials for the manufacture of 2,500 actual units of product are as follows:

Standard Costs
Direct materials   2,500 kilograms @ $8

Actual Costs
Direct materials   2,600 kilograms @ $8.75

The amount of the direct materials quantity variance is:
a. $875 favorable
b. $800 unfavorable
c. $800 favorable
d. $875 unfavorable

ANS: B   PTS: 1   DIF: Moderate   OBJ: LO: 23-03
NAT: BUSPROG: Analytic   KEY: Bloom's: Application

The following data relate to direct materials costs for November:

Actual costs   4,700 pounds at $5.40
Standard costs   4,500 pounds at $6.20

13. What is the direct materials price variance?
   a. $3,600 favorable
   b. $160 favorable
   c. $3,760 favorable
   d. $3,600 unfavorable

   ANS: C   PTS: 1   DIF: Moderate   OBJ: LO: 23-03
   NAT: BUSPROG: Analytic   KEY: Bloom's: Application

14. What is the direct materials quantity variance?
   a. $3,600 favorable
   b. $1,240 favorable
   c. $3,600 favorable
   d. $1,240 unfavorable

   ANS: D   PTS: 1   DIF: Moderate   OBJ: LO: 23-03
   NAT: BUSPROG: Analytic   KEY: Bloom's: Application

15. If the actual quantity of direct materials used in producing a commodity differs from the standard quantity, the variance is termed a:
   a. controllable variance
   b. price variance
   c. quantity variance
   d. rate variance

   ANS: C   PTS: 1   DIF: Easy   OBJ: LO: 23-03
   NAT: BUSPROG: Analytic   KEY: Bloom's: Knowledge

16. If the price paid per unit differs from the standard price per unit for direct materials, the variance is termed a:
   a. variable variance
   b. controllable variance
   c. price variance
   d. volume variance

   ANS: C   PTS: 1   DIF: Easy   OBJ: LO: 23-03
   NAT: BUSPROG: Analytic   KEY: Bloom's: Knowledge

The following data is given for the Stringer Company:

Budgeted production	26,000 units
Actual production	27,500 units
Materials:	
Standard price per ounce	$6.50
Standard ounces per completed unit	8
Actual ounces purchased and used in production	228,000
Actual price paid for materials	$1,504,800
Labor:	
Standard hourly labor rate	$22 per hour
Standard hours allowed per completed unit	6.6
Actual labor hours worked	183,000
Actual total labor costs	$4,020,000

Overhead:
    Actual and budgeted fixed overhead $1,029,600
    Standard variable overhead rate $24.50 per standard labor hour
    Actual variable overhead costs $4,520,000
    Overhead is applied on standard labor hours.

17.   The direct material price variance is:
    a.   22,800U
    b.   22,800F
    c.   52,000U
    d.   52,000F

ANS: A   PTS: 1   DIF: Moderate   OBJ: LO: 23-03
NAT: BUSPROG: Analytic   KEY: Bloom's: Application

18.   The direct material quantity variance is:
    a.   22,800F
    b.   22,800U
    c.   52,000F
    d.   52,000U

ANS: D   PTS: 1   DIF: Moderate   OBJ: LO: 23-03
NAT: BUSPROG: Analytic   KEY: Bloom's: Application

The Lucy Corporation purchased and used 129,000 board feet of lumber in production, at a total cost of $1,548,000. Original production had been budgeted for 22,000 units with a standard material quantity of 5.7 board feet per unit and a standard price of $12 per board foot. Actual production was 23,500 units.

19.   Compute the material price variance.
    a.   0
    b.   59,400U
    c.   59,400F
    d.   6,000U

ANS: A   PTS: 1   DIF: Moderate   OBJ: LO: 23-03
NAT: BUSPROG: Analytic   KEY: Bloom's: Application

20.   Compute the material quantity variance.
    a.   63,000F
    b.   63,000U
    c.   59,400F
    d.   59,400U

ANS: C   PTS: 1   DIF: Moderate   OBJ: LO: 23-03
NAT: BUSPROG: Analytic   KEY: Bloom's: Application

21.   If the wage rate paid per hour differs from the standard wage rate per hour for direct labor, the variance is termed a:
    a.   variable variance
    b.   rate variance
    c.   quantity variance
    d.   volume variance

22. If the actual direct labor hours spent producing a commodity differs from the standard hours, the
     variance is termed a:
     a. time variance
     b. price variance
     c. quantity variance
     d. rate variance

23. The following data relate to direct labor costs for the current period:

     Standard costs   7,500 hours at $11.40
     Actual costs   6,000 hours at $12.00

     What is the direct labor time variance?
     a. $ 4,500 favorable
     b. $18,000 unfavorable
     c. $ 3,600 favorable
     d. $17,100 favorable

24. The following data relate to direct labor costs for the current period:

     Standard costs   6,000 hours at $12.00
     Actual costs   7,500 hours at $11.40

     What is the direct labor rate variance?
     a. $18,000 unfavorable
     b. $ 4,500 favorable
     c. $17,100 unfavorable
     d. $ 3,600 favorable

25. The following data relate to direct labor costs for the current period:

     Standard costs   9,000 hours at $5.50
     Actual costs   8,500 hours at $5.75

     What is the direct labor rate variance?
     a. $2,250.00 unfavorable
     b. $2,125.00 unfavorable
     c. $2,250.00 favorable
     d. $2,125.00 favorable

ANS: B   PTS: 1   DIF: Moderate   OBJ: LO: 23-03
NAT: BUSPROG: Analytic   KEY: Bloom's: Application

26. The following data relate to direct labor costs for the current period:

Standard costs   36,000 hours at $22.00
Actual costs   35,000 hours at $23.00

What is the direct labor time variance?
a. $36,000 unfavorable
b. $35,000 unfavorable
c. $23,000 favorable
d. $22,000 favorable

ANS: D   PTS: 1   DIF: Moderate   OBJ: LO: 23-03
NAT: BUSPROG: Analytic   KEY: Bloom's: Application

27. The standard costs and actual costs for direct labor for the manufacture of 2,500 actual units of product are as follows:

Standard Costs	
Direct labor	7,500 hours @ $11.80

Actual Costs	
Direct labor	7,400 hours @ $11.40

The amount of the direct labor rate variance is:
a. $2,960 unfavorable
b. $4,500 favorable
c. $2,960 favorable
d. $4,500 unfavorable

ANS: C   PTS: 1   DIF: Moderate   OBJ: LO: 23-03
NAT: BUSPROG: Analytic   KEY: Bloom's: Application

28. The standard costs and actual costs for direct materials, direct labor, and factory overhead for the manufacture of 2,500 units of product are as follows:

Standard Costs	
Direct labor	7,500 hours @ $11.80

Actual Costs	
Direct labor	7,400 hours @ $11.40

The amount of the direct labor time variance is:
a. $1,180 favorable
b. $1,140 unfavorable
c. $1,180 unfavorable
d. $1,140 favorable

ANS: A   PTS: 1   DIF: Moderate   OBJ: LO: 23-03
NAT: BUSPROG: Analytic   KEY: Bloom's: Application

The following data relate to direct labor costs for February:

Actual costs	7,700 hours at $14.00
Standard costs	7,000 hours at $16.00

29. What is the direct labor time variance?
   a. $7,700 favorable
   b. $7,700 unfavorable
   c. $11,200 unfavorable
   d. $11,200 favorable

   ANS: C   PTS: 1   DIF: Moderate   OBJ: LO: 23-03
   NAT: BUSPROG: Analytic   KEY: Bloom's: Application

30. What is the direct labor rate variance?
   a. $14,000 favorable
   b. $14,000 unfavorable
   c. $15,400 favorable
   d. $15,400 unfavorable

   ANS: C   PTS: 1   DIF: Moderate   OBJ: LO: 23-03
   NAT: BUSPROG: Analytic   KEY: Bloom's: Application

The following data is given for the Harry Company:

Budgeted production	26,000 units
Actual production	27,500 units
Materials:	
Standard price per ounce	$6.50
Standard ounces per completed unit	8
Actual ounces purchased and used in production	228,000
Actual price paid for materials	$1,504,800
Labor:	
Standard hourly labor rate	$22 per hour
Standard hours allowed per completed unit	6.6
Actual labor hours worked	183,000
Actual total labor costs	$4,020,000
Overhead:	
Actual and budgeted fixed overhead	$1,029,600
Standard variable overhead rate	$24.50 per standard labor hour
Actual variable overhead costs	$4,520,000
Overhead is applied on standard labor hours.	

31. The direct labor rate variance is:
   a. 6,000U
   b. 6,000F
   c. 33,000F
   d. 33,000U

   ANS: B   PTS: 1   DIF: Moderate   OBJ: LO: 23-03
   NAT: BUSPROG: Analytic   KEY: Bloom's: Application

32. The direct labor time variance is:
    a. 6,000F
    b. 6,000U
    c. 33,000U
    d. 33,000F

    ANS: C   PTS: 1   DIF: Moderate   OBJ: LO: 23-03
    NAT: BUSPROG: Analytic   KEY: Bloom's: Application

    The Flapjack Corporation had 8,200 actual direct labor hours at an actual rate of $12.40 per hour. Original production had been budgeted for 1,100 units, but only 1,000 units were actually produced. Labor standards were 7.6 hours per completed unit at a standard rate of $13.00 per hour.

33. Compute the labor rate variance.
    a. 4,920U
    b. 4,920F
    c. 4,560U
    d. 4,560U

    ANS: B   PTS: 1   DIF: Moderate   OBJ: LO: 23-03
    NAT: BUSPROG: Analytic   KEY: Bloom's: Application

34. Compute the labor time variance.
    a. 9,880F
    b. 9,880U
    c. 7,800U
    d. 7,800F

    ANS: C   PTS: 1   DIF: Moderate   OBJ: LO: 23-03
    NAT: BUSPROG: Analytic   KEY: Bloom's: Application

	Standard	Actual
Material Cost Per Yard	$2.00	$2.10
Standard Yards per Unit	4.5 yards	4.75 yards
Units of Production		9,500

35. Calculate the Total Direct Materials cost variance using the above information:
    a. $9,262.50 Unfavorable
    b. $9,262.50 Favorable
    c. $3,780.00 Unfavorable
    d. $3,562.50 Favorable

    ANS: A   PTS: 1   DIF: Moderate   OBJ: LO: 23-03
    NAT: BUSPROG: Analytic   KEY: Bloom's: Application

36. Calculate the Direct Materials Price variance using the above information:
    a. $1,795.50 Favorable
    b. $378.00 Favorable
    c. $4,512.50 Unfavorable
    d. $378.00 Unfavorable

    ANS: C   PTS: 1   DIF: Moderate   OBJ: LO: 23-03
    NAT: BUSPROG: Analytic   KEY: Bloom's: Application

37. Calculate the Direct Materials Quantity variance using the above information:
    a. $4,512.50 Unfavorable
    b. $4,512.50 Favorable
    c. $4,750 Unfavorable
    d. $4,750 Favorable

ANS: C   PTS: 1   DIF: Moderate   OBJ: LO: 23-03
NAT: BUSPROG: Analytic   KEY: Bloom's: Application

	Standard	Actual
Rate	$12.00	$12.25
Hours	18,500	17,955
Units of Production		9,450

38. Calculate the Total Direct Labor Variance using the above information
    a. $2,051.25 Favorable
    b. $2,051.25 Unfavorable
    c. $2,362.50 Unfavorable
    d. $2,362.50 Favorable

ANS: A   PTS: 1   DIF: Moderate   OBJ: LO: 23-03
NAT: BUSPROG: Analytic   KEY: Bloom's: Application

39. Calculate the Direct Labor Time Variance using the above information
    a. $2,362.50 Favorable
    b. $2,362,50 Unfavorable
    c. $6,540.00 Favorable
    d. $6,540.00 Unfavorable

ANS: C   PTS: 1   DIF: Moderate   OBJ: LO: 23-03
NAT: BUSPROG: Analytic   KEY: Bloom's: Application

40. Calculate the Direct Labor Rate Variance using the above information
    a. $4,488.75 Unfavorable
    b. $6,851.25 Favorable
    c. $4,488.75 Favorable
    d. $6,851.25 Unfavorable

ANS: A   PTS: 1   DIF: Moderate   OBJ: LO: 23-03
NAT: BUSPROG: Analytic   KEY: Bloom's: Application

41. Which of the following is not a reason for a direct materials quantity variance?
    a. Malfunctioning equipment
    b. Purchasing of inferior raw materials
    c. Increased material cost per unit
    d. Spoilage of materials

ANS: C   PTS: 1   DIF: Moderate   OBJ: LO: 23-03
NAT: BUSPROG: Analytic   KEY: Bloom's: Knowledge

42. The formula to compute direct labor rate variance is to calculate the difference between
    a. actual costs + (actual hours * standard rate)
    b. actual costs − standard cost

c.   (actual hours * standard rate) − standard costs
d.   actual costs − (actual hours * standard rate)

ANS: D   PTS: 1   DIF: Moderate   OBJ: LO: 23-03
NAT: BUSPROG: Analytic   KEY: Bloom's: Knowledge

43.   The formula to compute direct labor time variance is to calculate the difference between
a.   actual costs − standard costs
b.   actual costs + standard costs
c.   (actual hours * standard rate) − standard costs
d.   actual costs − (actual hours * standard rate)

ANS: C   PTS: 1   DIF: Moderate   OBJ: LO: 23-03
NAT: BUSPROG: Analytic   KEY: Bloom's: Knowledge

44.   The formula to compute direct materials price variance is to calculate the difference between
a.   actual costs − (actual quantity * standard price)
b.   actual cost + standard costs
c.   actual cost − standard costs
d.   (actual quantity * standard price) -standard costs

ANS: A   PTS: 1   DIF: Moderate   OBJ: LO: 23-03
NAT: BUSPROG: Analytic   KEY: Bloom's: Knowledge

45.   The formula to compute direct material quantity variance is to calculate the difference between
a.   actual costs − standard costs
b.   standard costs − actual costs
c.   (actual quantity * standard price) − standard costs
d.   actual costs − (standard price * standard costs)

ANS: C   PTS: 1   DIF: Moderate   OBJ: LO: 23-03
NAT: BUSPROG: Analytic   KEY: Bloom's: Knowledge

46.   Which of the following would not lend itself to applying direct labor variances?
a.   Help desk
b.   Research and development scientist
c.   Customer service personnel
d.   Telemarketer

ANS: B   PTS: 1   DIF: Easy   OBJ: LO: 23-03
NAT: BUSPROG: Analytic   KEY: Bloom's: Knowledge

The standard costs and actual costs for factory overhead for the manufacture of 2,500 units of actual production are as follows:

	Standard Costs
Fixed overhead (based on 10,000 hours)	3 hours @ $.80 per hour
Variable overhead	3 hours @ $2.00 per hour

Actual Costs
Total variable cost, $18,000
Total fixed cost, $8,000

47. The amount of the factory overhead volume variance is:
   a. $2,000 favorable
   b. $2,000 unfavorable
   c. $2,500 unfavorable
   d. $0

ANS: B   PTS: 1   DIF: Moderate   OBJ: LO: 23-04
NAT: BUSPROG: Analytic   KEY: Bloom's: Application

48. The amount of the total factory overhead cost variance is:
   a. $2,000 favorable
   b. $5,000 unfavorable
   c. $2,500 unfavorable
   d. $0

ANS: B   PTS: 1   DIF: Moderate   OBJ: LO: 23-04
NAT: BUSPROG: Analytic   KEY: Bloom's: Application

49. The amount of the factory overhead controllable variance is:
   a. $2,000 unfavorable
   b. $3,000 favorable
   c. $0
   d. $3,000 unfavorable

ANS: D   PTS: 1   DIF: Moderate   OBJ: LO: 23-04
NAT: BUSPROG: Analytic   KEY: Bloom's: Application

The standard factory overhead rate is $10 per direct labor hour ($8 for variable factory overhead and $2 for fixed factory overhead) based on 100% capacity of 30,000 direct labor hours. The standard cost and the actual cost of factory overhead for the production of 5,000 units during May were as follows:

Standard:	25,000 hours at $10	$250,000
Actual:	Variable factory overhead	$202,500
	Fixed factory overhead	60,000

50. What is the amount of the factory overhead volume variance?
   a. $12,500 favorable
   b. $10,000 unfavorable
   c. $12,500 unfavorable
   d. $10,000 favorable

ANS: B   PTS: 1   DIF: Moderate   OBJ: LO: 23-04
NAT: BUSPROG: Analytic   KEY: Bloom's: Application

51. What is the amount of the factory overhead controllable variance?
   a. $10,000 favorable
   b. $2,500 unfavorable
   c. $10,000 unfavorable
   d. $2,500 favorable

ANS: B   PTS: 1   DIF: Moderate   OBJ: LO: 23-04
NAT: BUSPROG: Analytic   KEY: Bloom's: Application

52. Assuming that the standard fixed overhead rate is based on full capacity, the cost of available but unused productive capacity is indicated by the:
    a. factory overhead cost volume variance
    b. direct labor cost time variance
    c. direct labor cost rate variance
    d. factory overhead cost controllable variance

ANS: A   PTS: 1   DIF: Easy   OBJ: LO: 23-04
NAT: BUSPROG: Analytic   KEY: Bloom's: Knowledge

The standard factory overhead rate is $7.50 per machine hour ($6.20 for variable factory overhead and $1.30 for fixed factory overhead) based on 100% capacity of 80,000 machine hours. The standard cost and the actual cost of factory overhead for the production of 15,000 units during August were as follows:

Actual:	Variable factory overhead	$360,000
	Fixed factory overhead	104,000
Standard hours allowed for units produced:	60,000 hours	

53. What is the amount of the factory overhead volume variance?
    a. $12,000 unfavorable
    b. $12,000 favorable
    c. $14,000 unfavorable
    d. $26,000 unfavorable

ANS: D   PTS: 1   DIF: Moderate   OBJ: LO: 23-04
NAT: BUSPROG: Analytic   KEY: Bloom's: Application

54. What is the amount of the factory overhead controllable variance?
    a. $12,000 unfavorable
    b. $12,000 favorable
    c. $14,000 unfavorable
    d. $26,000 unfavorable

ANS: B   PTS: 1   DIF: Moderate   OBJ: LO: 23-04
NAT: BUSPROG: Analytic   KEY: Bloom's: Application

55. Incurring actual indirect factory wages in excess of budgeted amounts for actual production results in a:
    a. quantity variance
    b. controllable variance
    c. volume variance
    d. rate variance

ANS: B   PTS: 1   DIF: Moderate   OBJ: LO: 23-04
NAT: BUSPROG: Analytic   KEY: Bloom's: Knowledge

56. The controllable variance measures:
     a. operating results at less than normal capacity
     b. the efficiency of using variable overhead resources
     c. operating results at more than normal capacity
     d. control over fixed overhead costs

     ANS: B   PTS: 1   DIF: Easy   OBJ: LO: 23-04
     NAT: BUSPROG: Analytic   KEY: Bloom's: Knowledge

57. The unfavorable volume variance may be due to all of the following factors except:
     a. failure to maintain an even flow of work
     b. machine breakdowns
     c. unexpected increases in the cost of utilities
     d. failure to obtain enough sales orders

     ANS: C   PTS: 1   DIF: Easy   OBJ: LO: 23-04
     NAT: BUSPROG: Analytic   KEY: Bloom's: Knowledge

58. Favorable volume variances may be harmful when:
     a. machine repairs cause work stoppages
     b. supervisors fail to maintain an even flow of work
     c. production in excess of normal capacity cannot be sold
     d. all of the above

     ANS: C   PTS: 1   DIF: Moderate   OBJ: LO: 23-04
     NAT: BUSPROG: Analytic   KEY: Bloom's: Knowledge

59. The following data is given for the Bahia Company:

Budgeted production	1,000 units
Actual production	980 units
Materials:	
Standard price per pound	$2.00
Standard pounds per completed unit	12
Actual pounds purchased and used in production	11,800
Actual price paid for materials	$23,000
Labor:	
Standard hourly labor rate	$14 per hour
Standard hours allowed per completed unit	4.5
Actual labor hours worked	4,560
Actual total labor costs	$62,928
Overhead:	
Actual and budgeted fixed overhead	$27,000
Standard variable overhead rate	$3.50 per standard direct labor hour
Actual variable overhead costs	$15,500
Overhead is applied on standard labor hours.	

     The factory overhead controllable variance is:
     a. $65U
     b. $65F
     c. $540U
     d. $540F

ANS: A   PTS: 1   DIF: Moderate   OBJ: LO: 23-04
NAT: BUSPROG: Analytic   KEY: Bloom's: Application

60. The following data is given for the Bahia Company:

Budgeted production (at 100% production capacity)	1,000 units
Actual production	980 units
Materials:	
Standard price per pound	$2.00
Standard pounds per completed unit	12
Actual pounds purchased and used in production	11,800
Actual price paid for materials	$23,000
Labor:	
Standard hourly labor rate	$14 per hour
Standard hours allowed per completed unit	4.5
Actual labor hours worked	4,560
Actual total labor costs	$62,928
Overhead:	
Actual and budgeted fixed overhead	$27,000
Standard variable overhead rate	$3.50 per standard labor hour
Actual variable overhead costs	$15,500
Overhead is applied on standard labor hours.	

The factory overhead volume variance is:
a. $65U
b. $65F
c. $540U
d. $540F

ANS: C   PTS: 1   DIF: Moderate   OBJ: LO: 23-04
NAT: BUSPROG: Analytic   KEY: Bloom's: Application

The following data is given for the Zoyza Company:

Budgeted production (at 100% production capacity)	26,000 units
Actual production	27,500 units
Materials:	
Standard price per ounce	$6.50
Standard ounces per completed unit	8
Actual ounces purchased and used in production	228,000
Actual price paid for materials	$1,504,800
Labor:	
Standard hourly labor rate	$22 per hour
Standard hours allowed per completed unit	6.6
Actual labor hours worked	183,000
Actual total labor costs	$4,020,000
Overhead:	
Actual and budgeted fixed overhead	$1,029,600
Standard variable overhead rate	$24.50 per standard labor hour
Actual variable overhead costs	$4,520,000
Overhead is applied on standard labor hours.	

61. The factory overhead controllable variance is:
    a. $73,250F
    b. $73,250U
    c. $59,400F
    d. $59,400U

    ANS: B   PTS: 1   DIF: Moderate   OBJ: LO: 23-04
    NAT: BUSPROG: Analytic   KEY: Bloom's: Application

62. The factory overhead volume variance is:
    a. $73,250U
    b. $73,250F
    c. $59,400F
    d. $59,400U

    ANS: C   PTS: 1   DIF: Moderate   OBJ: LO: 23-04
    NAT: BUSPROG: Analytic   KEY: Bloom's: Application

The St. Augustine Corporation originally budgeted for $360,000 of fixed overhead at 100% production capacity. Production was budgeted to be 12,000 units. The standard hours for production were 5 hours per unit. The variable overhead rate was $3 per hour. Actual fixed overhead was $360,000 and actual variable overhead was $170,000. Actual production was 11,700 units.

63. Compute the factory overhead controllable variance.
    a. $9,000F
    b. $9,000U
    c. $5,500F
    d. $5,500U

    ANS: C   PTS: 1   DIF: Moderate   OBJ: LO: 23-04
    NAT: BUSPROG: Analytic   KEY: Bloom's: Application

64. Compute the factory overhead volume variance.
    a. $9,000F
    b. $9,000U
    c. $5,500F
    d. $5,500U

    ANS: B   PTS: 1   DIF: Moderate   OBJ: LO: 23-04
    NAT: BUSPROG: Analytic   KEY: Bloom's: Application

	Standard	Actual
Variable OH Rate	$ 3.35	
Fixed OH Rate	$ 1.80	
Hours	18,900	17,955
Fixed Overhead	$46,000	
Actual Variable Overhead		$ 67,430
Total Factory Overhead		$101,450

65. Calculate the total factory overhead cost variance using the above information:
    a. $4,866.75 Unfavorable
    b. $4,866.75 Favorable

c. $8,981.75 Favorable
d. $8,981.75 Unfavorable

ANS: D   PTS: 1   DIF: Moderate   OBJ: LO: 23-04
NAT: BUSPROG: Analytic   KEY: Bloom's: Application

66. Calculate the fixed factory overhead volume variance using the above information:
a. $1,701 Favorable
b. $4,866.75 Unfavorable
c. $1,701 Unfavorable
d. $4,866.75 Favorable

ANS: C   PTS: 1   DIF: Moderate   OBJ: LO: 23-04
NAT: BUSPROG: Analytic   KEY: Bloom's: Application

67. Calculate the variable factory overhead controllable variance using the above information:
a. $8,981.75 Favorable
b. $7,280.75 Unfavorable
c. $8,981.75 Unfavorable
d. $7,280.75 Favorable

ANS: B   PTS: 1   DIF: Moderate   OBJ: LO: 23-04
NAT: BUSPROG: Analytic   KEY: Bloom's: Application

68. A negative fixed overhead volume variance can be caused due to the following except:
a. Sales orders at a low level
b. Machine breakdowns
c. Employee inexperience
d. Increase in utility costs

ANS: D   PTS: 1   DIF: Moderate   OBJ: LO: 23-04
NAT: BUSPROG: Analytic   KEY: Bloom's: Knowledge

69. At the end of the fiscal year, variances from standard costs are usually transferred to the:
a. direct labor account
b. factory overhead account
c. cost of goods sold account
d. direct materials account

ANS: C   PTS: 1   DIF: Easy   OBJ: LO: 23-05
NAT: BUSPROG: Analytic   KEY: Bloom's: Knowledge

70. Variances from standard costs are usually reported to:
a. suppliers
b. stockholders
c. management
d. creditors

ANS: C   PTS: 1   DIF: Easy   OBJ: LO: 23-05
NAT: BUSPROG: Analytic   KEY: Bloom's: Knowledge

71. If at the end of the fiscal year the variances from standard are significant, the variances should be transferred to the:
    a. work in process account only
    b. cost of goods sold account only
    c. finished goods account only
    d. work in process, cost of goods sold, and finished goods accounts

    ANS: D   PTS: 1   DIF: Moderate   OBJ: LO: 23-05
    NAT: BUSPROG: Analytic   KEY: Bloom's: Knowledge

72. Assuming that the Morocco Desk Co. purchases 6,000 feet of lumber at $6.00 per foot and the standard price for direct materials is $5.00, the entry to record the purchase and unfavorable direct materials price variance is:

    a. Direct Materials   30,000
           Direct Materials Price Variance   6,000
             Accounts Payable   36,000
    b. Direct Materials   30,000
             Accounts Payable   30,000
    c. Direct Materials   36,000
           Direct Materials Price Variance   6,000
             Accounts Payable   30,000
    d. Work in Process   36,000
           Direct Materials Price Variance   6,000
             Accounts Payable   30,000

    ANS: A   PTS: 1   DIF: Easy   OBJ: LO: 23-05
    NAT: BUSPROG: Analytic   KEY: Bloom's: Knowledge

73. A company records their inventory purchases at standard cost but also records purchase price variances. The company purchased 5,000 widgets $8.00. The standard cost for the widgets is $7.60. Which of the following would be included in the journal entry?
    a. $38,000 Debit to Accounts Payable
    b. $ 2,000 Credit to Direct Materials Price Variance
    c. $ 2,000 Debit to Accounts Payable
    d. $ 2,000 Debit to Direct Materials Price Variance

    ANS: D   PTS: 1   DIF: Easy   OBJ: LO: 23-05
    NAT: BUSPROG: Analytic   KEY: Bloom's: Knowledge

74. The use of standards for nonmanufacturing expenses is:
    a. not as common as it is for manufacturing costs
    b. as common as it is for manufacturing costs
    c. not useful
    d. impossible

    ANS: A   PTS: 1   DIF: Moderate   OBJ: LO: 23-06
    NAT: BUSPROG: Analytic   KEY: Bloom's: Knowledge

75. The total manufacturing cost variance is
    a. the difference between actual costs and standard costs for units produced.
    b. the flexible budget variance plus the time variance

c. the difference between planned costs and standard costs for units produced
d. none of the above.

ANS: A   PTS: 1   DIF: Moderate   OBJ: LO: 23-02
NAT: BUSPROG: Analytic   KEY: Bloom's: Knowledge

OTHER

1. Ruby Company produces a chair that requires 5 yds. of material per unit. The standard price of one yard of material is $7.50. During the month, 8,500 chairs were manufactured, using 43,600 yards at a cost of $7.55 per yard. Determine the (a) price variance, (b) quantity variance, and (c) cost variance.

ANS:
(a) Price variance = ($7.50 − $7.55) × 43,600 = $2,180 unfavorable

(b) Quantity variance = ((5 × 8,500) − 43,600) × $7.50 = $8,250 unfavorable

(c) Cost variance = $10,430 unfavorable

PTS: 1   DIF: Moderate   OBJ: LO: 23-03   NAT: BUSPROG: Analytic
KEY: Bloom's: Application

2. Ruby Company produces a chair that requires 5 yds. of material per unit. The standard price of one yard of material is $7.50. During the month, 8,400 chairs were manufactured, using 43,700 yards at a cost of $7.30 per yard. Determine the (a) price variance, (b) quantity variance, and (c) cost variance.

ANS:
(a) Price variance = ($7.50 − $7.30) × 43,700 = $8,740 favorable

(b) Quantity variance = ((5 × 8,400) − 43,700)) × $7.50 = $12,750 unfavorable

(c) Cost variance = $4,010 unfavorable

PTS: 1   DIF: Moderate   OBJ: LO: 23-03   NAT: BUSPROG: Analytic
KEY: Bloom's: Application

3. Ruby Company produces a chair that requires 5 yds. of material per unit. The standard price of one yard of material is $7.60. During the month, 8,500 chairs were manufactured, using 40,000 yards at a cost of $7.50. Determine the (a) price variance, (b) quantity variance, and (c) cost variance.

ANS:
(a) Price variance = ($7.60 − $7.50) × 40,000 = $4,000 favorable

(b) Quantity variance = ((8,500 × 5) − 40,000) × $7.60 = $19,000 favorable

(c) Cost variance = $23,000 favorable

PTS: 1   DIF: Moderate   OBJ: LO: 23-03   NAT: BUSPROG: Analytic
KEY: Bloom's: Application

4. Japan Company produces lamps that require 2.25 standard hours per unit at an hourly rate of $15.00 per hour. If 7,700 units required 19,250 hours at an hourly rate of $14.90 per hour, what is the direct labor (a) rate variance, (b) time variance, and (c) cost variance?

    ANS:
    (a) Rate variance = ($15.00 − $14.90) × 19,250 = $1,925 favorable

    (b) Time variance = (19,250 − (7,700 × 2.25)) × $15.00 = $28,875 unfavorable

    (c) Cost variance = (19,250 × $14.90) − (7,700 × 2.25 × $15.00) = $26,950 unfavorable

    PTS: 1   DIF: Moderate   OBJ: LO: 23-03   NAT: BUSPROG: Analytic
    KEY: Bloom's: Application

5. Tippi Company produces lamps that require 2.25 standard hours per unit at an hourly rate of $15.00 per hour. If 7,700 units required 17,550 hours at an hourly rate of $15.20 per hour, what is the direct labor (a) rate variance, (b) time variance, and (c) cost variance?

    ANS:
    (a) Rate variance = ($15.00 − $15.20) × 17,550 = $3,510 unfavorable

    (b) Time variance = (17,550 − (2.25 × 7,700)) × $15.00 = $3,375 unfavorable

    (c) Cost variance = (17,550 × $15.20) − ((2.25 × 7,700 × $15) = $6,885 unfavorable
                        or $3,510 + $3,375 = $6,885 unfavorable

    PTS: 1   DIF: Moderate   OBJ: LO: 23-03   NAT: BUSPROG: Analytic
    KEY: Bloom's: Application

6. Trumpet Company produced 8,700 units of product that required 3.25 standard hours per unit. The standard variable overhead cost per unit is $4.00 per hour. The actual variance factory overhead was $111,000. Determine the variable factory overhead controllable variance.

    ANS:
    (8,700 × 3.25 × $4.00) − $111,000 = $2,100 favorable

    PTS: 1   DIF: Easy   OBJ: LO: 23-04   NAT: BUSPROG: Analytic
    KEY: Bloom's: Application

7. The Trumpet Company produced 8,700 units of a product that required 3.25 standard hours per unit. The standard fixed overhead cost per unit is $1.20 per hour at 29,000 hours, which is 100% of normal capacity. Determine the fixed factory overhead volume variance.

    ANS:
    (29,000 hours − (8,700 units × 3.25 hours)) × $1.20 = $870 unfavorable

    PTS: 1   DIF: Easy   OBJ: LO: 23-04   NAT: BUSPROG: Analytic
    KEY: Bloom's: Application

8. Oak Company produces a chair that requires 6 yds. of material per unit. The standard price of one yard of material is $7.50. During the month, 8,500 chairs were manufactured, using 48,875 yards. Journalize the entry to record the standard direct materials used in production.

ANS:

Work in Process (8,500 × 6 × $7.50)	382,500.00	
Direct Materials Quantity Variance ((48,875 − 51,000) × $7.50)		15,937.50
Materials (48,875 × $7.50)		366,562.50

PTS: 1   DIF: Moderate   OBJ: LO: 23-05   NAT: BUSPROG: Analytic
KEY: Bloom's: Application

9. Prepare an income statement for the year ended December 31, 2012, through gross profit for Aframe Company using the following information. Assume Aframe Company sold 8,600 units at $125 per unit. (Note: Normal production is 9,000 units)

Standard: 5 yards per unit @ $6.30 per yard	Actual yards used: 43,240 yards @ $6.25 per yard
Standard: 2.25 hours per unit @ $15.00	Actual hours worked: 19,100 @ $14.90 per hour
Standard: Variable overhead $1.05 per unit	
Standard: Fixed overhead $211,500 (budgeted and actual amount)	Actual total factory overhead $235,500

ANS:

Aframe Company
Income Statement Through Gross Profit
For the year ended December 31, 2012

		Favorable	Unfavorable	
Sales				$1,075,000
Cost of goods sold − at standard *				772,280
Gross profit − at standard				302,720
Less variances from standard cost				
Direct materials price		$2,162		
Direct materials quantity			$1,512	
Direct labor rate		1,910		
Direct labor time		3,750		
Factory overhead controllable			14,970	
Factory overhead volume			9,400	
				18,060
Gross profit − actual				284,660

* (5 × $6.30) + (2.25 × $15.00) + $1.05 + ($211,500/9,000) = $89.90 × 8,600 units

PTS: 1   DIF: Moderate   OBJ: LO: 23-05   NAT: BUSPROG: Analytic
KEY: Bloom's: Application

10. If a company records inventory purchases at standard cost and also records purchase price variances, prepare the journal entry for a purchase of 6,000 widgets that were bought at $8.00 and have a standard cost of $8.15.

ANS:

	Dr	Cr
Materials (6,000 × $8.15)	48,900	
Direct Materials Price Variance		900
Accounts Payable (6,000 × $8.00)		48,000

PTS: 1   DIF: Easy   OBJ: LO: 23-05   NAT: BUSPROG: Analytic
KEY: Bloom's: Application

11. The following are inputs and outputs to the help desk.

Operator training
Number of calls per day
Maintenance of computer equipment
Number of operators
Number of complaints

Identify whether each is an input or an output to the help desk.

ANS:
Operator training − Input
Number of calls per day − Output
Maintenance of computer equipment − Input
Number of operators − Input
Number of complaints − Output

PTS: 1   DIF: Moderate   OBJ: LO: 23-06   NAT: BUSPROG: Analytic
KEY: Bloom's: Application

12. Greyson Company produced 8,300 units of their product that required 4.25 standard hours per unit. Determine the standard fixed overhead cost per unit at 27,000 hours, which is 100% of normal capacity, if the favorable fixed factory overhead volume variance is $14,895.

ANS:
(27,000 − (8,300 × 4.25)) × $X = $14,895 favorable

X = $1.80

PTS: 1   DIF: Easy   OBJ: LO: 23-04   NAT: BUSPROG: Analytic
KEY: Bloom's: Application

13. Hsu Company produces a part with a standard of 5 yds. of material per unit. The standard price of one yard of material is $8.50. During the month, 8,800 parts were manufactured, using 45,700 yards of material at a cost of $8.30.

Required:

Determine the (a) price variance, (b) quantity variance, and (c) cost variance.

ANS:
(a) Price variance = ($8.50 − $8.30) × 45,700 = $9,140 favorable

(b) Quantity variance = (45,700 − (5 × 8,800)) × $8.50 = $14,450 unfavorable

(c) Cost variance = (45,700 × $8.30) − (8,800 × 5 × $8.50) = $5,310 unfavorable

PTS: 1   DIF: Moderate   OBJ: LO: 23-03   NAT: BUSPROG: Analytic
KEY: Bloom's: Application

14.   Aquatic Corp.'s standard material requirement to produce a single of Model 2000 is 15 pounds of
      material @ $110.00 per pound.

      Last month, Aquatic purchased 170,000 pounds of material at a total cost of $17,850,000. They
      used 162,000 pounds to produce 10,000 units of Model 2000.

Required:

Calculate the material price variance and material quantity variance, and indicate whether each
variance is favorable or unfavorable.

ANS:
Actual cost = $17,850,000/ 170,000 pounds = $105 per pound

Material price variance = ($105.00 − $110.00) × 170,000 = $850,000 favorable

Material quantity variance = [162,000 − (15 × 10,000)] × $110.00 =$1,320,000 unfavorable

PTS: 1   DIF: Moderate   OBJ: LO: 23-03   NAT: BUSPROG: Analytic
KEY: Bloom's: Application

15.   If a company records inventory purchases at standard cost and also records purchase price variances,
      prepare the journal entry for a purchase of widgets that were bought at $7.45 per unit and have a
      standard cost of $7.15.   The total amount owed to the vendor for this purchase is $33,525.

ANS:

	Dr	Cr
Materials (4,500 × $7.15)	32,175	
Direct Materials Price Variance	1,350	
Accounts Payable (X × $7.45)		33,525

X= 4,500 units

PTS: 1   DIF: Easy   OBJ: LO: 23-05   NAT: BUSPROG: Analytic
KEY: Bloom's: Application

16. Rosser Company produces a container that requires 4 yds. of material per unit. The standard price of one yard of material is $4.50. During the month, 9,500 chairs were manufactured, using 37,300 yards.

Required: Journalize the entry to record the standard direct materials used in production.

ANS:

Work in Process (9,500 × 4 × $4.50)	171,000	
Direct Materials Quantity Variance		3,150
Materials (37,300 × $4.50)		167,850

PTS: 1   DIF: Moderate   OBJ: LO: 23-05   NAT: BUSPROG: Analytic
KEY: Bloom's: Application

The following data is given for the Taylor Company:

Budgeted production	1,000 units
Actual production	980 units
Materials:	
Standard price per lb	$2.00
Standard pounds per completed unit	12
Actual pounds purchased and used in production	11,800
Actual price paid for materials	$23,000
Labor:	
Standard hourly labor rate	$14 per hour
Standard hours allowed per completed unit	4.5
Actual labor hours worked	4,560
Actual total labor costs	$62,928
Overhead:	
Actual and budgeted fixed overhead	$27,000
Standard variable overhead rate	$3.50 per standard labor hour
Actual variable overhead costs	$15,500
Overhead is applied on standard labor hours.	

17. Compute the direct material price and quantity variances for Taylor Company.

ANS:
Direct material price: $23,000 − ($2.00 × 11,800) = $600 F

Direct material quantity variance: (11,800 − (980 × 12)) × $2.00 = $80 U

PTS: 1   DIF: Moderate   OBJ: LO: 23-03   NAT: BUSPROG: Analytic
KEY: Bloom's: Application

18. Compute the direct labor rate and time variances for Taylor Company.

ANS:
Direct labor rate: $62,928 − ($14.00 × 4,560) = $912 F

Direct labor time variance: (4,560 − (980 × 4.5)) × $14.00 = $2,100 U

PTS: 1   DIF: Moderate   OBJ: LO: 23-03   NAT: BUSPROG: Analytic
KEY: Bloom's: Application

19. Define ideal and currently attainable standards. Which type of standard should be used and why?

ANS:
Ideal standards are standards that are only achievable under perfect operating conditions Currently attainable standards (also called normal standards) allow for normal difficulties and mistakes. They can be attained with reasonable effort.

Companies should use currently attainable standards as employees are more likely to put forth their best effort when standards are reasonable. The use of ideal standards may have a negative impact on performance as they are likely to be viewed by employees as unrealistic.

PTS: 1   DIF: Moderate   OBJ: LO: 23-01   NAT: BUSPROG: Analytic
KEY: Bloom's: Knowledge

20. Define nonfinancial performance measures. What are they used for and what are some common examples?

ANS:
Nonfinancial performance measures evaluate performance in a measure other than dollars. They are used to evaluate the time, quality or quantity of a business activity and bring additional perspective to performance evaluation.

Common examples include: Inventory turnover; Percent of on-time delivery; Employee satisfaction; and Number of customer complaints.

PTS: 1   DIF: Moderate   OBJ: LO: 23-06   NAT: BUSPROG: Analytic
KEY: Bloom's: Knowledge

MATCHING

Match the following terms with the best definition given.
a. Ideal standard
b. Nonfinancial performance measure
c. Currently attainable standard
d. Unfavorable cost variance
e. Favorable cost variance

1. An example is number of customer complaints.
2. Actual cost > standard cost at actual volumes
3. Actual cost < standard cost at actual volumes
4. Normal standard
5. Theoretical standard

1. ANS: B   PTS: 1   DIF: Easy   OBJ: LO: 23-06
   NAT: BUSPROG: Analytic   KEY: Bloom's: Knowledge
2. ANS: D   PTS: 1   DIF: Easy   OBJ: LO: 23-02
   NAT: BUSPROG: Analytic   KEY: Bloom's: Knowledge
3. ANS: E   PTS: 1   DIF: Easy   OBJ: LO: 23-02
   NAT: BUSPROG: Analytic   KEY: Bloom's: Knowledge
4. ANS: C   PTS: 1   DIF: Easy   OBJ: LO: 23-01
   NAT: BUSPROG: Analytic   KEY: Bloom's: Knowledge
5. ANS: A   PTS: 1   DIF: Easy   OBJ: LO: 23-01
   NAT: BUSPROG: Analytic   KEY: Bloom's: Knowledge

Match the following terms with the best definition given.
a.   Direct materials price variance
b.   Direct labor rate variance
c.   Direct labor time variance
d.   Direct materials quantity variance
e.   Budgeted variable factory overhead

6.   (Actual direct hours − Standard direct hours) × Standard Rate per Hour
7.   (Actual rate per hour − Standard rate per hour) × Actual hours
8.   (Actual price − Standard price) × Actual quantity
9.   (Actual quantity − Standard quantity) × Standard Price
10. Standard variable overhead for actual units produced

6.   ANS: C   PTS: 1   DIF: Easy   OBJ: LO: 23-03
     NAT: BUSPROG: Analytic   KEY: Bloom's: Knowledge
7.   ANS: B   PTS: 1   DIF: Easy   OBJ: LO: 23-03
     NAT: BUSPROG: Analytic   KEY: Bloom's: Knowledge
8.   ANS: A   PTS: 1   DIF: Easy   OBJ: LO: 23-03
     NAT: BUSPROG: Analytic   KEY: Bloom's: Knowledge
9.   ANS: D   PTS: 1   DIF: Easy   OBJ: LO: 23-03
     NAT: BUSPROG: Analytic   KEY: Bloom's: Knowledge
10. ANS: E   PTS: 1   DIF: Easy   OBJ: LO: 23-04
     NAT: BUSPROG: Analytic   KEY: Bloom's: Knowledge

PROBLEM

1.   Compute the standard cost for one hat, based on the following standards for each hat:

     Standard Material Quantity: 3/4 yard of fabric at $5.00 per yard
     Standard Labor: 2 hours at $5.75 per hour
     Factory Overhead: $3.20 per direct labor hour

     ANS:
     Standard Material: 3/4 yard at $5.00 per yard $ 3.75
     Standard Labor: 2 hours at $5.75 per hour   11.50
     Factory Overhead: 2 hours at $3.20 per hour   6.40
        Total standard cost $21.65

     PTS: 1   DIF: Easy   OBJ: LO: 23-02   NAT: BUSPROG: Analytic
     KEY: Bloom's: Application

2.   Standard and actual costs for direct materials for the manufacture of 1,000 units of product were as follows:

     Actual costs   1,550 lbs. @ $9.10
     Standard costs   1,600 lbs. @ $9.00

     Determine the (a) quantity variance, (b) price variance, and (c) total direct materials cost variance.

ANS:
(a)

Actual quantity	1,550 lbs.
Standard quantity	1,600 lbs.
Quantity variance--favorable	50 lbs. favorable
× standard price	$ 9.00
	$ 450 favorable

(b)

Actual price	$ 9.10 per lb.
Standard price	9.00 per lb.
Price variance	$ .10 per lb. unfavorable
× actual quantity	1,550
	$ 155 unfavorable

(c)

Quantity variance	$ 450 favorable
Price variance	155 unfavorable
Total direct materials cost variance	$ 295 favorable

PTS: 1   DIF: Moderate   OBJ: LO: 23-03   NAT: BUSPROG: Analytic
KEY: Bloom's: Application

3.   Standard and actual costs for direct labor for the manufacture of 1,000 units of product were as follows:

Actual costs	950 hours @ $37.00
Standard costs	975 hours @ $36.00

Determine the (a) time variance, (b) rate variance, and (c) total direct labor cost variance.

ANS:
(a)

Actual time	950 hours
Standard time	975 hours
Time variance--favorable	25 hours
× standard rate	$ 36
	$ 900 favorable

(b)

Actual rate	$ 37.00 per hour
Standard rate	36.00 per hour
Rate variance--unfavorable	$ 1.00 per hour
× actual time	950
	$ 950 unfavorable

(c)

Time variance	$900 favorable
Rate variance	950 unfavorable
Total direct labor cost variance	$ 50 unfavorable

PTS: 1   DIF: Moderate   OBJ: LO: 23-03   NAT: BUSPROG: Analytic
KEY: Bloom's: Application

4.   The following information is for the standard and actual costs for the Happy Corporation.

Standard Costs:
Budgeted units of production - 16,000 (80% of capacity)
Standard labor hours per unit - 4
Standard labor rate - $26 per hour
Standard material per unit - 8 lbs.
Standard material cost - $ 12 per pound
Standard variable overhead rate - $15 per labor hour
Budgeted fixed overhead - $640,000
Fixed overhead rate is based on budgeted labor hours at 80% capacity.

Actual Cost:
Actual production - 16,500 units
Actual material purchased and used - 130,000 pounds
Actual total material cost - $1,600,000
Actual labor - 65,000 hours
Actual total labor costs - $1,700,000
Actual variable overhead - $1,000,000
Actual fixed overhead - $640,000
Actual variable overhead - $1,000,000

Determine: (a) the quantity variance, price variance, and total direct materials cost variance;
(b) the time variance, rate variance, and total direct labor cost variance; and (c) the volume variance,
controllable variance, and total factory overhead cost variance.

ANS:
(a)
Quantity variance:

Actual quantity × standard price: 130,000 × $12 =	$1,560,000
Standard quantity × standard price: 16,500 × 8 × $12 =	1,584,000
Quantity variance (favorable)	$ 24,000

Price variance:

Actual total price	$1,600,000
Actual quantity × standard price: 130,000 × $12 =	1,560,000
Price variance (unfavorable)	$ 40,000

Total direct material cost variance:

Price variance (unfavorable)	$ 40,000
Quantity variance (favorable)	24,000
Total (unfavorable)	$ 16,000

(b)
Time variance:

Actual hours × standard rate: 65,000 × $26 =	$1,690,000
Standard hours × standard rate: 16,500 × 4 × $26 =	1,716,000
Time variance (favorable)	$ 26,000

Rate variance:

Actual labor costs	$ 1,700,000
Actual hours × standard rate 65,000 × $26 =	1,690,000
rate variance (unfavorable)	$ 10,000

Total direct labor cost variance:

Time variance (favorable)	$ 26,000
Rate variance (unfavorable)	10,000
Total (favorable)	$ 16,000

(c)
Volume variance:

Actual fixed overhead	$ 640,000
Applied fixed overhead (16,500 × 4) × ($640,000/64,000) =	660,000
Volume variance (favorable)	$ 20,000

Controllable variance:

Actual variable overhead	$1,000,000
Applied variable overhead (16,500 × 4) × $15 =	990,000
Controllable variance (unfavorable)	$ 10,000

Total factory overhead cost variance:

Volume variance (favorable)	$ 20,000
Controllable variance (unfavorable)	10,000
Total (favorable)	$ 10,000

PTS: 1 DIF: Challenging OBJ: LO: 23-03 | LO: 23-04
NAT: BUSPROG: Analytic KEY: Bloom's: Application

5. The Finishing Department of Pinnacle Manufacturing Co. prepared the following factory overhead cost budget for October of the current year, during which it expected to operate at a 100% capacity of 10,000 machine hours:

Variable cost:		
Indirect factory wages	$18,000	
Power and light	12,000	
Indirect materials	4,000	
Total variable cost		$34,000
Fixed cost:		
Supervisory salaries	$12,000	
Depreciation of plant and equipment	8,800	
Insurance and property taxes	3,200	
Total fixed cost		24,000
Total factory overhead		$58,000

During October, the plant was operated for 9,000 machine hours and the factory overhead costs incurred were as follows: indirect factory wages, $16,400; power and light, $10,000; indirect materials, $3,000; supervisory salaries, $12,000; depreciation of plant and equipment, $8,800; insurance and property taxes, $3,200.

Prepare a factory overhead cost variance report for October. (The budgeted amounts for actual amount produced should be based on 9,000 machine hours.)

ANS:

Pinnacle Manufacturing Co. - Finishing Department
Factory Overhead Cost Variance Report
For Month Ended October 31, 20--

Productive capacity for the month			10,000 hours	
Actual production for the month			9,000 hours	

			Variances	
	Budget	Actual	Favorable	Unfavorable
Variable cost:				
Indirect factory wages	$16,200	$16,400		$ 200
Power and light	10,800	10,000	$ 800	
Indirect materials	3,600	3,000	600	
Total variable cost	$30,600	$29,400		
Fixed costs:				
Supervisory salaries	$12,000	$12,000		
Depreciation of plant and equipment	8,800	8,800		
Insurance and property taxes	3,200	3,200		
Total fixed cost	$24,000	$24,000		
Total factory overhead cost	$54,600	$53,400		
Total controllable variances			$1,400	$ 200
Net controllable variance--favorable				$1,200
Volume variance--unfavorable:				
Idle hours at the standard rate for fixed overhead-- 1,000 × $2.40				2,400
Total factory overhead cost variance--unfavorable				$1,200

PTS: 1   DIF: Moderate   OBJ: LO: 23-04   NAT: BUSPROG: Analytic
KEY: Bloom's: Application

6. The following information relates to manufacturing overhead for the Chapman Company:

Standards:
Total fixed factory overhead - $450,000
Estimated production - 25,000 units (100% of capacity)
Overhead rates are based on machine hours.
Standard hours allowed per unit produced - 2
Fixed overhead rate - $9.00 per machine hour
Variable overhead rate - $3.50 per hour

Actual:
Fixed factory overhead - $450,000
Production - 24,000 units
Variable overhead - $170,000

Required:
(a)   Compute the volume variance.
(b)   Compute the controllable variance.
(c)   Compute the total factory overhead cost variance.

ANS:
(a)

Productive capacity of 25,000 units	50,000 hours
Standard for product produced (24,000 units)	48,000 hours
Productive capacity not used	2,000 hours
Standard fixed factory overhead cost rate	$ 9.00 per hour
Volume variance (unfavorable)	$18,000

(b)

Actual Variable overhead incurred	$170,000
Budgeted factory overhead for standard units product produced (applied)	
24,000 × 2 × $3.50 =	168,000
Controllable variance (unfavorable)	$ 2,000

(c)

Volume variance (unfavorable)	$18,000
Controllable variance (unfavorable)	2,000
Cost variance (unfavorable)	$20,000

PTS: 1   DIF: Moderate   OBJ: LO: 23-04   NAT: BUSPROG: Analytic
KEY: Bloom's: Application

7.   Using the following information, prepare a factory overhead flexible budget for Andover Company where the total factory overhead cost is $75,500 at normal capacity (100%). Include capacity at 75%, 90%, 100%, and 110%. Total variable cost is $6.25 per unit and total fixed costs are $38,000. The information is for month ended August 31, 2012.   (Hint: Determine units produced at normal capacity.)

ANS:

Andover Company
Factory Overhead Cost Budget
For the Month Ending August 31, 2012

Percent of normal capacity	75%	90%	100%	110%
Units produced	4,500	5,400	X	6,600
Variable costs per unit $6.25	$28,125	$33,750	$37,500	$41,250
Fixed costs	38,000	38,000	38,000	38,000
Total factory overhead cost	$66,125	$71,750	$75,500	$79,250

X=$37,500/$6.25
X= 6,000 units

8. Prepare an income statement (through income before income tax) for presentation to management, using the following data from the records of Greenway Manufacturing Company for November of the current year:

Administrative expenses	$ 73,500
Cost of goods sold (at standard)	470,000
Direct materials quantity variance-favorable	1,200
Direct materials price variance-favorable	2,400
Direct labor time variance-unfavorable	900
Direct labor rate variance-favorable	500
Factory overhead volume variance-unfavorable	10,000
Factory overhead controllable variance-favorable	1,500
Sales	950,000
Selling expenses	165,800

ANS:

Greenway Manufacturing Company
Income Statement
For Month Ended November 30, 20--

	Favorable	Unfavorable	
Sales			$950,000
Cost of goods sold--at standard			470,000
Gross profit--at standard			$480,000
Less variances from standard cost:			
Direct materials price	$2,400		
Direct materials quantity	1,200		
Direct labor rate	500		
Direct labor time		900	
Factory overhead controllable	1,500		
Factory overhead volume		10,000	5,300
Gross profit			$474,700
Operating expenses:			
Selling expenses		$165,800	
Administrative expenses		73,500	239,300
Income before income tax			$235,400

9. Robin Company purchased and used 520 pounds of direct materials to produce a product with a 510 pound standard direct materials requirement. The standard materials price is $2.10 per pound. The actual materials price was $2.00 per pound. Prepare the journal entries to record (1) the purchase of the materials and (2) the material entering production. Robin records standards and variances in the general ledger.

ANS:

Materials (520 × $2.10)	1,092	
Direct Materials Price Variance		52
Accounts Payable (520 × $2.00)		1,040
Work in Process (510 × $2.10)	1,071	
Direct Materials Quantity Variance	21	
Materials		1,092

PTS: 1   DIF: Moderate   OBJ: LO: 23-05   NAT: BUSPROG: Analytic
KEY: Bloom's: Knowledge

10.   Robin Company purchased and used 500 pounds of direct materials to produce a product with a 520 pound standard direct materials requirement. The standard materials price is $1.90 per pound. The actual materials price was $2.00 per pound. Prepare the journal entries to record (1) the purchase of the materials and (2) the material entering production.   Robin records standards and variances in the general ledger.

ANS:

Materials (500 × $1.90)	950	
Direct Materials Price Variance (500 × $0.10)	50	
Accounts Payable (500 × $2.00)		1,000
Work in Process (520 × $1.90)	988	
Direct Materials Quantity Variance		38
Materials		950

PTS: 1   DIF: Moderate   OBJ: LO: 23-05   NAT: BUSPROG: Analytic
KEY: Bloom's: Knowledge

TRUE/FALSE

1. Separation of businesses into more manageable operating units is termed decentralization.

   ANS: T   PTS: 1   DIF: Easy   OBJ: LO: 24-01
   NAT: BUSPROG: Analytic   KEY: Bloom's: Knowledge

2. The process of measuring and reporting operating data by areas of responsibility is termed responsibility accounting.

   ANS: T   PTS: 1   DIF: Easy   OBJ: LO: 24-01
   NAT: BUSPROG: Analytic   KEY: Bloom's: Knowledge

3. A decentralized business organization is one in which all major planning and operating decisions are made by top management.

   ANS: F   PTS: 1   DIF: Easy   OBJ: LO: 24-01
   NAT: BUSPROG: Analytic   KEY: Bloom's: Knowledge

4. A centralized business organization is one in which all major planning and operating decisions are made by top management.

   ANS: T   PTS: 1   DIF: Easy   OBJ: LO: 24-01
   NAT: BUSPROG: Analytic   KEY: Bloom's: Knowledge

5. The primary disadvantage of decentralized operations is that decisions made by one manager may affect other managers in such a way that the profitability of the entire company may suffer.

   ANS: T   PTS: 1   DIF: Easy   OBJ: LO: 24-01
   NAT: BUSPROG: Analytic   KEY: Bloom's: Knowledge

6. The three common types of responsibility centers are referred to as cost centers, profit centers, and investment centers.

   ANS: T   PTS: 1   DIF: Easy   OBJ: LO: 24-01
   NAT: BUSPROG: Analytic   KEY: Bloom's: Knowledge

7. One of the advantages of decentralization is that delegating authority to managers closest to the operation *always* results in better decisions.

   ANS: F   PTS: 1   DIF: Easy   OBJ: LO: 24-01
   NAT: BUSPROG: Analytic   KEY: Bloom's: Knowledge

8. Developing and retaining quality managers is an advantage of decentralization.

   ANS: T   PTS: 1   DIF: Easy   OBJ: LO: 24-01
   NAT: BUSPROG: Analytic   KEY: Bloom's: Knowledge

9. A responsibility center in which the department manager has responsibility for and authority over costs, revenues, and assets invested in the department is termed a cost center.

    ANS: F   PTS: 1   DIF: Easy   OBJ: LO: 24-02
    NAT: BUSPROG: Analytic   KEY: Bloom's: Knowledge

10. Budget performance reports prepared for the vice-president of production would generally contain less detail than reports prepared for the various plant managers.

    ANS: T   PTS: 1   DIF: Challenging   OBJ: LO: 24-02
    NAT: BUSPROG: Analytic   KEY: Bloom's: Knowledge

11. The amount of detail presented in a budget performance report for a cost center depends upon the level of management to which the report is directed.

    ANS: T   PTS: 1   DIF: Moderate   OBJ: LO: 24-02
    NAT: BUSPROG: Analytic   KEY: Bloom's: Knowledge

12. The primary accounting tool for controlling and reporting for cost centers is a budget.

    ANS: T   PTS: 1   DIF: Easy   OBJ: LO: 24-02
    NAT: BUSPROG: Analytic   KEY: Bloom's: Knowledge

13. Responsibility accounting reports that are given to lower level managers are usually very detailed, in turn, higher level managers will be given a summary report.

    ANS: T   PTS: 1   DIF: Easy   OBJ: LO: 24-02
    NAT: BUSPROG: Analytic   KEY: Bloom's: Knowledge

14. A manager in a cost center also has responsibility and authority over the revenues and the costs.

    ANS: F   PTS: 1   DIF: Easy   OBJ: LO: 24-02
    NAT: BUSPROG: Analytic   KEY: Bloom's: Knowledge

15. The plant managers in a cost center can be held responsible for major differences between budgeted and actual costs in their plants.

    ANS: T   PTS: 1   DIF: Easy   OBJ: LO: 24-02
    NAT: BUSPROG: Analytic   KEY: Bloom's: Knowledge

16. A responsibility center in which the authority over and responsibility for costs and revenues is vested in the department manager is termed a profit center.

    ANS: T   PTS: 1   DIF: Easy   OBJ: LO: 24-03
    NAT: BUSPROG: Analytic   KEY: Bloom's: Knowledge

17. Operating expenses directly traceable to or incurred for the sole benefit of a specific department and usually subject to the control of the department manager are termed direct expenses.

    ANS: T   PTS: 1   DIF: Easy   OBJ: LO: 24-03
    NAT: BUSPROG: Analytic   KEY: Bloom's: Knowledge

18. Sales commissions expense for a department store is an example of a direct expense.

    ANS: T   PTS: 1   DIF: Easy   OBJ: LO: 24-03
    NAT: BUSPROG: Analytic   KEY: Bloom's: Knowledge

19. Operating expenses incurred for the entire business as a unit that are not subject to the control of individual department managers are called indirect expenses.

    ANS: T   PTS: 1   DIF: Easy   OBJ: LO: 24-03
    NAT: BUSPROG: Analytic   KEY: Bloom's: Knowledge

20. Office salaries expense for a department store is an indirect expense.

    ANS: T   PTS: 1   DIF: Easy   OBJ: LO: 24-03
    NAT: BUSPROG: Analytic   KEY: Bloom's: Knowledge

21. The underlying principle of allocating operating expenses to departments is to assign to each department an amount of expense proportional to the revenues of that department.

    ANS: F   PTS: 1   DIF: Moderate   OBJ: LO: 24-03
    NAT: BUSPROG: Analytic   KEY: Bloom's: Knowledge

22. Property tax expense for a department store's store equipment is an example of a direct expense.

    ANS: T   PTS: 1   DIF: Challenging   OBJ: LO: 24-03
    NAT: BUSPROG: Analytic   KEY: Bloom's: Knowledge

23. Depreciation expense on store equipment for a department store is an indirect expense.

    ANS: F   PTS: 1   DIF: Moderate   OBJ: LO: 24-03
    NAT: BUSPROG: Analytic   KEY: Bloom's: Knowledge

24. Responsibility accounting reports for profit centers are normally in the form of income statements.

    ANS: T   PTS: 1   DIF: Moderate   OBJ: LO: 24-03
    NAT: BUSPROG: Analytic   KEY: Bloom's: Knowledge

25. The manager of a profit center does not make decisions concerning the fixed assets invested in the center.

    ANS: T   PTS: 1   DIF: Easy   OBJ: LO: 24-03
    NAT: BUSPROG: Analytic   KEY: Bloom's: Knowledge

26. The profit center income statement should include only revenues and expenses that are controlled by the manager.

    ANS: T   PTS: 1   DIF: Easy   OBJ: LO: 24-03
    NAT: BUSPROG: Analytic   KEY: Bloom's: Knowledge

27. The manager of the furniture department of a leading retailer does not control the salaries of departmental personnel.

   ANS: F   PTS: 1   DIF: Easy   OBJ: LO: 24-03
   NAT: BUSPROG: Analytic   KEY: Bloom's: Knowledge

28. Service department charges are similar to the expenses of a profit center that purchased services from a source outside the company.

   ANS: T   PTS: 1   DIF: Easy   OBJ: LO: 24-03
   NAT: BUSPROG: Analytic   KEY: Bloom's: Knowledge

29. Purchase requisitions for Purchasing and the number of payroll checks for Payroll Accounting are examples of activity bases.

   ANS: T   PTS: 1   DIF: Easy   OBJ: LO: 24-03
   NAT: BUSPROG: Analytic   KEY: Bloom's: Knowledge

30. The rates at which services are charged to each division are called service department charge rates.

   ANS: T   PTS: 1   DIF: Easy   OBJ: LO: 24-03
   NAT: BUSPROG: Analytic   KEY: Bloom's: Knowledge

31. The service department will determine its service department charge rate and charge the company's divisions or departments according to their use of that particular service department.

   ANS: T   PTS: 1   DIF: Easy   OBJ: LO: 24-03
   NAT: BUSPROG: Analytic   KEY: Bloom's: Knowledge

32. The profit center income statement should include only controllable revenues and expenses.

   ANS: T   PTS: 1   DIF: Easy   OBJ: LO: 24-03
   NAT: BUSPROG: Analytic   KEY: Bloom's: Knowledge

33. Controllable expenses are those that can be influenced by the decisions of the profit center management.

   ANS: T   PTS: 1   DIF: Moderate   OBJ: LO: 24-03
   NAT: BUSPROG: Analytic   KEY: Bloom's: Knowledge

34. In an investment center, the manager has the responsibility and the authority to make decisions that affect not only costs and revenues, but also the plant assets invested in the center.

   ANS: T   PTS: 1   DIF: Easy   OBJ: LO: 24-04
   NAT: BUSPROG: Analytic   KEY: Bloom's: Knowledge

35. Three measures of investment center performance are income from operations, rate of return on investment, and residual income.

   ANS: T   PTS: 1   DIF: Easy   OBJ: LO: 24-04
   NAT: BUSPROG: Analytic   KEY: Bloom's: Knowledge

36. The major shortcoming of income from operations as an investment center performance measure is that it ignores the amount of revenues earned by the center.

ANS: F   PTS: 1   DIF: Easy   OBJ: LO: 24-04
NAT: BUSPROG: Analytic   KEY: Bloom's: Knowledge

37. If Division Q's income from operations was $30,000 on invested assets of $200,000, the rate of return on investment is 15%.

ANS: T   PTS: 1   DIF: Moderate   OBJ: LO: 24-04
NAT: BUSPROG: Analytic   KEY: Bloom's: Knowledge

38. The rate of return on investment may be computed by multiplying investment turnover by the profit margin.

ANS: T   PTS: 1   DIF: Easy   OBJ: LO: 24-04
NAT: BUSPROG: Analytic   KEY: Bloom's: Knowledge

39. If the profit margin for a division is 8% and the investment turnover is 1.20, the rate of return on investment is 9.6%.

ANS: T   PTS: 1   DIF: Challenging   OBJ: LO: 24-04
NAT: BUSPROG: Analytic   KEY: Bloom's: Knowledge

40. If the profit margin for a division is 11% and the investment turnover is 1.5, the rate of return on investment is 7.3%.

ANS: F   PTS: 1   DIF: Challenging   OBJ: LO: 24-04
NAT: BUSPROG: Analytic   KEY: Bloom's: Knowledge

41. Investment turnover (as used in determining the rate of return on investment) focuses on the rate of profit earned on each sales dollar.

ANS: F   PTS: 1   DIF: Easy   OBJ: LO: 24-04
NAT: BUSPROG: Analytic   KEY: Bloom's: Knowledge

42. The ratio of sales to investment is termed the rate of return on investment.

ANS: F   PTS: 1   DIF: Easy   OBJ: LO: 24-04
NAT: BUSPROG: Analytic   KEY: Bloom's: Knowledge

43. The major advantage of the rate of return on investment over income from operations as a divisional performance measure is that divisional investment is directly considered and thus comparability of divisions is facilitated.

ANS: T   PTS: 1   DIF: Easy   OBJ: LO: 24-04
NAT: BUSPROG: Analytic   KEY: Bloom's: Knowledge

44. By using the rate of return on investment as a divisional performance measure, divisional managers will always be motivated to invest in proposals which will increase the overall rate of return for the company.

ANS: F   PTS: 1   DIF: Easy   OBJ: LO: 24-04
NAT: BUSPROG: Analytic   KEY: Bloom's: Knowledge

45. The excess of divisional income from operations over a minimum amount of desired income from operations is termed the residual income.

   ANS: T   PTS: 1   DIF: Moderate   OBJ: LO: 24-04
   NAT: BUSPROG: Analytic   KEY: Bloom's: Knowledge

46. The minimum amount of desired divisional income from operations is set by top management by establishing a maximum rate of return considered acceptable for invested assets.

   ANS: F   PTS: 1   DIF: Easy   OBJ: LO: 24-04
   NAT: BUSPROG: Analytic   KEY: Bloom's: Knowledge

47. The major advantage of residual income as a performance measure is that it gives consideration to not only a minimum rate of return on investment but also the total magnitude of income from operations earned by each division.

   ANS: T   PTS: 1   DIF: Moderate   OBJ: LO: 24-04
   NAT: BUSPROG: Analytic   KEY: Bloom's: Knowledge

48. The ratio of income from operations to sales is termed the profit margin component of the rate of return on investment.

   ANS: T   PTS: 1   DIF: Easy   OBJ: LO: 24-04
   NAT: BUSPROG: Analytic   KEY: Bloom's: Knowledge

49. The ratio of sales to invested assets is termed the investment turnover component of the rate of return on investment.

   ANS: T   PTS: 1   DIF: Moderate   OBJ: LO: 24-04
   NAT: BUSPROG: Analytic   KEY: Bloom's: Knowledge

50. If income from operations for a division is $5,000, invested assets are $25,000, and sales are $30,000, the profit margin is 20%.

   ANS: F   PTS: 1   DIF: Moderate   OBJ: LO: 24-04
   NAT: BUSPROG: Analytic   KEY: Bloom's: Application

51. If income from operations for a division is $6,000, invested assets are $25,000, and sales are $30,000, the profit margin is 20%.

   ANS: T   PTS: 1   DIF: Moderate   OBJ: LO: 24-04
   NAT: BUSPROG: Analytic   KEY: Bloom's: Application

52. If income from operations for a division is $6,000, invested assets are $25,000, and sales are $30,000, the investment turnover is 1.2.

   ANS: T   PTS: 1   DIF: Moderate   OBJ: LO: 24-04
   NAT: BUSPROG: Analytic   KEY: Bloom's: Application

53. If income from operations for a division is $6,000, invested assets are $25,000, and sales are $30,000, the investment turnover is 5.

ANS: F PTS: 1 DIF: Moderate OBJ: LO: 24-04
NAT: BUSPROG: Analytic KEY: Bloom's: Application

54. If income from operations for a division is $30,000, sales are $263,750, and invested assets are $187,500, the investment turnover is 1.3.

ANS: F PTS: 1 DIF: Moderate OBJ: LO: 24-04
NAT: BUSPROG: Analytic KEY: Bloom's: Application

55. If income from operations for a division is $120,000, sales are $975,000, and invested assets are $750,000, the investment turnover is 1.3.

ANS: T PTS: 1 DIF: Moderate OBJ: LO: 24-04
NAT: BUSPROG: Analytic KEY: Bloom's: Application

56. If divisional income from operations is $75,000, invested assets are $737,500, and the minimum rate of return on invested assets is 6%, the residual income is $36,750.

ANS: F PTS: 1 DIF: Moderate OBJ: LO: 24-04
NAT: BUSPROG: Analytic KEY: Bloom's: Application

57. If divisional income from operations is $100,000, invested assets are $850,000, and the minimum rate of return on invested assets is 8%, the residual income is $68,000.

ANS: F PTS: 1 DIF: Moderate OBJ: LO: 24-04
NAT: BUSPROG: Analytic KEY: Bloom's: Application

58. The profit margin component of rate of return on investment analysis focuses on profitability by indicating the rate of profit earned on each sales dollar.

ANS: T PTS: 1 DIF: Easy OBJ: LO: 24-04
NAT: BUSPROG: Analytic KEY: Bloom's: Knowledge

59. In rate of return on investment analysis, the investment turnover component focuses on efficiency in the use of assets and indicates the rate at which sales are being generated for each dollar of invested assets.

ANS: T PTS: 1 DIF: Easy OBJ: LO: 24-04
NAT: BUSPROG: Analytic KEY: Bloom's: Knowledge

60. The minimum amount of desired divisional income from operations is set by top management by establishing a minimum rate of return considered acceptable for invested assets.

ANS: T PTS: 1 DIF: Easy OBJ: LO: 24-04
NAT: BUSPROG: Analytic KEY: Bloom's: Knowledge

61. A disadvantage to using the residual income performance measure is that it encourages managers to spend only the minimum acceptable rate of return on assets set by upper management.

ANS: F   PTS: 1   DIF: Easy   OBJ: LO: 24-04
NAT: BUSPROG: Analytic   KEY: Bloom's: Knowledge

62. The DuPont formula uses financial information to measure the performance of a business.

ANS: T   PTS: 1   DIF: Moderate   OBJ: LO: 24-04
NAT: BUSPROG: Analytic   KEY: Bloom's: Knowledge

63. The DuPont formula uses financial and nonfinancial information to measure the performance of a business.

ANS: F   PTS: 1   DIF: Easy   OBJ: LO: 24-04
NAT: BUSPROG: Analytic   KEY: Bloom's: Knowledge

64. The balanced scorecard is a set of financial and nonfinancial measures that reflect the performance of the business.

ANS: T   PTS: 1   DIF: Easy   OBJ: LO: 24-04
NAT: BUSPROG: Analytic   KEY: Bloom's: Knowledge

65. The objective of transfer pricing is to encourage each division manager to transfer goods and services between divisions if overall company income can be increased by doing so.

ANS: T   PTS: 1   DIF: Easy   OBJ: LO: 24-05
NAT: BUSPROG: Analytic   KEY: Bloom's: Knowledge

66. Transfer prices may be used when decentralized units are organized as cost, profit, or investment centers.

ANS: T   PTS: 1   DIF: Easy   OBJ: LO: 24-05
NAT: BUSPROG: Analytic   KEY: Bloom's: Knowledge

67. Under the cost price approach, the transfer price is the price at which the product or service transferred could be sold to outside buyers.

ANS: F   PTS: 1   DIF: Easy   OBJ: LO: 24-05
NAT: BUSPROG: Analytic   KEY: Bloom's: Knowledge

68. Under the negotiated price approach, the transfer price is the price at which the product or service transferred could be sold to outside buyers.

ANS: F   PTS: 1   DIF: Easy   OBJ: LO: 24-05
NAT: BUSPROG: Analytic   KEY: Bloom's: Knowledge

69. The negotiated price approach allows the managers of decentralized units to agree among themselves as to the transfer price.

ANS: T   PTS: 1   DIF: Easy   OBJ: LO: 24-05
NAT: BUSPROG: Analytic   KEY: Bloom's: Knowledge

70. It is beneficial for divisions in a company to negotiate a transfer price when the supplying division has unused capacity in its plant.

ANS: T   PTS: 1   DIF: Easy   OBJ: LO: 24-05
NAT: BUSPROG: Analytic   KEY: Bloom's: Knowledge

71. It is beneficial for two related companies to use the cost price approach for transfer pricing when both of the companies operate as cost centers and are not concerned with the revenue.

ANS: T   PTS: 1   DIF: Easy   OBJ: LO: 24-05
NAT: BUSPROG: Analytic   KEY: Bloom's: Knowledge

MATCHING

An activity base is used to charge service department expenses. Match each of the following questions with an activity base.
   a. Purchasing
   b. Payroll Accounting
   c. Human Resources
   d. Maintenance
   e. Information Systems
   f. Marketing
   g. President's office
   h. Transportation

1. Number of work orders
2. Number of employees
3. Number of payroll checks
4. Number of purchase requisitions
5. Equally amongst divisions
6. Number of advertising campaigns
7. Number of miles
8. Number of computers in department

1. ANS: D   PTS: 1   DIF: Moderate   OBJ: LO: 24-03
   NAT: BUSPROG: Analytic   KEY: Bloom's: Knowledge
2. ANS: C   PTS: 1   DIF: Moderate   OBJ: LO: 24-03
   NAT: BUSPROG: Analytic   KEY: Bloom's: Knowledge
3. ANS: B   PTS: 1   DIF: Moderate   OBJ: LO: 24-03
   NAT: BUSPROG: Analytic   KEY: Bloom's: Knowledge
4. ANS: A   PTS: 1   DIF: Moderate   OBJ: LO: 24-03
   NAT: BUSPROG: Analytic   KEY: Bloom's: Knowledge
5. ANS: G   PTS: 1   DIF: Moderate   OBJ: LO: 24-03
   NAT: BUSPROG: Analytic   KEY: Bloom's: Knowledge
6. ANS: F   PTS: 1   DIF: Moderate   OBJ: LO: 24-03
   NAT: BUSPROG: Analytic   KEY: Bloom's: Knowledge
7. ANS: H   PTS: 1   DIF: Moderate   OBJ: LO: 24-03
   NAT: BUSPROG: Analytic   KEY: Bloom's: Knowledge
8. ANS: E   PTS: 1   DIF: Moderate   OBJ: LO: 24-03
   NAT: BUSPROG: Analytic   KEY: Bloom's: Knowledge

Match the following as either an advantage, disadvantage, or neither of decentralization.
   a.   Advantage of decentralization
   b.   Disadvantage of decentralization
   c.   Neither an advantage or disadvantage

9.   Responsibilties delegated to unit managers
10. Internal price wars
11. Operational issues are made by managers closest to the operations
12. Separate office staff
13. Separate sales forces

9.   ANS: A   PTS: 1   DIF: Moderate   OBJ: LO: 24-01
     NAT: BUSPROG: Analytic   KEY: Bloom's: Knowledge
10. ANS: B   PTS: 1   DIF: Moderate   OBJ: LO: 24-01
     NAT: BUSPROG: Analytic   KEY: Bloom's: Knowledge
11. ANS: A   PTS: 1   DIF: Moderate   OBJ: LO: 24-01
     NAT: BUSPROG: Analytic   KEY: Bloom's: Knowledge
12. ANS: B   PTS: 1   DIF: Moderate   OBJ: LO: 24-01
     NAT: BUSPROG: Analytic   KEY: Bloom's: Knowledge
13. ANS: B   PTS: 1   DIF: Moderate   OBJ: LO: 24-01
     NAT: BUSPROG: Analytic   KEY: Bloom's: Knowledge

Match the following terms with the best definition given below.
   a.   Controllable revenues
   b.   Profit margin
   c.   Investment turnover
   d.   Rate of return on investments
   e.   Residual income

14. Income from operations minus minimum acceptable income from operations
15. Income from operations divided by invested assets
16. Ratio of income from operations to sales
17. Earned by profit centers.
18. Ratio of sales to invested assets

14. ANS: E   PTS: 1   DIF: Moderate   OBJ: LO: 24-04
     NAT: BUSPROG: Analytic   KEY: Bloom's: Knowledge
15. ANS: D   PTS: 1   DIF: Moderate   OBJ: LO: 24-04
     NAT: BUSPROG: Analytic   KEY: Bloom's: Knowledge
16. ANS: B   PTS: 1   DIF: Moderate   OBJ: LO: 24-04
     NAT: BUSPROG: Analytic   KEY: Bloom's: Knowledge
17. ANS: A   PTS: 1   DIF: Moderate   OBJ: LO: 24-04
     NAT: BUSPROG: Analytic   KEY: Bloom's: Knowledge
18. ANS: C   PTS: 1   DIF: Moderate   OBJ: LO: 24-04
     NAT: BUSPROG: Analytic   KEY: Bloom's: Knowledge

MULTIPLE CHOICE

1. Which of the following would be most effective in a small owner/manager-operated business?
   a. Profit centers
   b. Centralization
   c. Investment centers
   d. Cost centers

   ANS: B   PTS: 1   DIF: Moderate   OBJ: LO: 24-01
   NAT: BUSPROG: Analytic   KEY: Bloom's: Knowledge

2. Businesses that are separated into two or more manageable units in which managers have authority and responsibility for operations are said to be:
   a. decentralized
   b. consolidated
   c. diversified
   d. centralized

   ANS: A   PTS: 1   DIF: Easy   OBJ: LO: 24-01
   NAT: BUSPROG: Analytic   KEY: Bloom's: Knowledge

3. Which of the following is NOT a disadvantage of decentralized operation?
   a. Competition among managers decreases profits
   b. Duplication of operations
   c. Price cutting by departments that are competing in the same product market
   d. Top management freed from everyday tasks to do strategic planning

   ANS: D   PTS: 1   DIF: Challenging   OBJ: LO: 24-01
   NAT: BUSPROG: Analytic   KEY: Bloom's: Knowledge

4. Which is the best example of a decentralized operation?
   a. One owner who prepares plans and makes decisions for the entire company.
   b. Each unit is responsible for their own operations and decision making.
   c. In a major company, operating decisions are made by top management.
   d. None of the above. All are examples of a centralized management.

   ANS: B   PTS: 1   DIF: Easy   OBJ: LO: 24-01
   NAT: BUSPROG: Analytic   KEY: Bloom's: Knowledge

5. All of the following are advantages of decentralization except:
   a. Managers make better decisions when closer to the operation of the company.
   b. Expertise in all areas of the business is difficult, decentralization makes it better to delegate certain responsibilities.
   c. Each decentralized operation purchases their own assets and pays for operating costs.
   d. Decentralized managers can respond quickly to customer satisfaction and quality service.

   ANS: C   PTS: 1   DIF: Easy   OBJ: LO: 24-01
   NAT: BUSPROG: Analytic   KEY: Bloom's: Knowledge

6. Which of the following is not one of the common types of responsibility centers?
   a. Cost Center
   b. Profit Center
   c. Investment Center
   d. Revenue Center

ANS: D   PTS: 1   DIF: Easy   OBJ: LO: 24-01
NAT: BUSPROG: Analytic   KEY: Bloom's: Knowledge

7. Which of the following is a disadvantage of decentralization?
   a. Decisions made by one manager may negatively affect the profitability of the entire company.
   b. Helps retain quality managers.
   c. Decision making by managers closest to the operations.
   d. Managers are able to acquire expertise in their areas of responsibility.

ANS: A   PTS: 1   DIF: Easy   OBJ: LO: 24-01
NAT: BUSPROG: Analytic   KEY: Bloom's: Knowledge

8. A manager is responsible for costs only in a(n):
   a. profit center
   b. investment center
   c. volume center
   d. cost center

ANS: D   PTS: 1   DIF: Easy   OBJ: LO: 24-02
NAT: BUSPROG: Analytic   KEY: Bloom's: Knowledge

9. In a cost center, the manager has responsibility and authority for making decisions that affect:
   a. revenues
   b. assets
   c. both costs and revenues
   d. costs

ANS: D   PTS: 1   DIF: Easy   OBJ: LO: 24-02
NAT: BUSPROG: Analytic   KEY: Bloom's: Knowledge

10. For higher levels of management, responsibility accounting reports:
    a. are more detailed than for lower levels of management
    b. are more summarized than for lower levels of management
    c. contain about the same level of detail as reports for lower levels of management
    d. are rarely provided or reviewed

ANS: B   PTS: 1   DIF: Moderate   OBJ: LO: 24-02
NAT: BUSPROG: Analytic   KEY: Bloom's: Knowledge

11. Most manufacturing plants are considered cost centers because they have control over
    a. sales and costs.
    b. fixed assets and costs.
    c. costs only.
    d. fixed assets and sales.

ANS: C   PTS: 1   DIF: Easy   OBJ: LO: 24-02
NAT: BUSPROG: Analytic   KEY: Bloom's: Knowledge

12. The following is a measure of a manager's performance working in a cost center.
    a. budget performance report
    b. rate of return and residual income measures
    c. divisional income statements
    d. balance sheet

ANS: A   PTS: 1   DIF: Easy   OBJ: LO: 24-02
NAT: BUSPROG: Analytic   KEY: Bloom's: Knowledge

13. A responsibility center in which the department manager has responsibility for and authority over costs and revenues is called a(n):
    a. profit center
    b. investment center
    c. volume center
    d. cost center

ANS: A   PTS: 1   DIF: Easy   OBJ: LO: 24-03
NAT: BUSPROG: Analytic   KEY: Bloom's: Knowledge

14. In a profit center, the department manager has responsibility for and the authority to make decisions that affect:
    a. not only costs and revenues, but also assets invested in the center
    b. the assets invested in the center, but not costs and revenues
    c. both costs and revenues for the department or division
    d. costs and assets invested in the center, but not revenues

ANS: C   PTS: 1   DIF: Easy   OBJ: LO: 24-03
NAT: BUSPROG: Analytic   KEY: Bloom's: Knowledge

15. Which of the following expenses incurred by the sporting goods department of a department store is a direct expense?
    a. Depreciation expense--office equipment
    b. Insurance on inventory of sporting goods
    c. Uncollectible accounts expense
    d. Office salaries

ANS: B   PTS: 1   DIF: Challenging   OBJ: LO: 24-03
NAT: BUSPROG: Analytic   KEY: Bloom's: Knowledge

16. Which of the following expenses incurred by a department store is an indirect expense?
    a. Insurance on merchandise inventory
    b. Sales salaries
    c. Depreciation on store equipment
    d. Salary of vice-president of finance

ANS: D   PTS: 1   DIF: Challenging   OBJ: LO: 24-03
NAT: BUSPROG: Analytic   KEY: Bloom's: Knowledge

17. In a profit center, the manager has responsibility and authority for making decisions that affect:
    a. liabilities
    b. assets
    c. investments
    d. costs

ANS: D   PTS: 1   DIF: Easy   OBJ: LO: 24-03
NAT: BUSPROG: Analytic   KEY: Bloom's: Knowledge

18. Operating expenses directly traceable to or incurred for the sole benefit of a specific department and usually subject to the control of the department manager are termed:
    a. miscellaneous administrative expenses
    b. direct expenses
    c. indirect expenses
    d. fixed expenses

    ANS: B   PTS: 1   DIF: Easy   OBJ: LO: 24-03
    NAT: BUSPROG: Analytic   KEY: Bloom's: Knowledge

19. In evaluating the profit center manager, the income from operations should be compared:
    a. across profit centers
    b. to historical performance or budget
    c. to the competitor's net income
    d. to the total company earnings per share

    ANS: B   PTS: 1   DIF: Easy   OBJ: LO: 24-03
    NAT: BUSPROG: Analytic   KEY: Bloom's: Knowledge

20. Income from operations of the Commercial Aviation Division is $2,225,000. If income from operations before service department charges is $3,250,000:
    a. operating expenses are $1,025,000
    b. total service department charges are $1,025,000
    c. noncontrollable charges are $1,025,000
    d. direct manufacturing charges are $1,025,000

    ANS: B   PTS: 1   DIF: Moderate   OBJ: LO: 24-03
    NAT: BUSPROG: Analytic   KEY: Bloom's: Application

21. The costs of services charged to a profit center on the basis of its use of those services are called:
    a. operating expenses
    b. noncontrollable charges
    c. service department charges
    d. activity charges

    ANS: C   PTS: 1   DIF: Easy   OBJ: LO: 24-03
    NAT: BUSPROG: Analytic   KEY: Bloom's: Knowledge

22. Division X reported income from operations of $975,000 and total service department charges of $575,000. Therefore:
    a. net income was $400,000
    b. the gross profit margin was $400,000
    c. income from operations before service department charges was $1,550,000
    d. consolidated net income was $400,000

    ANS: C   PTS: 1   DIF: Moderate   OBJ: LO: 24-03
    NAT: BUSPROG: Analytic   KEY: Bloom's: Application

23. To calculate income from operations, total service department charges are:
    a. added to income from operations before service department charges
    b. subtracted from operating expenses
    c. subtracted from income from operations before service department charges
    d. subtracted from gross profit margin

ANS: C   PTS: 1   DIF: Easy   OBJ: LO: 24-03
NAT: BUSPROG: Analytic   KEY: Bloom's: Knowledge

24. Income from operations for Division Z is $250,000, total service department charges are $400,000 and operating expenses are $2,266,000. What are the revenues for Division Z?
   a. $650,000
   b. $2,516,000
   c. $2,916,000
   d. $2,666,000

ANS: C   PTS: 1   DIF: Moderate   OBJ: LO: 24-03
NAT: BUSPROG: Analytic   KEY: Bloom's: Application

25. Income from operations for Division K is $220,000, and income from operations before service department charges is $975,000. Therefore:
   a. total operating expenses are $755,000
   b. total manufacturing expenses are $755,000
   c. direct materials, direct labor, and factory overhead total $755,000
   d. total service department charges are $755,000

ANS: D   PTS: 1   DIF: Moderate   OBJ: LO: 24-03
NAT: BUSPROG: Analytic   KEY: Bloom's: Application

26. The following data are taken from the management accounting reports of Dulcimer Co.:

	Div. A	Div. B	Div. C
Income from operations	$1,900,000	$1,450,000	$1,450,000
Total service department charges	1,700,000	1,050,000	1,100,000

If an incentive bonus is paid to the manager who achieved the highest income from operations before service department charges, it follows that:
   a. Division A's manager is given the bonus
   b. Division B's manager is given the bonus
   c. Division C's manager is given the bonus
   d. The managers of Divisions B and C divide the bonus

ANS: A   PTS: 1   DIF: Moderate   OBJ: LO: 24-03
NAT: BUSPROG: Analytic   KEY: Bloom's: Application

27. What is the term used to describe expenses that are incurred for the benefit of a specific department?
   a. Indirect expenses
   b. Margin expenses
   c. Departmental expenses
   d. Direct expenses

ANS: D   PTS: 1   DIF: Easy   OBJ: LO: 24-03
NAT: BUSPROG: Analytic   KEY: Bloom's: Knowledge

The following financial information was summarized from the accounting records of Train Corporation for the current year ended December 31:

	Rails Division	Locomotive Division	Corporate Total
Cost of goods sold	$47,200	$30,720	
Direct operating expenses	27,200	20,040	
Net sales	108,000	78,000	
Interest expense			$2,040
General overhead			18,160
Income tax			4,700

28. The gross profit for the Rails Division is:
   a. $60,800
   b. $33,600
   c. $8,700
   d. $21,150

   ANS: A   PTS: 1   DIF: Moderate   OBJ: LO: 24-03
   NAT: BUSPROG: Analytic   KEY: Bloom's: Application

29. The income from operations for the Rails Division is:
   a. $60,800
   b. $33,600
   c. $8,700
   d. $21,150

   ANS: B   PTS: 1   DIF: Moderate   OBJ: LO: 24-03
   NAT: BUSPROG: Analytic   KEY: Bloom's: Application

30. The gross profit for the Locomotive Division is:
   a. $57,960
   b. $14,790
   c. $27,240
   d. $47,280

   ANS: D   PTS: 1   DIF: Moderate   OBJ: LO: 24-03
   NAT: BUSPROG: Analytic   KEY: Bloom's: Application

31. The income from operations for the Locomotive Division is:
   a. $57,960
   b. $14,790
   c. $27,240
   d. $47,280

   ANS: C   PTS: 1   DIF: Moderate   OBJ: LO: 24-03
   NAT: BUSPROG: Analytic   KEY: Bloom's: Application

32. The net income for Train Corporation is:
   a. $83,180
   b. $35,940
   c. $48,390
   d. $60,840

ANS: B   PTS: 1   DIF: Challenging   OBJ: LO: 24-03
NAT: BUSPROG: Analytic   KEY: Bloom's: Application

33. Responsibility accounting reports for profit centers will include
     a. costs.
     b. revenues.
     c. expenses and fixed assets.
     d. revenues, expenses, net income or loss from operations.

ANS: D   PTS: 1   DIF: Easy   OBJ: LO: 24-03
NAT: BUSPROG: Analytic   KEY: Bloom's: Knowledge

34. Some organizations use internal service departments to provide like services to several divisions or
     departments within an organization. Which of the following would probably not lend itself as a
     service department?
     a. Inventory Control
     b. Payroll Accounting
     c. Information Systems
     d. Human Resources

ANS: A   PTS: 1   DIF: Easy   OBJ: LO: 24-03
NAT: BUSPROG: Analytic   KEY: Bloom's: Knowledge

35. The following is a measure of a manager's performance working in a profit center.
     a. balance sheet
     b. rate of return and residual income measures
     c. budget performance report
     d. divisional income statements

ANS: D   PTS: 1   DIF: Easy   OBJ: LO: 24-03
NAT: BUSPROG: Analytic   KEY: Bloom's: Knowledge

36. Which of the following would not be considered an internal centralized service department?
     a. Payroll accounting department
     b. Manufacturing department
     c. Information systems department
     d. Purchasing department

ANS: B   PTS: 1   DIF: Easy   OBJ: LO: 24-03
NAT: BUSPROG: Analytic   KEY: Bloom's: Knowledge

37. Avey Corporation had $275,000 in invested assets, sales of $330,000, income from operations
     amounting to $49,500 and a desired minimum rate of return of 7.5%. The rate of return on
     investment for Avey Corporation is:
     a. 8%
     b. 10%
     c. 18%
     d. 7.5%

ANS: C   PTS: 1   DIF: Moderate   OBJ: LO: 24-04
NAT: BUSPROG: Analytic   KEY: Bloom's: Application

     Mason Corporation had $650,000 in invested assets, sales of $700,000, income from operations
     amounting to $99,000, and a desired minimum rate of return of 15%.

38. The profit margin for Mason is:
    a. 7.1%
    b. 20%
    c. 15.2%
    d. 14.1%

    ANS: D   PTS: 1   DIF: Moderate   OBJ: LO: 24-04
    NAT: BUSPROG: Analytic   KEY: Bloom's: Application

39. The investment turnover for Mason is:
    a. 1.08
    b. .93
    c. 6.57
    d. 7.07

    ANS: A   PTS: 1   DIF: Moderate   OBJ: LO: 24-04
    NAT: BUSPROG: Analytic   KEY: Bloom's: Application

40. The residual income for Mason is:
    a. $0
    b. $84,150
    c. ($6,000)
    d. $1,500

    ANS: D   PTS: 1   DIF: Moderate   OBJ: LO: 24-04
    NAT: BUSPROG: Analytic   KEY: Bloom's: Application

41. Hamlin Corporation had $220,000 in invested assets, sales of $242,000, income from operations amounting to $70,400, and a desired minimum rate of return of 3%. The rate of return on investment for Hamlin is:
    a. 7%
    b. 32%
    c. 3%
    d. 29%

    ANS: B   PTS: 1   DIF: Moderate   OBJ: LO: 24-04
    NAT: BUSPROG: Analytic   KEY: Bloom's: Application

    Chicks Corporation had $1,100,000 in invested assets, sales of $1,210,000, income from operations amounting to $302,500, and a desired minimum rate of return of 15%.

42. The profit margin for Chicks is:
    a. 25%
    b. 22%
    c. 15%
    d. 27.5%

    ANS: A   PTS: 1   DIF: Moderate   OBJ: LO: 24-04
    NAT: BUSPROG: Analytic   KEY: Bloom's: Application

43. The investment turnover for Chicks is:
    a. 1.3
    b. 1.5

c. 1.0
d. 1.1

ANS: D   PTS: 1   DIF: Moderate   OBJ: LO: 24-04
NAT: BUSPROG: Analytic   KEY: Bloom's: Application

44. The residual income for Chicks is:
a. $165,000
b. $302,500
c. $137,500
d. $191,500

ANS: C   PTS: 1   DIF: Moderate   OBJ: LO: 24-04
NAT: BUSPROG: Analytic   KEY: Bloom's: Application

The Clydesdale Company has sales of $4,500,000. It also has invested assets of $2,000,000 and operating expenses of $3,600,000. The company has established a minimum rate of return of 7%.

45. What is Clydesdale Company's profit margin?
a. 20%
b. 80%
c. 44.4%
d. 18%

ANS: A   PTS: 1   DIF: Moderate   OBJ: LO: 24-04
NAT: BUSPROG: Analytic   KEY: Bloom's: Application

46. What is Clydesdale Company's investment turnover?
a. 1.80
b. 2.25
c. 1.25
d. 1.4

ANS: B   PTS: 1   DIF: Moderate   OBJ: LO: 24-04
NAT: BUSPROG: Analytic   KEY: Bloom's: Application

47. What is Clydesdale Company's rate of return on investment?
a. 56%
b. 20%
c. 45%
d. 25%

ANS: C   PTS: 1   DIF: Moderate   OBJ: LO: 24-04
NAT: BUSPROG: Analytic   KEY: Bloom's: Application

48. What is Clydesdale Company's residual income?
a. $252,000
b. $900,000
c. $1,400,000
d. $760,000

ANS: D   PTS: 1   DIF: Moderate   OBJ: LO: 24-04
NAT: BUSPROG: Analytic   KEY: Bloom's: Application

49. Managers of what type of decentralized units have authority and responsibility for revenues, costs, and assets invested in the unit?
    a. Profit center
    b. Investment center
    c. Production center
    d. Cost center

    ANS: B   PTS: 1   DIF: Easy   OBJ: LO: 24-04
    NAT: BUSPROG: Analytic   KEY: Bloom's: Knowledge

50. A responsibility center in which the department manager is responsible for costs, revenues, and assets for a department is called:
    a. a cost center
    b. a profit center
    c. an operating center
    d. an investment center

    ANS: D   PTS: 1   DIF: Easy   OBJ: LO: 24-04
    NAT: BUSPROG: Analytic   KEY: Bloom's: Knowledge

51. In an investment center, the manager has the responsibility for and the authority to make decisions that affect:
    a. the assets invested in the center, but not costs and revenues
    b. costs and assets invested in the center, but not revenues
    c. both costs and revenues for the department or division
    d. not only costs and revenues, but also assets invested in the center

    ANS: D   PTS: 1   DIF: Easy   OBJ: LO: 24-04
    NAT: BUSPROG: Analytic   KEY: Bloom's: Knowledge

52. In an investment center, the manager has responsibility and authority for making decisions that affect:
    a. costs
    b. revenues
    c. assets
    d. costs, revenues, and assets

    ANS: D   PTS: 1   DIF: Easy   OBJ: LO: 24-04
    NAT: BUSPROG: Analytic   KEY: Bloom's: Knowledge

53. The profit margin is the:
    a. ratio of income from operations to sales
    b. ratio of income from operations to invested assets
    c. ratio of assets to liabilities
    d. ratio of sales to invested assets

    ANS: A   PTS: 1   DIF: Easy   OBJ: LO: 24-04
    NAT: BUSPROG: Analytic   KEY: Bloom's: Knowledge

54. The investment turnover is the:
    a. ratio of income from operations to sales
    b. ratio of income from operations to invested assets
    c. ratio of assets to liabilities
    d. ratio of sales to invested assets

ANS: D PTS: 1   DIF: Easy   OBJ: LO: 24-04
NAT: BUSPROG: Analytic   KEY: Bloom's: Knowledge

55. Identify the formula for the rate of return on investment.
  a. Invested Assets/Income From Operations
  b. Sales/Invested Assets
  c. Income From Operations/Sales
  d. Income From Operations/Invested Assets

ANS: D PTS: 1   DIF: Easy   OBJ: LO: 24-04
NAT: BUSPROG: Analytic   KEY: Bloom's: Knowledge

56. Which of the following expressions is termed the profit margin factor as used in determining the rate of return on investment?
  a. Sales/Income From Operations
  b. Income From Operations/Sales
  c. Invested Assets/Sales
  d. Sales/Invested Assets

ANS: B PTS: 1   DIF: Easy   OBJ: LO: 24-04
NAT: BUSPROG: Analytic   KEY: Bloom's: Knowledge

57. Which of the following expressions is termed the investment turnover factor as used in determining the rate of return on investment?
  a. Invested Assets/Sales
  b. Income From Operations/Invested Assets
  c. Income From Operations/Sales
  d. Sales/Invested Assets

ANS: D PTS: 1   DIF: Easy   OBJ: LO: 24-04
NAT: BUSPROG: Analytic   KEY: Bloom's: Knowledge

58. The profit margin for Atlantic Division is 28% and the investment turnover is 2.8. What is the rate of return on investment for Atlantic Division?
  a. 20%
  b. 28%
  c. 14%
  d. 78.4%

ANS: D PTS: 1   DIF: Moderate OBJ: LO: 24-04
NAT: BUSPROG: Analytic   KEY: Bloom's: Application

59. Pacific Division for Bean Company has a rate of return on investment of 28% and an investment turnover of 1.4. What is the profit margin?
  a. 28%
  b. 20%
  c. 14%
  d. 39.2%

ANS: B PTS: 1   DIF: Moderate OBJ: LO: 24-04
NAT: BUSPROG: Analytic   KEY: Bloom's: Application

60. The Eastern Division of Kentucky Company has a rate of return on investment of 28% and a profit margin of 20%. What is the investment turnover?
    a. 3.6
    b. 1.4
    c. 5.0
    d. .7

    ANS: B   PTS: 1   DIF: Moderate   OBJ: LO: 24-04
    NAT: BUSPROG: Analytic   KEY: Bloom's: Application

61. What additional information is needed to find the rate of return on investment if income from operations is known?
    a. Invested assets
    b. Residual income
    c. Direct expenses
    d. Sales

    ANS: A   PTS: 1   DIF: Challenging   OBJ: LO: 24-04
    NAT: BUSPROG: Analytic   KEY: Bloom's: Knowledge

62. The Western Division of Bestboot Company has a rate of return on investment of 15% and an investment turnover of 1.2. What is the profit margin?
    a. 10%
    b. 12.5%
    c. 9%
    d. 6%

    ANS: B   PTS: 1   DIF: Moderate   OBJ: LO: 24-04
    NAT: BUSPROG: Analytic   KEY: Bloom's: Application

63. The best measure of managerial efficiency in the use of investments in assets is:
    a. rate of return on stockholders' equity
    b. investment turnover
    c. income from operations
    d. inventory turnover

    ANS: B   PTS: 1   DIF: Challenging   OBJ: LO: 24-04
    NAT: BUSPROG: Analytic   KEY: Bloom's: Knowledge

64. Two divisions of Central Company (Divisions X and Y) have the same profit margins. Division X's investment turnover is larger than that of Division Y (1.2 to 1.0). Income from operations for Division X is $55,000, and income from operations for Division Y is $43,000. Division X has a higher return on investment than Division Y by:
    a. using income from operations as a performance measure
    b. comparing the profit margins
    c. applying a negotiated price measure
    d. using its assets more efficiently in generating sales

    ANS: D   PTS: 1   DIF: Challenging   OBJ: LO: 24-04
    NAT: BUSPROG: Analytic   KEY: Bloom's: Application

65. The profit margin for Division B is 8% and the investment turnover is 1.20. What is the rate of return on investment for Division B?
    a. 8%
    b. 6.7%
    c. 7.3%
    d. 9.6%

    ANS: D   PTS: 1   DIF: Moderate   OBJ: LO: 24-04
    NAT: BUSPROG: Analytic   KEY: Bloom's: Application

66. The excess of divisional income from operations over a minimum amount of divisional income from operations is termed:
    a. profit margin
    b. residual income
    c. rate of return on investment
    d. gross profit

    ANS: B   PTS: 1   DIF: Easy   OBJ: LO: 24-04
    NAT: BUSPROG: Analytic   KEY: Bloom's: Knowledge

67. Assume that divisional income from operations amounts to $192,000 and top management has established 15% as the minimum rate of return on divisional assets totaling $1,000,000. The residual income for the division is:
    a. $42,000
    b. $28,800
    c. $92,000
    d. $0

    ANS: A   PTS: 1   DIF: Moderate   OBJ: LO: 24-04
    NAT: BUSPROG: Analytic   KEY: Bloom's: Application

68. Which one of the following is NOT a measure that management can use in evaluating and controlling investment center performance?
    a. Rate of return on investment
    b. Negotiated price
    c. Residual income
    d. Income from operations

    ANS: B   PTS: 1   DIF: Easy   OBJ: LO: 24-04
    NAT: BUSPROG: Analytic   KEY: Bloom's: Knowledge

69. A factor in determining the rate of return on investment--the ratio of income from operations to sales--is called:
    a. profit margin
    b. indirect expenses
    c. investment turnover
    d. cost

    ANS: A   PTS: 1   DIF: Easy   OBJ: LO: 24-04
    NAT: BUSPROG: Analytic   KEY: Bloom's: Knowledge

70. A factor in determining the rate of return on investment--the ratio of sales to invested assets--is called:
    a. profit margin
    b. indirect margin
    c. investment turnover
    d. cost ratio

    ANS: C   PTS: 1   DIF: Easy   OBJ: LO: 24-04
    NAT: BUSPROG: Analytic   KEY: Bloom's: Knowledge

71. Assume that Division J has achieved income from operations of $165,000 using $900,000 of invested assets. If management desires a minimum rate of return of 11%, the residual income is:
    a. $99,000
    b. $18,150
    c. $264,000
    d. $66,000

    ANS: D   PTS: 1   DIF: Moderate   OBJ: LO: 24-04
    NAT: BUSPROG: Analytic   KEY: Bloom's: Application

    Division A of Mocha Company has sales of $155,000, cost of goods sold of $83,000, operating expenses of $43,000, and invested assets of $150,000.

72. What is the rate of return on investment for Division A?
    a. 19.3%
    b. 48.0%
    c. 18.7%
    d. 5.47%

    ANS: A   PTS: 1   DIF: Moderate   OBJ: LO: 24-04
    NAT: BUSPROG: Analytic   KEY: Bloom's: Application

73. What is the profit margin for Division A?
    a. 19.3%
    b. 48.0%
    c. 18.7%
    d. 5.47%

    ANS: C   PTS: 1   DIF: Moderate   OBJ: LO: 24-04
    NAT: BUSPROG: Analytic   KEY: Bloom's: Application

74. What is the investment turnover for Division A?
    a. 1.03
    b. 1.0
    c. 5.17
    d. 5.34

    ANS: A   PTS: 1   DIF: Moderate   OBJ: LO: 24-04
    NAT: BUSPROG: Analytic   KEY: Bloom's: Application

    Division X of O'Blarney Company has sales of $300,000, cost of goods sold of $120,000, operating expenses of $58,000, and invested assets of $150,000.

75. What is the rate of return on investment for Division X?
    a. 9.15%
    b. 81.3%
    c. 40.7%
    d. 200%

    ANS: B   PTS: 1   DIF: Moderate   OBJ: LO: 24-04
    NAT: BUSPROG: Analytic   KEY: Bloom's: Application

76. What is the profit margin for Division X?
    a. 81.3%
    b. 20.2%
    c. 40.7%
    d. 60%

    ANS: C   PTS: 1   DIF: Moderate   OBJ: LO: 24-04
    NAT: BUSPROG: Analytic   KEY: Bloom's: Application

77. Investment centers differ from profit centers in that they
    a. are responsible for net income only.
    b. are able to invest in assets.
    c. have less responsibilities than cost centers and profit centers.
    d. are only responsible for revenues.

    ANS: B   PTS: 1   DIF: Easy   OBJ: LO: 24-04
    NAT: BUSPROG: Analytic

78. Moon Shoe Factory is an investment center and is responsible for all of their net income and the use of their assets. In 2012, the invested assets totaled $475,000 and net income was $125,000. What is the rate of return on assets?
    a. 26.3%
    b. 25.0%
    c. 4.0%
    d. 380.0%

    ANS: A   PTS: 1   DIF: Easy   OBJ: LO: 24-04
    NAT: BUSPROG: Analytic   KEY: Bloom's: Application

79. The balanced scorecard measures financial and nonfinancial performance of a business. The balanced scorecard measures four areas. Identify one of the following that is not included as a performance measurement.
    a. Internal Process
    b. Financial
    c. Innovation and Learning
    d. Employees

    ANS: D   PTS: 1   DIF: Easy   OBJ: LO: 24-04
    NAT: BUSPROG: Analytic   KEY: Bloom's: Knowledge

80. The following is a measure of a manager's performance working in an investment center.
    a. rate of return on investment
    b. residual income
    c. divisional income statements
    d. all of the responses

ANS: D   PTS: 1   DIF: Easy   OBJ: LO: 24-04
NAT: BUSPROG: Analytic   KEY: Bloom's: Knowledge

The Everest Company has income from operations of $80,000, invested assets of $500,000, and sales of $1,050,000.

81. What is the profit margin?
    a. 47.6%
    b. 7.6%
    c. 55.2%
    d. 4.8%

    ANS: B   PTS: 1   DIF: Easy   OBJ: LO: 24-04
    NAT: BUSPROG: Analytic   KEY: Bloom's: Application

82. What is the investment turnover?
    a. 1.8
    b. 2.1
    c. .48
    d. 13.13

    ANS: B   PTS: 1   DIF: Easy   OBJ: LO: 24-04
    NAT: BUSPROG: Analytic   KEY: Bloom's: Application

83. The balanced scorecard measures
    a. only financial information
    b. only nonfinancial information
    c. both financial and nonfinancial information
    d. external and internal information

    ANS: C   PTS: 1   DIF: Easy   OBJ: LO: 24-04
    NAT: BUSPROG: Analytic   KEY: Bloom's: Knowledge

84. Which of the following is not a commonly used approach to setting transfer prices?
    a. Market price approach
    b. Revenue price approach
    c. Negotiated price approach
    d. Cost price approach

    ANS: B   PTS: 1   DIF: Moderate   OBJ: LO: 24-05
    NAT: BUSPROG: Analytic   KEY: Bloom's: Knowledge

85. Determining the transfer price as the price at which the product or service transferred could be sold to outside buyers is known as the:
    a. Cost price approach
    b. Negotiated price approach
    c. Revenue price approach
    d. Market price approach

    ANS: D   PTS: 1   DIF: Easy   OBJ: LO: 24-05
    NAT: BUSPROG: Analytic   KEY: Bloom's: Knowledge

Materials used by Square Yard Products Inc. in producing Division 3's product are currently purchased from outside suppliers at a cost of $5 per unit. However, the same materials are available from Division 6. Division 6 has unused capacity and can produce the materials needed by Division 3 at a variable cost of $3 per unit. A transfer price of $3.20 per unit is established, and 40,000 units of material are transferred, with no reduction in Division 6's current sales.

86. How much would Division 3's income from operations increase?
    a. $150,000
    b. $50,000
    c. $32,000
    d. $72,000

    ANS: D   PTS: 1   DIF: Moderate   OBJ: LO: 24-05
    NAT: BUSPROG: Analytic   KEY: Bloom's: Application

87. How much would Division 6's income from operations increase?
    a. $8,000
    b. $15,000
    c. $80,000
    d. $150,000

    ANS: A   PTS: 1   DIF: Moderate   OBJ: LO: 24-05
    NAT: BUSPROG: Analytic   KEY: Bloom's: Application

88. How much would Square Yard Products total income from operations increase?
    a. $32,000
    b. $112,000
    c. $80,000
    d. $150,000

    ANS: C   PTS: 1   DIF: Moderate   OBJ: LO: 24-05
    NAT: BUSPROG: Analytic   KEY: Bloom's: Application

Materials used by Jefferson Company in producing Division C's product are currently purchased from outside suppliers at a cost of $10 per unit. However, the same materials are available from Division A. Division A has unused capacity and can produce the materials needed by Division C at a variable cost of $8.50 per unit. A transfer price of $9.50 per unit is negotiated and 25,000 units of material are transferred, with no reduction in Division A's current sales.

89. How much would Division C's income from operations increase?
    a. $0
    b. $75,000
    c. $12,500
    d. $50,000

    ANS: C   PTS: 1   DIF: Moderate   OBJ: LO: 24-05
    NAT: BUSPROG: Analytic   KEY: Bloom's: Application

90. How much would Division A's income from operations increase?
    a. $0
    b. $75,000
    c. $25,000
    d. $50,000

ANS: C   PTS: 1   DIF: Moderate   OBJ: LO: 24-05
NAT: BUSPROG: Analytic   KEY: Bloom's: Application

91. How much would Jefferson's total income from operations increase?
     a. $37,500
     b. $100,000
     c. $62,500
     d. $150,000

     ANS: A   PTS: 1   DIF: Moderate   OBJ: LO: 24-05
     NAT: BUSPROG: Analytic   KEY: Bloom's: Application

The Ukulele Company's radio division currently is purchasing transistors from the Xiang Co. for
$3.50 each. The total number of transistors needed is 8,000 per month. Ukulele Company's
electronics division can produce the transistors for a cost of $4.00 each and they have plenty of
capacity to manufacture the units.   The $4 is made up of $3.25 in variable costs, and $0.75 in
allocated fixed costs.

92. What should be the range of a possible transfer price?
     a. No transfer should take place.
     b. $3.51 to $3.99
     c. $3.26 to $3.99
     d. $3.26 to $3.49

     ANS: D   PTS: 1   DIF: Moderate   OBJ: LO: 24-05
     NAT: BUSPROG: Analytic   KEY: Bloom's: Application

93. Which transfer price approach is used when the transfer price is set at the amount sold to outside
     buyers?
     a. Market Price
     b. Cost Price
     c. Negotiated Price
     d. Variable Price

     ANS: A   PTS: 1   DIF: Easy   OBJ: LO: 24-05
     NAT: BUSPROG: Analytic   KEY: Bloom's: Application

94. The transfer price which uses a variety of cost concepts is the
     a. Negotiated price approach
     b. Standard cost approach
     c. Cost price approach
     d. Market price approach

     ANS: C   PTS: 1   DIF: Easy   OBJ: LO: 24-05
     NAT: BUSPROG: Analytic   KEY: Bloom's: Application

95. The transfer price that must be less than the market price but greater than the supplying division's
     variable costs per unit is called
     a. the cost price approach
     b. the negotiated cost approach
     c. the standard cost approach
     d. the market price approach

ANS: B PTS: 1   DIF: Moderate OBJ: LO: 24-05
NAT: BUSPROG: Analytic   KEY: Bloom's: Application

96. Mandolin Company has two divisions. Division A is interested in purchasing 10,000 units from Division B. Capacity is available for Division B to produce these units. The per unit market price is $30 per unit, with a variable cost of $17. The manager of Division A has offered to purchase the units at $15 per unit. In an effort to make this transfer price beneficial for the company as a whole, what is the range of prices that should be used during negotiations between the two divisions?
 a. $15 to $30
 b. $15 to $17
 c. over $30
 d. $17 to $30

ANS: D PTS: 1   DIF: Moderate OBJ: LO: 24-05
NAT: BUSPROG: Analytic   KEY: Bloom's: Application

ABC Corporation has three service departments with the following costs and activity base:

Service Department	Cost	Activity Base for Allocation
Graphics Production	$200,000	# of copies
Accounting	$500,000	# of invoices processed
Personnel Department	$400,000	# of employees

ABC has three operating divisions, Micro, Macro and Super. Their revenue, cost and activity information are as follows:

	Micro	Macro	Super
Direct Revenues	$700,000	$850,000	$650,000
Direct Operating Expenses	$ 50,000	$ 70,000	$100,000
# of copies made	20,000	30,000	50,000
# invoices processed	700	800	500
# of employees	130	145	125

97. What is the service department charge rate for Graphics Production?
 a. $2.00
 b. $10.00
 c. $6.66
 d. $.50

ANS: A PTS: 1   DIF: Moderate OBJ: LO: 24-03
NAT: BUSPROG: Analytic   KEY: Bloom's: Application

98. What is the service department charge rate for the Personnel Department?
 a. $2,758
 b. $3,200
 c. $3,077
 d. $1,000

ANS: D PTS: 1   DIF: Moderate OBJ: LO: 24-03
NAT: BUSPROG: Analytic   KEY: Bloom's: Application

99. What is the service department charge rate for the Accounting Department?
     a. $714
     b. $250
     c. $625
     d. $.004

     ANS: B   PTS: 1   DIF: Moderate   OBJ: LO: 24-03
     NAT: BUSPROG: Analytic   KEY: Bloom's: Application

100. How much service department cost will be allocated to the Micro Division?
     a. $200,000
     b. $145,000
     c. $60,000
     d. $345,000

     ANS: D   PTS: 1   DIF: Challenging   OBJ: LO: 24-03
     NAT: BUSPROG: Analytic   KEY: Bloom's: Application

101. How much service department cost would be allocated to the Macro Division?
     a. $405,000
     b. $175,000
     c. $130,000
     d. $305,000

     ANS: A   PTS: 1   DIF: Challenging   OBJ: LO: 24-03
     NAT: BUSPROG: Analytic   KEY: Bloom's: Application

102. How much service department cost would be allocated to the Super Division?
     a. $350,000
     b. $100,000
     c. $125,000
     d. $550,000

     ANS: A   PTS: 1   DIF: Challenging   OBJ: LO: 24-03
     NAT: BUSPROG: Analytic   KEY: Bloom's: Application

103. What will the income of the Micro Division be after all service department allocations?
     a. $305,000
     b. $650,000
     c. $345,000
     d. $610,000

     ANS: A   PTS: 1   DIF: Challenging   OBJ: LO: 24-03
     NAT: BUSPROG: Analytic   KEY: Bloom's: Application

104. What will the income of the Macro Division be after all service department allocations?
     a. $780,000
     b. $375,000
     c. $575,000
     d. $435,000

     ANS: B   PTS: 1   DIF: Challenging   OBJ: LO: 24-03
     NAT: BUSPROG: Analytic   KEY: Bloom's: Application

105.   What will the income of the Super Division be after all service department allocations?
       a. $300,000
       b. $325,000
       c. $550,000
       d. $200,000

ANS: D   PTS: 1   DIF: Challenging   OBJ: LO: 24-03
NAT: BUSPROG: Analytic   KEY: Bloom's: Application

OTHER

1.   Piano Company's costs were over budget by $47,000. The Piano Company is divided in two
     regions. The first region's costs were over budget by $5,000. Determine the amount that the second
     region's cost was over or under budget.

     ANS:
     $42,000 over budget

     PTS: 1   DIF: Easy   OBJ: LO: 24-03   NAT: BUSPROG: Analytic
     KEY: Bloom's: Application

2.   Using the data from the Ace Guitar Company, determine the divisional income from operations for
     the A and B regions.

	A Region	B Region	
Sales	$500,000	$900,000	
Cost of goods sold	200,000	300,000	
Selling expenses	150,000	275,000	
Service department expenses			
Purchasing			$90,000
Payroll accounting			30,000

     Allocate service department expenses proportional to the sales of each region. Round percentage of
     sales allocation to one decimal place.

     ANS:
     % of Sales Allocation:
     A Region = $500,000 / $1,400,000 = 35.7%
     B Region = $900,000 / $,1400,000 = 64.3%

     A Region = 35.7% × $120,000 = $42,840 allocation of service costs
     A Region Income = $500,000 − $200,000 − $150,000 − $42,840 = $107,160
     B Region = 64.3% × $120,000 = $77,160 allocation of service costs
     B Region Income = $900,000 − $300,000 − $275,000 − $77,160 = $247,840

     PTS: 1   DIF: Moderate   OBJ: LO: 24-03   NAT: BUSPROG: Analytic
     KEY: Bloom's: Application

3. The Bottlebrush Company has income from operations of $60,000, invested assets of $345,000, and sales of $786,000. Use the DuPont formula to calculate the rate of return on investment, and show (a) the profit margin, (b) the investment turnover, and (c) rate of return on investment. Round profit margin percentage to two decimal places and investment turnover to three decimal places.

    ANS:
    a) Profit margin = $60,000 / $786,000 = 7.63%
    b) Investment turnover = $786,000 / $345,000 = 2.278
    c) Rate of return on investment = 7.63% × 2.278 = 17.38%

    PTS: 1   DIF: Moderate   OBJ: LO: 24-04   NAT: BUSPROG: Analytic
    KEY: Bloom's: Application

4. The Magnolia Company Division A has income from operations of $80,000 and assets of $400,000. The minimum acceptable rate of return on assets is 12%. What is the residual income for the division?

    ANS:

Income from operations	$80,000
Minimum acceptable income from operations as a percent of assets:	48,000
$400,000 * 12%	
Residual income	$32,000

    PTS: 1   DIF: Easy   OBJ: LO: 24-04   NAT: BUSPROG: Analytic
    KEY: Bloom's: Application

5. The materials used by the Hibiscus Company Division A are currently purchased from outside supplier at $55 per unit. Division B is able to supply Division A with 20,000 units at a variable cost of $42 per unit. The two divisions have recently negotiated a transfer price of $48 per unit for the 20,000 units. By how much will each division's income increase as a result of this transfer?

    ANS:

Division A	
Change in sales	$ 0
Decrease in variable costs (20,000 * ($55 − $48))	140,000
Increase in income	$140,000
Division B	
Increase in sales (20,000 * $48)	$960,000
Increase in variable cost (20,000 * $42)	840,000
Increase in income	$120,000
Total increase in income for Hibiscus Company	$260,000

    PTS: 1   DIF: Moderate   OBJ: LO: 24-05   NAT: BUSPROG: Analytic
    KEY: Bloom's: Application

6. The materials used by the Holly Company Division A are currently purchased from outside supplier. Division B is able to supply Division A with 20,000 units at a variable cost of $42 per unit. The normal price that Division B normally sells its units is $53 per unit. What is the range of transfer prices that the two division managers should negotiate?

ANS:
$42 to $53 per unit.

PTS: 1   DIF: Easy   OBJ: LO: 24-05   NAT: BUSPROG: Analytic
KEY: Bloom's: Application

7. Xang Company's costs were over budget by $46,000. The Xang Company is divided in two regions. The first region's costs were over budget by $7,000.

Required:

Determine the amount that the second region's cost was over or under budget.

ANS:
$46,000 − $7,000 = $39,000 over budget

PTS: 1   DIF: Easy   OBJ: LO: 24-03   NAT: BUSPROG: Analytic
KEY: Bloom's: Application

8. Ralston Company has income from operations of $75,000, invested assets of $360,000, and sales of $790,000.

Required:

Use the DuPont formula to calculate the rate of return on investment, and show (a) the profit margin, (b) the investment turnover, and (c) rate of return on investment.
Round profit margin percentage to two decimal places and investment turnover to three decimal places.

ANS:
a) Profit margin = $75,000 / $790,000 = 9.49%
b) Investment turnover = $790,000 / $360,000 = 2.194
c) Rate of return on investment = 9.49% × 2.194 = 20.82%

PTS: 1   DIF: Moderate   OBJ: LO: 24-04   NAT: BUSPROG: Analytic
KEY: Bloom's: Application

9. Materials used by the Layton Company Division 1 are currently purchased from outside supplier at $58 per unit. Division 2 is able to supply Division 1 with 22,000 units at a variable cost of $46 per unit. The two divisions have recently negotiated a transfer price of $50 per unit for the 20,000 units.

Required:

By how much will each division's income increase as a result of this transfer?

ANS:

Division 1	
Change in sales	$ 0
Decrease in variable costs (20,000 * ($58 − $50))	160,000
Increase in income	$ 160,000
Division 2	
Increase in sales (20,000 * $50)	$1,000,000
Increase in variable cost (20,000 * $46)	920,000
Increase in income	$ 80,000
Total increase in income for Layton Company	$ 240,000

PTS: 1   DIF: Moderate   OBJ: LO: 24-05   NAT: BUSPROG: Analytic
KEY: Bloom's: Application

10.   Using the data from the Terrace Industries, determine the divisional   income from operations for
      Districts 1 & 2.

	District 1	District 2	
Sales	$300,000	$600,000	
Cost of goods sold	120,000	150,000	
Selling expenses	55,000	75,000	
Service department expenses			
Purchasing			$70,000
Payroll accounting			80,000

Allocate service department expenses proportional to the sales of each district.

ANS:
% of Sales Allocation:
District 1 = $300,000 / $900,000 = 33.3%
District 2 = $600,000 / $900,000 = 66.7%

District 1 = 33.3% × $150,000 = $50,000 allocation of service costs
District 1 Income = $300,000 − $120,000 − $55,000 − $50,000 = $75,000
District 2 = 66.7% × $150,000 = $100,000 allocation of service costs
District 2 Income = $600,000 − $150,000 − $75,000 − $100,000 = $275,000

PTS: 1   DIF: Moderate   OBJ: LO: 24-03   NAT: BUSPROG: Analytic
KEY: Bloom's: Application

11.   Franklin Industries has several divisions. The Northern Division has $350,000 of invested assets,
      income from operations of $200,000, and residual income of $158,000.   Determine the minimum
      acceptable rate of return on divisional assets.

ANS:
$200,000 − ($350,000 × X%) = $158,000

X = 12%

PTS: 1   DIF: Easy   OBJ: LO: 24-04   NAT: BUSPROG: Analytic
KEY: Bloom's: Application

12. The Creative Division of the Barry Company reported the following results for December 2012:

Invested Assets	$1,200,000
Profit Margin	25%
Return on Investment	30%

Required: Based on this information, what were the sales?

ANS:
$1,200,000 × 30% = $360,000 / 25% = $1,440,000

PTS: 1   DIF: Moderate   OBJ: LO: 24-03   NAT: BUSPROG: Analytic
KEY: Bloom's: Application

PROBLEM

1. The budget for Department 10 of Treble Company for the current month ending March 31 is as follows:

Materials	$208,000
Factory wages	265,000
Supervisory salaries	67,800
Depreciation of plant and equipment	35,000
Power and light	22,500
Insurance and property taxes	15,500
Maintenance	9,700

During March, the costs incurred in Department 10 of Treble Company were materials, $204,000; factory wages, $285,000; supervisory salaries, $63,600; depreciation of plant and equipment, $35,000; power and light, $21,360; insurance and property taxes, $14,400; maintenance, $9,456.

(a) Prepare a budget performance report for the supervisor of Department 10 of Treble Company for the month of March.
(b) Are there any significant variances (5% or greater) of the budgeted amounts that should be examined by the supervisor?

ANS:

(a)

BUDGET PERFORMANCE REPORT
Supervisor, Department 10--Treble Company
For Month Ended March 31, 20--

	Budget	Actual	Over	Under
Materials	$208,000	$204,000		$ 4,000
Factory wages	265,000	285,000	$20,000	
Supervisory salaries	67,800	63,600		$ 4,200
Depreciation of plant and equipment	35,000	35,000	—	—
Power and light	22,500	21,360		1,140
Insurance and property taxes	15,500	14,400		1,100
Maintenance	9,700	9,456		244
	$623,500	$632,816	$20,000	$10,684

(b)   The factory wages, supervisory salaries, power and light, and insurance and property taxes
       should be examined by the supervisor.

PTS: 1   DIF: Moderate   OBJ: LO: 24-03   NAT: BUSPROG: Analytic
KEY: Bloom's: Application

2. A department store apportions payroll costs on the basis of the number of payroll checks issued.
    Accounting costs are apportioned on the basis of the number of reports. The payroll costs for the
    year were $231,000 and the accounting costs for the year totaled $75,500. The departments and the
    number of payroll checks and accounting reports for each are as follows:

	Number of Payroll Checks	Number of Reports
Department R	483	70
Department S	1,470	85
Department T	147	345

Determine the amount of (a) payroll cost and (b) accounting cost to be apportioned to each
department.

ANS:
(a)

	Total	Department R	S	T
Number of payroll checks	2,100	483	1,470	147
Percent	100%	23%	70%	7%
Payroll cost	$231,000	$53,130	$161,700	$16,170

(b)

	Total	R	S	T
Number of reports	500	70	85	345
Percent	100%	14%	17%	69%
Accounting cost	$75,500	$10,570	$12,835	$52,095

PTS: 1   DIF: Moderate   OBJ: LO: 24-03   NAT: BUSPROG: Analytic
KEY: Bloom's: Application

3. A portion of the divisional income statement for the year just ended is presented below in condensed
    form.

	Department B
Net sales	$ 250,000
Cost of goods sold	190,000
Gross profit	$ 60,000
Operating expenses	90,000
Loss from operations	$ (30,000)

The operating expenses of Department B include $50,000 for direct expenses.

It is estimated that the discontinuance of Department B would not have affected the sales of the other
departments nor have reduced the indirect expenses of the business. Assuming the accuracy of these
estimates, determine the effect (increase or decrease and amount) on the income from operations of
the business if Department B had been discontinued.

ANS:

$10,000 decrease, which is the income from operations for Department B ($250,000 net sales − $190,000 cost of goods sold − $50,000 direct expenses).

PTS: 1   DIF: Moderate   OBJ: LO: 24-03   NAT: BUSPROG: Analytic
KEY: Bloom's: Application

4. Some items are omitted from each of the following condensed divisional income statements of Demi Inc.

	Eastern Division	Western Division	Central Division
Sales	$ (1)	$420,000	$580,000
Cost of goods sold	480,000	120,000	$ (5)
Gross profit	$230,000	$ (3)	$200,000
Operating expenses	95,000	160,000	$ (6)
Income from operations	$ (2)	$ (4)	$ 75,000

(a) Determine the amount of the missing items, identifying them by number.
(b) Based on income from operations, which division is the most profitable?

ANS:
(a) (1) $710,000
     (2) $135,000
     (3) $300,000
     (4) $140,000
     (5) $380,000
     (6) $125,000

(b) Western Division

PTS: 1   DIF: Moderate   OBJ: LO: 24-03   NAT: BUSPROG: Analytic
KEY: Bloom's: Application

5. Using the data from the Coffee & Cocoa Company,
    (a) determine the divisional income from operations for the three regions by allocating the service department expenses proportional to the sales of the regions.
    (b) determine the increase or decrease in net income if C Region did not operate.

	A Region	B Region	C Region
Sales	$600,000	$900,000	$300,000
Cost of goods sold	200,000	350,000	190,000
Selling expenses	150,000	275,000	100,000
Service department expenses			
Purchasing			120,000
Payroll accounting			80,000

ANS:

(a)

	A Region	B Region	C Region	Total
Sales	$600,000	$900,000	$300,000	$1,800,000
Cost of goods sold	200,000	350,000	190,000	740,000
Selling expenses	150,000	275,000	100,000	525,000
Serv. dept. expenses	66,667	100,000	33,333	200,000
Net income	$183,333	$175,000	$(23,333)	$ 335,000

(b) $10,000 decrease

PTS: 1   DIF: Challenging   OBJ: LO: 24-03   NAT: BUSPROG: Analytic
KEY: Bloom's: Application

6.   Bentz Co. has two divisions, A and B. Invested assets and condensed income statement data for each
     division for the past year ended December 31 are as follows:

	Division A	Division B
Revenues	$190,000	$125,500
Operating expenses	112,500	92,750
Service department charges	29,500	12,625
Invested assets	225,000	99,000

(a)   Prepare condensed income statements for the past year for each division.
(b)   Using the expanded expression, determine the profit margin, investment turnover, and rate of
      return on investment for each division.

ANS:

(a)

Bentz Co.
Divisional Income Statements
For the Year Ended December 31, 20--

	Division A	Division B
Revenues	$190,000	$125,500
Operating expenses	112,500	92,750
Income from operations before service department charges	$ 77,500	$ 32,750
Service department charges	29,500	12,625
Income from operations	$ 48,000	$ 20,125

(b)   Rate of return on investment (ROI) = Profit margin × investment turnover

$$\text{ROI} = \frac{\text{Income From Operations}}{\text{Sales}} \times \frac{\text{Sales}}{\text{Invested Assets}}$$

$$\text{Division A} = \frac{\$48,000}{\$190,000} \times \frac{\$190,000}{\$225,000}$$

ROI = 25.26% × .8444
ROI = 21.3%

$$\text{Division B} = \frac{\$20{,}125}{\$125{,}500} \times \frac{\$125{,}500}{\$99{,}000}$$

ROI = 16.04% × 1.2677
ROI = 20.3%

PTS: 1   DIF: Moderate   OBJ: LO: 24-04   NAT: BUSPROG: Analytic
KEY: Bloom's: Application

7.   Data for Divisions A, B, C, D, and E are as follows:

Div.	Sales	Income from Operations	Inv. Assets	Rate of Return on Inv.	Profit Margin	Invest. Turnover
A	(1)	$35,000	$200,000	(2)	(3)	1.6
B	$455,000	(4)	$284,375	16%	(5)	(6)
C	$525,000	$73,500	(7)	(8)	(9)	1.2
D	$800,000	(10)	(11)	(12)	13.0%	2.5
E	(13)	(14)	$250,000	(15)	16.0%	2.0

(a)   Determine the missing items, identifying each by number.
(b)   Which division is most profitable in terms of income from operations?
(c)   Which division is most profitable in terms of rate of return on investment?

Round percentage values to one decimal point.

ANS:
(a)   (1) $320,000 ($200,000 × 1.6)
       (2)   17.5% ($35,000/$200,000)
       (3)   10.9% ($35,000/$320,000)
       (4) $45,500 ($284,375 × 16%)
       (5)   10% ($45,500/$455,000)
       (6)   1.6 ($455,000/$284,375)
       (7) $437,500 ($525,000/1.2)
       (8)   16.8% ($73,500/$437,500)
       (9)   14% ($73,500/$525,000)
       (10) $104,000 ($800,000 × 13.0%)
       (11) $320,000 ($800,000/2.5)
       (12) 32.5% ($104,000/$320,000)
       (13) $500,000 ($250,000 × 2.0)
       (14) $80,000 ($500,000 × 16%)
       (15) 32% (16% × 2.0)

(b)   Division D

(c)   Division D

PTS: 1   DIF: Challenging   OBJ: LO: 24-04   NAT: BUSPROG: Analytic
KEY: Bloom's: Application

8. Several items are missing from the following table of rate of return on investment and residual income. Determine the missing items, identifying each item by the appropriate letter.

Invested Assets	Income from Oper.	Rate of Return on Inv.	Min. Rate of Return	Min. Amt. of Income from Oper.	Residual Income
(a)	(b)	(c)	16%	$128,000	$10,000
$850,000	$153,000	(d)	12%	(e)	(f)
$825,000	(g)	20%	(h)	(i)	$24,000
(j)	$129,000	24%	(k)	$ 60,000	(l)

Round percentage values to one decimal point.

ANS:
(a) $800,000 ($128,000/16%)
(b) $138,000 ($128,000 + $10,000)
(c) 17.3% ($138,000/$800,000)
(d) 18% ($153,000/$850,000)
(e) $102,000 ($850,000 × 12%)
(f) $51,000 ($153,000 − $102,000)
(g) $165,000 ($825,000 × 20%)
(h) 17.1% ($141,000/$825,000)
(i) $141,000 ($165,000 − $24,000)
(j) $537,500 ($129,000/24%)
(k) 11.2% ($60,000/$537,500)
(l) $69,000 ($129,000 − $60,000)

PTS: 1   DIF: Challenging   OBJ: LO: 24-04   NAT: BUSPROG: Analytic
KEY: Bloom's: Application

9. The sales, income from operations, and invested assets for each division of Grosbeak Company are as follows:

	Sales	Income from Operations	Invested Assets
Division E	$5,000,000	$550,000	$2,400,000
Division F	4,800,000	860,000	2,500,000
Division G	7,000,000	860,000	2,900,000

(a) Using the expanded expression, determine the profit margin, investment turnover, and rate of return on investment for each division. Round profit margin percentage to two decimal places, investment turnover to four decimal places, and rate of return on investment to one decimal place.
(b) Which division is the most profitable per dollar invested?

ANS:

(a) Rate of Return on Investment:

ROI = Profit Margin × Investment Turnover

$$ROI = \frac{\text{Income from Operations}}{\text{Sales}} \times \frac{\text{Sales}}{\text{Invested Assets}}$$

Division E: $ROI = \frac{\$550,000}{\$5,000,000} \times \frac{\$5,000,000}{\$2,400,000}$

ROI = 11.00% × 2.0833

ROI = 22.9%

Division F: $ROI = \frac{\$860,000}{\$4,800,000} \times \frac{\$4,800,000}{\$2,500,000}$

ROI = 17.92% × 1.92

ROI = 34.4%

Division G: $ROI = \frac{\$860,000}{\$7,000,000} \times \frac{\$7,000,000}{\$2,900,000}$

ROI = 12.29% × 2.4138

ROI = 29.7%

(b) Divisions F is the most profitable.

PTS: 1   DIF: Moderate   OBJ: LO: 24-04   NAT: BUSPROG: Analytic
KEY: Bloom's: Application

10. The sales, income from operations, and invested assets for each division of Wren Company are as follows:

	Sales	Income from Operations	Invested Assets
Division C	$5,000,000	$630,000	$4,000,000
Division D	6,800,000	760,000	3,900,000
Division E	3,750,000	750,000	7,500,000

Management has established a minimum rate of return for invested assets of 8%.

(a) Determine the residual income for each division.

(b) Based on residual income, which of the divisions is the most profitable?

ANS:
(a) Division C: $630,000 − ($4,000,000 × 8%) = $310,000
     Division D: $760,000 − ($3,900,000 × 8%) = $448,000
     Division E: $750,000 − ($7,500,000 × 8%) = $150,000

(b) Division D

PTS: 1   DIF: Moderate   OBJ: LO: 24-04   NAT: BUSPROG: Analytic
KEY: Bloom's: Application

Chapter 24—Performance Evaluation for Decentralized Operations

11. Materials used by Best Bread Company in producing Division A's product are currently purchased from outside suppliers at a cost of $30 per unit. However, the same materials are available from Division B. Division B has unused capacity and can produce the materials needed by Division A at a variable cost of $20 per unit.

   (a) If a transfer price of $25 per unit is established and 60,000 units of material are transferred, with no reductions in Division B's current sales, how much would Best Bread Company's total income from operations increase?

   (b) Assuming transfer price of $25 per unit is established and 60,000 units of material are transferred, with no reductions in Division B's current sales, how much would the income from operations of Division A increase?

   (c) Assuming transfer price of $25 per unit is established and 60,000 units of material are transferred, with no reductions in Division B's current sales, how much would the income from operations of Division B increase?

   (d) If the negotiated price approach is used, what would be the range of acceptable transfer prices?

   ANS:
   (a) $600,000

   (b) Division A would save $5 per unit on 60,000 units or $300,000.

   (c) Division B would earn an additional $300,000 by selling 60,000 units at $5 above the variable cost.

   (d) $20 to $30

   PTS: 1   DIF: Moderate   OBJ: LO: 24-05   NAT: BUSPROG: Analytic
   KEY: Bloom's: Application

12. The sales, income from operations, and invested assets for each division of Marcus Company are as follows:

	Sales	Income from Operations	Invested Assets	Residual Income
Division X		$5,000,000 $ 645,000	$4,100,000	$235,000
Division Y		6,800,000 777,000	4,000,000	377,000
Division Z		3,750,000 760,000	7,600,000	0

   Determine the minimum rate of return for invested assets.

   ANS:
   Division X: $645,000 − ($4,100,000 × X%) = $235,000
   Division Y: $777,000 − ($4,000,000 × X%) = $377,000
   Division Z: $760,000 − ($7,600,000 × X%) = $0

   X = 10%

   PTS: 1   DIF: Moderate   OBJ: LO: 24-04   NAT: BUSPROG: Analytic
   KEY: Bloom's: Application

© 2014 Cengage Learning. All Rights Reserved. May not be scanned, copied or duplicated, or posted to a publicly accessible website, in whole or in part.

TRUE/FALSE

1. Differential revenue is the amount of income that would result from the best available alternative proposed use of cash.

   ANS: F   PTS: 1   DIF: Easy   OBJ: LO: 25-01
   NAT: BUSPROG: Analytic   KEY: Bloom's: Knowledge

2. Differential revenue is the amount of increase or decrease in revenue expected from a particular course of action as compared with an alternative.

   ANS: T   PTS: 1   DIF: Easy   OBJ: LO: 25-01
   NAT: BUSPROG: Analytic   KEY: Bloom's: Knowledge

3. If the total unit cost of manufacturing Product Y is currently $36 and the total unit cost after modifying the style is estimated to be $48, the differential cost for this situation is $48.

   ANS: F   PTS: 1   DIF: Moderate   OBJ: LO: 25-01
   NAT: BUSPROG: Analytic   KEY: Bloom's: Application

4. If the total unit cost of manufacturing Product Y is currently $36 and the total unit cost after modifying the style is estimated to be $48, the differential cost for this situation is $12.

   ANS: T   PTS: 1   DIF: Moderate   OBJ: LO: 25-01
   NAT: BUSPROG: Analytic   KEY: Bloom's: Application

Hill Co. can further process Product O to produce Product P. Product O is currently selling for $60 per pound and costs $42 per pound to produce. Product P would sell for $82 per pound and would require an additional cost of $13 per pound to produce.

5. The differential revenue of producing Product P is $82 per pound.

   ANS: F   PTS: 1   DIF: Challenging   OBJ: LO: 25-01
   NAT: BUSPROG: Analytic   KEY: Bloom's: Application

6. The differential revenue of producing Product P is $22 per pound.

   ANS: T   PTS: 1   DIF: Moderate   OBJ: LO: 25-01
   NAT: BUSPROG: Analytic   KEY: Bloom's: Application

7. The differential cost of producing Product P is $13 per pound.

   ANS: T   PTS: 1   DIF: Moderate   OBJ: LO: 25-01
   NAT: BUSPROG: Analytic   KEY: Bloom's: Application

8. The differential cost of producing Product P is $55 per pound.

    ANS: F   PTS: 1   DIF: Moderate   OBJ: LO: 25-01
    NAT: BUSPROG: Analytic   KEY: Bloom's: Application

9. Opportunity cost is the amount of increase or decrease in cost that would result from the best
    available alternative to the proposed use of cash or its equivalent.

    ANS: F   PTS: 1   DIF: Easy   OBJ: LO: 25-01
    NAT: BUSPROG: Analytic   KEY: Bloom's: Knowledge

10. Differential analysis can aid management in making decisions on a variety of alternatives, including
    whether to discontinue an unprofitable segment and whether to replace usable plant assets.

    ANS: T   PTS: 1   DIF: Moderate   OBJ: LO: 25-01
    NAT: BUSPROG: Analytic   KEY: Bloom's: Knowledge

11. A cost that will not be affected by later decisions is termed a sunk cost.

    ANS: T   PTS: 1   DIF: Easy   OBJ: LO: 25-01
    NAT: BUSPROG: Analytic   KEY: Bloom's: Knowledge

12. A cost that will not be affected by later decisions is termed an opportunity cost.

    ANS: F   PTS: 1   DIF: Easy   OBJ: LO: 25-01
    NAT: BUSPROG: Analytic   KEY: Bloom's: Knowledge

13. The amount of income that would result from an alternative use of cash is called opportunity cost.

    ANS: T   PTS: 1   DIF: Easy   OBJ: LO: 25-01
    NAT: BUSPROG: Analytic   KEY: Bloom's: Knowledge

14. Since the costs of producing an intermediate product do not change regardless of whether the
    intermediate product is sold or processed further, these costs are not considered in deciding whether
    to further process a product.

    ANS: T   PTS: 1   DIF: Moderate   OBJ: LO: 25-01
    NAT: BUSPROG: Analytic   KEY: Bloom's: Knowledge

15. The costs of initially producing an intermediate product should be considered in deciding whether to
    further process a product, even though the costs will not change, regardless of the decision.

    ANS: F   PTS: 1   DIF: Moderate   OBJ: LO: 25-01
    NAT: BUSPROG: Analytic   KEY: Bloom's: Knowledge

16. In deciding whether to accept business at a special price, the short-run price should be set high
    enough to cover all variable costs and expenses.

    ANS: T   PTS: 1   DIF: Moderate   OBJ: LO: 25-01
    NAT: BUSPROG: Analytic   KEY: Bloom's: Knowledge

17. Eliminating a product or segment may have the long-term effect of reducing fixed costs.

ANS: T   PTS: 1   DIF: Easy   OBJ: LO: 25-01
NAT: BUSPROG: Analytic   KEY: Bloom's: Knowledge

18. Make or buy options often arise when a manufacturer has excess productive capacity in the form of unused equipment, space, and labor.

ANS: T   PTS: 1   DIF: Easy   OBJ: LO: 25-01
NAT: BUSPROG: Analytic   KEY: Bloom's: Knowledge

19. In addition to the differential costs in an equipment replacement decision, the remaining useful life of the old equipment and the estimated life of the new equipment are important considerations.

ANS: T   PTS: 1   DIF: Easy   OBJ: LO: 25-01
NAT: BUSPROG: Analytic   KEY: Bloom's: Knowledge

20. Manufacturers must conform to the Robinson-Patman Act which prohibits price discrimination within the United States unless differences in prices can be justified by different costs of serving different customers.

ANS: T   PTS: 1   DIF: Easy   OBJ: LO: 25-01
NAT: BUSPROG: Analytic   KEY: Bloom's: Knowledge

21. When a company is showing a net loss, it is always best to discontinue the segment in order not to continue with losses.

ANS: F   PTS: 1   DIF: Easy   OBJ: LO: 25-01
NAT: BUSPROG: Analytic   KEY: Bloom's: Knowledge

22. Discontinuing a segment or product may not be the best choice when the segment is contributing to fixed expenses.

ANS: T   PTS: 1   DIF: Easy   OBJ: LO: 25-01
NAT: BUSPROG: Analytic   KEY: Bloom's: Knowledge

23. Make or buy decisions should be made only with related parties.

ANS: F   PTS: 1   DIF: Easy   OBJ: LO: 25-01
NAT: BUSPROG: Analytic   KEY: Bloom's: Knowledge

24. Depending on the capacity of the plant, a company may best be served by further processing some of the product and leaving the rest as is, with no further processing.

ANS: T   PTS: 1   DIF: Moderate   OBJ: LO: 25-01
NAT: BUSPROG: Analytic   KEY: Bloom's: Knowledge

25. A practical approach which is frequently used by managers when setting normal long-run prices is the cost-plus approach.

ANS: T   PTS: 1   DIF: Easy   OBJ: LO: 25-02
NAT: BUSPROG: Analytic   KEY: Bloom's: Knowledge

26. The total cost concept includes all manufacturing costs plus selling and administrative expenses in the cost amount to which the markup is added to determine product price.

   ANS: T   PTS: 1   DIF: Easy   OBJ: 25-APP
   NAT: BUSPROG: Analytic   KEY: Bloom's: Knowledge

27. The product cost concept includes all manufacturing costs plus selling and administrative expenses in the cost amount to which the markup is added to determine product price.

   ANS: F   PTS: 1   DIF: Easy   OBJ: LO: 25-02
   NAT: BUSPROG: Analytic   KEY: Bloom's: Knowledge

28. The product cost concept includes all manufacturing costs in the cost amount to which the markup is added to determine product price.

   ANS: T   PTS: 1   DIF: Easy   OBJ: LO: 25-02
   NAT: BUSPROG: Analytic   KEY: Bloom's: Knowledge

29. In using the total cost concept of applying the cost-plus approach to product pricing, selling expenses, administrative expenses, and profit are covered in the markup.

   ANS: F   PTS: 1   DIF: Easy   OBJ: 25-APP
   NAT: BUSPROG: Analytic   KEY: Bloom's: Knowledge

30. In using the product cost concept of applying the cost-plus approach to product pricing, selling expenses, administrative expenses, and profit are covered in the markup.

   ANS: T   PTS: 1   DIF: Easy   OBJ: LO: 25-02
   NAT: BUSPROG: Analytic   KEY: Bloom's: Knowledge

31. In using the variable cost concept of applying the cost-plus approach to product pricing, fixed manufacturing costs and fixed selling and administrative expenses must be covered by the markup.

   ANS: T   PTS: 1   DIF: Easy   OBJ: 25-APP
   NAT: BUSPROG: Analytic   KEY: Bloom's: Knowledge

32. In using the variable cost concept of applying the cost-plus approach to product pricing, fixed manufacturing costs and both fixed and variable selling and administrative expenses must be covered by the markup.

   ANS: F   PTS: 1   DIF: Easy   OBJ: 25-APP
   NAT: BUSPROG: Analytic   KEY: Bloom's: Knowledge

33. When estimated costs are used in applying the cost-plus approach to product pricing, the estimates should be based upon normal levels of performance.

   ANS: T   PTS: 1   DIF: Moderate   OBJ: LO: 25-02
   NAT: BUSPROG: Analytic   KEY: Bloom's: Knowledge

34. When estimated costs are used in applying the cost-plus approach to product pricing, the estimates should be based upon ideal levels of performance.

ANS: F　　PTS: 1　　　DIF: Moderate　OBJ: LO: 25-02
NAT: BUSPROG: Analytic　　KEY: Bloom's: Knowledge

35. A bottleneck begins when demand for the company's product exceeds the ability to produce the product.

ANS: T　　PTS: 1　　　DIF: Easy　OBJ: LO: 25-03
NAT: BUSPROG: Analytic　　KEY: Bloom's: Knowledge

36. A bottleneck happens when a key piece of manufacturing machinery can produce 1000 units per hour and demand for the product supports a production rate of 1200 units per hour.

ANS: T　　PTS: 1　　　DIF: Easy　OBJ: LO: 25-03
NAT: BUSPROG: Analytic　　KEY: Bloom's: Knowledge

37. When a bottleneck occurs between two products, the company must determine the contribution margin for each product and manufacture the product that has the highest contribution margin per bottleneck hour.

ANS: T　　PTS: 1　　　DIF: Moderate　OBJ: LO: 25-03
NAT: BUSPROG: Analytic　　KEY: Bloom's: Knowledge

38. The theory of constraints is a manufacturing strategy that focuses on reducing the influence of bottlenecks on a process.

ANS: T　　PTS: 1　　　DIF: Moderate　OBJ: LO: 25-03
NAT: BUSPROG: Analytic　　KEY: Bloom's: Knowledge

39. The lowest contribution margin per scarce resource is the most profitable.

ANS: F　　PTS: 1　　　DIF: Moderate　OBJ: LO: 25-03
NAT: BUSPROG: Analytic　　KEY: Bloom's: Knowledge

40. Activity-based costing provides more accurate and useful cost data than traditional systems.

ANS: T　　PTS: 1　　　DIF: Easy　OBJ: LO: 25-04
NAT: BUSPROG: Analytic　　KEY: Bloom's: Knowledge

41. Activity-based costing is determined by charging products for only the services (activities) they used during production.

ANS: T　　PTS: 1　　　DIF: Easy　OBJ: LO: 25-04
NAT: BUSPROG: Analytic　　KEY: Bloom's: Knowledge

42. Cost plus methods determine the normal selling price by estimating a cost amount per unit and adding a markup.

ANS: T　　PTS: 1　　　DIF: Easy　OBJ: 25-APP
NAT: BUSPROG: Analytic　　KEY: Bloom's: Knowledge

43. Under the total cost concept, manufacturing cost plus desired profit is included in the total cost per unit.

     ANS: F   PTS: 1   DIF: Easy   OBJ: 25-APP
     NAT: BUSPROG: Analytic   KEY: Bloom's: Knowledge

44. Under the variable cost concept, only variable costs are included in the cost amount per unit to which the markup is added.

     ANS: T   PTS: 1   DIF: Easy   OBJ: 25-APP
     NAT: BUSPROG: Analytic   KEY: Bloom's: Knowledge

45. The desired selling price for a product will be the same under both variable and total cost.

     ANS: T   PTS: 1   DIF: Moderate   OBJ: 25-APP
     NAT: BUSPROG: Analytic   KEY: Bloom's: Knowledge

MULTIPLE CHOICE

1. The amount of increase or decrease in revenue that is expected from a particular course of action as compared with an alternative is termed:
    a. manufacturing margin
    b. contribution margin
    c. differential cost
    d. differential revenue

    ANS: D   PTS: 1   DIF: Easy   OBJ: LO: 25-01
    NAT: BUSPROG: Analytic   KEY: Bloom's: Knowledge

2. The amount of increase or decrease in cost that is expected from a particular course of action as compared with an alternative is termed:
    a. period cost
    b. product cost
    c. differential cost
    d. discretionary cost

    ANS: C   PTS: 1   DIF: Easy   OBJ: LO: 25-01
    NAT: BUSPROG: Analytic   KEY: Bloom's: Knowledge

3. A cost that will not be affected by later decisions is termed a(n):
    a. period cost
    b. differential cost
    c. sunk cost
    d. replacement cost

    ANS: C   PTS: 1   DIF: Easy   OBJ: LO: 25-01
    NAT: BUSPROG: Analytic   KEY: Bloom's: Knowledge

4. The condensed income statement for a business for the past year is presented as follows:

	Product			
	F	G	H	Total
Sales	$300,000	$210,000	$340,000	$850,000
Less variable costs	180,000	190,000	220,000	590,000
Contribution margin	$120,000	$ 20,000	$120,000	$260,000
Less fixed costs	50,000	50,000	40,000	140,000
Income (loss) from oper.	$ 70,000	$(30,000)	$ 80,000	$120,000

Management is considering the discontinuance of the manufacture and sale of Product G at the beginning of the current year. The discontinuance would have no effect on the total fixed costs and expenses or on the sales of Products F and H. What is the amount of change in net income for the current year that will result from the discontinuance of Product G?
a. $20,000 increase
b. $30,000 increase
c. $20,000 decrease
d. $30,000 decrease

ANS: C   PTS: 1   DIF: Moderate   OBJ: LO: 25-01
NAT: BUSPROG: Analytic   KEY: Bloom's: Application

5. The condensed income statement for a business for the past year is as follows:

	Product	
	T	U
Sales	$660,000	$320,000
Less variable costs	540,000	220,000
Contribution margin	$120,000	$100,000
Less fixed costs	145,000	40,000
Income (loss) from operations	$(25,000)	$ 60,000

Management is considering the discontinuance of the manufacture and sale of Product T at the beginning of the current year. The discontinuance would have no effect on the total fixed costs and expenses or on the sales of Product U. What is the amount of change in net income for the current year that will result from the discontinuance of Product T?
a. $120,000 increase
b. $250,000 increase
c. $25,000 decrease
d. $120,000 decrease

ANS: D   PTS: 1   DIF: Moderate   OBJ: LO: 25-01
NAT: BUSPROG: Analytic   KEY: Bloom's: Application

6. A business is operating at 90% of capacity and is currently purchasing a part used in its manufacturing operations for $15 per unit. The unit cost for the business to make the part is $20, including fixed costs, and $12, not including fixed costs. If 30,000 units of the part are normally purchased during the year but could be manufactured using unused capacity, what would be the amount of differential cost increase or decrease from making the part rather than purchasing it?
a. $150,000 cost increase
b. $ 90,000 cost decrease

  c. $150,000 cost increase
  d. $ 90,000 cost increase

  ANS: B   PTS: 1   DIF: Moderate   OBJ: LO: 25-01
  NAT: BUSPROG: Analytic   KEY: Bloom's: Application

7. A business is operating at 70% of capacity and is currently purchasing a part used in its
    manufacturing operations for $24 per unit. The unit cost for the business to make the part is $36,
    including fixed costs, and $28, not including fixed costs. If 15,000 units of the part are normally
    purchased during the year but could be manufactured using unused capacity, what would be the
    amount of differential cost increase or decrease from making the part rather than purchasing it?
    a. $60,000 cost decrease
    b. $180,000 cost increase
    c. $60,000 cost increase
    d. $180,000 cost decrease

    ANS: C   PTS: 1   DIF: Moderate   OBJ: LO: 25-01
    NAT: BUSPROG: Analytic   KEY: Bloom's: Application

8. The amount of income that would result from an alternative use of cash is called:
    a. differential income
    b. sunk cost
    c. differential revenue
    d. opportunity cost

    ANS: D   PTS: 1   DIF: Easy   OBJ: LO: 25-01
    NAT: BUSPROG: Analytic   KEY: Bloom's: Knowledge

9. Pheasant Co. can further process Product B to produce Product C. Product B is currently selling for
    $30 per pound and costs $28 per pound to produce. Product C would sell for $60 per pound and
    would require an additional cost of $24 per pound to produce. What is the differential cost of
    producing Product C?
    a. $30 per pound
    b. $24 per pound
    c. $28 per pound
    d. $60 per pound

    ANS: B   PTS: 1   DIF: Moderate   OBJ: LO: 25-01
    NAT: BUSPROG: Analytic   KEY: Bloom's: Application

    Partridge Co. can further process Product J to produce Product D. Product J is currently selling for
    $21 per pound and costs $15.75 per pound to produce. Product D would sell for $38 per pound and
    would require an additional cost of $9.25 per pound to produce.

10. What is the differential cost of producing Product D?
    a. $6.50 per pound
    b. $9.25 per pound
    c. $17 per pound
    d. $5.25 per pound

    ANS: B   PTS: 1   DIF: Moderate   OBJ: LO: 25-01
    NAT: BUSPROG: Analytic   KEY: Bloom's: Application

11. What is the differential revenue of producing Product D?
    a. $6.75 per pound
    b. $9.25 per pound
    c. $17 per pound
    d. $5.25 per pound

    ANS: C   PTS: 1   DIF: Moderate   OBJ: LO: 25-01
    NAT: BUSPROG: Analytic   KEY: Bloom's: Knowledge

12. Quail Co. can further process Product B to produce Product C. Product B is currently selling for $60 per pound and costs $42 per pound to produce. Product C would sell for $92 per pound and would require an additional cost of $13 per pound to produce. What is the differential revenue of producing and selling Product C?
    a. $32 per pound
    b. $42 per pound
    c. $50 per pound
    d. $18 per pound

    ANS: A   PTS: 1   DIF: Moderate   OBJ: LO: 25-01
    NAT: BUSPROG: Analytic   KEY: Bloom's: Application

13. Raven Company is considering replacing equipment which originally cost $500,000 and which has $420,000 accumulated depreciation to date. A new machine will cost $790,000. What is the sunk cost in this situation?
    a. $370,000
    b. $790,000
    c. $80,000
    d. $290,000

    ANS: C   PTS: 1   DIF: Moderate   OBJ: LO: 25-01
    NAT: BUSPROG: Analytic   KEY: Bloom's: Application

14. Raptor Company is considering replacing equipment which originally cost $500,000 and which has $420,000 accumulated depreciation to date. A new machine will cost $790,000 and the old equipment can be sold for $8,000. What is the sunk cost in this situation?
    a. $72,000
    b. $80,000
    c. $88,000
    d. $290,000

    ANS: B   PTS: 1   DIF: Moderate   OBJ: LO: 25-01
    NAT: BUSPROG: Analytic   KEY: Bloom's: Application

15. A business is considering a cash outlay of $250,000 for the purchase of land, which it could lease for $35,000 per year. If alternative investments are available which yield an 18% return, the opportunity cost of the purchase of the land is:
    a. $35,000
    b. $45,000
    c. $10,000
    d. $6,300

    ANS: B   PTS: 1   DIF: Moderate   OBJ: LO: 25-01
    NAT: BUSPROG: Analytic   KEY: Bloom's: Application

16. A business is considering a cash outlay of $300,000 for the purchase of land, which it could lease for $36,000 per year. If alternative investments are available which yield an 18% return, the opportunity cost of the purchase of the land is:
    a. $54,000
    b. $36,000
    c. $18,000
    d. $72,000

    ANS: A   PTS: 1   DIF: Moderate   OBJ: LO: 25-01
    NAT: BUSPROG: Analytic   KEY: Bloom's: Application

17. A business is considering a cash outlay of $400,000 for the purchase of land, which it could lease for $40,000 per year. If alternative investments are available which yield a 21% return, the opportunity cost of the purchase of the land is:
    a. $84,000
    b. $40,000
    c. $44,000
    d. $ 8,400

    ANS: A   PTS: 1   DIF: Moderate   OBJ: LO: 25-01
    NAT: BUSPROG: Analytic   KEY: Bloom's: Application

18. A business received an offer from an exporter for 20,000 units of product at $15 per unit. The acceptance of the offer will not affect normal production or domestic sales prices. The following data are available:

Domestic unit sales price	$21
Unit manufacturing costs:	
Variable	12
Fixed	5

    What is the differential revenue from the acceptance of the offer?
    a. $300,000
    b. $420,000
    c. $120,000
    d. $240,000

    ANS: A   PTS: 1   DIF: Moderate   OBJ: LO: 25-01
    NAT: BUSPROG: Analytic   KEY: Bloom's: Application

    A business received an offer from an exporter for 10,000 units of product at $17.50 per unit. The acceptance of the offer will not affect normal production or domestic sales prices. The following data is available:

Domestic unit sales price	$20
Unit manufacturing costs:	
Variable	11
Fixed	1

19. What is the differential revenue from the acceptance of the offer?
    a. $200,000
    b. $175,000

c. $130,000
d. $140,000

ANS: B   PTS: 1   DIF: Moderate   OBJ: LO: 25-01
NAT: BUSPROG: Analytic   KEY: Bloom's: Application

20.   What is the differential cost from the acceptance of the offer?
    a. $200,000
    b. $175,000
    c. $140,000
    d. $110,000

ANS: D   PTS: 1   DIF: Moderate   OBJ: LO: 25-01
NAT: BUSPROG: Analytic   KEY: Bloom's: Application

21.   What is the amount of gain or loss from acceptance of the offer?
    a. $65,000 gain
    b. $50,000 loss
    c. $30,000 loss
    d. $20,000 loss

ANS: A   PTS: 1   DIF: Moderate   OBJ: LO: 25-01
NAT: BUSPROG: Analytic   KEY: Bloom's: Application

A business received an offer from an exporter for 30,000 units of product at $16 per unit. The acceptance of the offer will not affect normal production or domestic sales prices. The following data are available:

Domestic unit sales price	$22
Unit manufacturing costs:	
Variable	11
Fixed	6

22.   What is the differential cost from the acceptance of the offer?
    a. $120,000
    b. $330,000
    c. $300,000
    d. $510,000

ANS: B   PTS: 1   DIF: Moderate   OBJ: LO: 25-01
NAT: BUSPROG: Analytic   KEY: Bloom's: Application

23.   What is the amount of the gain or loss from acceptance of the offer?
    a. $30,000 loss
    b. $40,000 gain
    c. $150,000 gain
    d. $50,000 gain

ANS: C   PTS: 1   DIF: Moderate   OBJ: LO: 25-01
NAT: BUSPROG: Analytic   KEY: Bloom's: Application

24. Relevant revenues and costs refer to:
     a. activities that occurred in the past
     b. monies already earned and/or spent
     c. last year's net income
     d. differences between the alternatives being considered

     ANS: D   PTS: 1   DIF: Easy   OBJ: LO: 25-01
     NAT: BUSPROG: Analytic   KEY: Bloom's: Knowledge

25. Assume that Penguin Co. is considering disposing of equipment that cost $50,000 and has $40,000
     of accumulated depreciation to date. Penguin Co. can sell the equipment through a broker for
     $25,000 less 5% commission. Alternatively, Teal Co. has offered to lease the equipment for five
     years for a total of $48,750. Penguin will incur repair, insurance, and property tax expenses
     estimated at $10,000. At lease-end, the equipment is expected to have no residual value. The net
     differential income from the lease alternative is:
     a. $15,000
     b. $ 5,000
     c. $25,000
     d. $12,500

     ANS: A   PTS: 1   DIF: Moderate   OBJ: LO: 25-01
     NAT: BUSPROG: Analytic   KEY: Bloom's: Application

26. Sparrow Co. is currently operating at 80% of capacity and is currently purchasing a part used in its
     manufacturing operations for $8.00 a unit. The unit cost for Sparrow Co. to make the part is $9.00,
     which includes $.60 of fixed costs. If 4,000 units of the part are normally purchased each year but
     could be manufactured using unused capacity, what would be the amount of differential cost
     increase or decrease for making the part rather than purchasing it?
     a. $12,000 cost decrease
     b. $4,000 cost increase
     c. $20,000 cost decrease
     d. $1,600 cost increase

     ANS: D   PTS: 1   DIF: Moderate   OBJ: LO: 25-01
     NAT: BUSPROG: Analytic   KEY: Bloom's: Application

27. Heston and Burton, CPAs, currently work a five-day week. They estimate that net income for the
     firm would increase by $75,000 annually if they worked an additional day each month. The cost
     associated with the decision to continue the practice of a five-day work week is an example of:
     a. differential revenue
     b. sunk cost
     c. differential income
     d. opportunity cost

     ANS: D   PTS: 1   DIF: Moderate   OBJ: LO: 25-01
     NAT: BUSPROG: Analytic   KEY: Bloom's: Knowledge

28. Starling Co. is considering disposing of a machine with a book value of $12,500 and estimated remaining life of five years. The old machine can be sold for $1,500. A new high-speed machine can be purchased at a cost of $25,000. It will have a useful life of five years and no residual value. It is estimated that the annual variable manufacturing costs will be reduced from $26,000 to $23,500 if the new machine is purchased. The total net differential increase or decrease in cost for the new equipment for the entire five years is:
    a. decrease of $11,000
    b. decrease of $15,000
    c. increase of $11,000
    d. increase of $15,000

    ANS: C   PTS: 1   DIF: Moderate   OBJ: LO: 25-01
    NAT: BUSPROG: Analytic   KEY: Bloom's: Application

29. Nighthawk Inc. is considering disposing of a machine with a book value of $22,500 and an estimated remaining life of three years. The old machine can be sold for $6,250. A new machine with a purchase price of $68,750 is being considered as a replacement. It will have a useful life of three years and no residual value. It is estimated that the annual variable manufacturing costs will be reduced from $43,750 to $20,000 if the new machine is purchased. The net differential increase or decrease in cost for the entire three years for the new equipment is:
    a. $8,750 increase
    b. $31,250 decrease
    c. $8,750 decrease
    d. $2,925 decrease

    ANS: C   PTS: 1   DIF: Moderate   OBJ: LO: 25-01
    NAT: BUSPROG: Analytic   KEY: Bloom's: Application

Falcon Co. produces a single product. Its normal selling price is $30.00 per unit. The variable costs are $19.00 per unit. Fixed costs are $25,000 for a normal production run of 5,000 units per month. Falcon received a request for a special order that would not interfere with normal sales. The order was for 1,500 units and a special price of $20.00 per unit. Falcon Co. has the capacity to handle the special order and, for this order, a variable selling cost of $1.00 per unit would be eliminated.

30. If the order is accepted, what would be the impact on net income?
    a. decrease of $750
    b. decrease of $4,500
    c. increase of $3,000
    d. increase of $1,500

    ANS: C   PTS: 1   DIF: Moderate   OBJ: LO: 25-01
    NAT: BUSPROG: Analytic   KEY: Bloom's: Application

31. Should the special order be accepted?
    a. Cannot determine from the data given
    b. Yes
    c. No
    d. There would be no difference in accepting or rejecting the special order

    ANS: B   PTS: 1   DIF: Moderate   OBJ: LO: 25-01
    NAT: BUSPROG: Analytic   KEY: Bloom's: Application

32. Mighty Safe Fire Alarm is currently buying 50,000 motherboard from MotherBoard, Inc. at a price of $65 per board. Mighty Safe is considering making its own boards. The costs to make the board are as follows: Direct Materials $32 per unit, Direct labor $10 per unit, Variable Factory Overhead $16.00, Fixed Costs for the plant would increase by $75,000. Which option should be selected and why?
    a. Buy - $75,000 more in profits
    b. Make - $275,000 increase in profits
    c. Buy - $275,000 more in profits
    d. Make - $350,000 increase in profits

    ANS: B   PTS: 1   DIF: Moderate   OBJ: LO: 25-01
    NAT: BUSPROG: Analytic   KEY: Bloom's: Application

33. Super Security Company manufacturers home alarms. Currently it is manufacturing one of its components at a variable cost of $45 and fixed costs of $15 per unit. An outside provider of this component has offered to sell Safe Security the component for $50. Determine the best plan and calculate the savings.
    a. $5 savings per unit - Manufacture
    b. $5 savings per unit - Purchase
    c. $10 savings per unit - Manufacture
    d. $15 savings per unit - Purchase

    ANS: A   PTS: 1   DIF: Easy   OBJ: LO: 25-01
    NAT: BUSPROG: Analytic   KEY: Bloom's: Application

34. Discontinuing a product or segment is a huge decision that must be carefully analyzed. Which of the following would be a valid reason not to discontinue an operation?
    a. The losses are minimal.
    b. The variable costs are less than revenues.
    c. The variable costs are more than revenues.
    d. The allocated fixed costs are more than revenues.

    ANS: B   PTS: 1   DIF: Moderate   OBJ: LO: 25-01
    NAT: BUSPROG: Analytic   KEY: Bloom's: Knowledge

35. Which of the following would be considered a sunk cost?
    a. Purchase price of new equipment
    b. Equipment rental for the production area
    c. Net book value of equipment that has no market value
    d. Warehouse lease expense

    ANS: C   PTS: 1   DIF: Challenging   OBJ: LO: 25-01
    NAT: BUSPROG: Analytic   KEY: Bloom's: Knowledge

36. All of the following should be considered in a make or buy decision except
    a. cost savings
    b. quality issues with the supplier
    c. future growth in the plant and other production opportunities
    d. whether the supplier will make a profit that would no longer belong to the business

    ANS: D   PTS: 1   DIF: Moderate   OBJ: LO: 25-01
    NAT: BUSPROG: Analytic   KEY: Bloom's: Knowledge

37. Which of the following reasons would cause a company to reject an offer to accept business at a special price?
     a. The additional sale will not conflict with regular sales.
     b. The additional sales will increase differential income.
     c. The additional sales will not increase fixed expenses.
     d. The additional sales will increase fixed expenses.

     ANS: D   PTS: 1   DIF: Moderate   OBJ: LO: 25-01
     NAT: BUSPROG: Analytic   KEY: Bloom's: Knowledge

38. A practical approach which is frequently used by managers when setting normal long-run prices is the:
     a. cost-plus approach
     b. economic theory approach
     c. price graph approach
     d. price skimming

     ANS: A   PTS: 1   DIF: Easy   OBJ: LO: 25-02
     NAT: BUSPROG: Analytic   KEY: Bloom's: Knowledge

39. Which of the following is NOT a cost concept commonly used in applying the cost-plus approach to product pricing?
     a. Total cost concept
     b. Product cost concept
     c. Variable cost concept
     d. Fixed cost concept

     ANS: D   PTS: 1   DIF: Easy   OBJ: LO: 25-02
     NAT: BUSPROG: Analytic   KEY: Bloom's: Knowledge

40. When using the total cost concept of applying the cost-plus approach to product pricing, what is included in the markup?
     a. Total selling and administrative expenses plus desired profit
     b. Total fixed manufacturing costs, total fixed selling and administrative expenses, and desired profit
     c. Total costs plus desired profit
     d. Desired profit

     ANS: D   PTS: 1   DIF: Easy   OBJ: 25-APP
     NAT: BUSPROG: Analytic   KEY: Bloom's: Knowledge

41. When using the product cost concept of applying the cost-plus approach to product pricing, what is included in the markup?
     a. Desired profit
     b. Total fixed manufacturing costs, total fixed selling and administrative expenses, and desired profit
     c. Total costs plus desired profit
     d. Total selling and administrative expenses plus desired profit

     ANS: D   PTS: 1   DIF: Easy   OBJ: LO: 25-02
     NAT: BUSPROG: Analytic   KEY: Bloom's: Knowledge

42. When using the variable cost concept of applying the cost-plus approach to product pricing, what is included in the markup?
    a. Total costs plus desired profit
    b. Desired profit
    c. Total selling and administrative expenses plus desired profit
    d. Total fixed manufacturing costs, total fixed selling and administrative expenses, and desired profit

    ANS: D   PTS: 1   DIF: Easy   OBJ: 25-APP
    NAT: BUSPROG: Analytic   KEY: Bloom's: Knowledge

43. What cost concept used in applying the cost-plus approach to product pricing covers selling expenses, administrative expenses, and desired profit in the "markup"?
    a. Total cost concept
    b. Product cost concept
    c. Variable cost concept
    d. Sunk cost concept

    ANS: B   PTS: 1   DIF: Challenging   OBJ: LO: 25-02
    NAT: BUSPROG: Analytic   KEY: Bloom's: Knowledge

44. What cost concept used in applying the cost-plus approach to product pricing includes only desired profit in the "markup"?
    a. Product cost concept
    b. Variable cost concept
    c. Sunk cost concept
    d. Total cost concept

    ANS: D   PTS: 1   DIF: Challenging   OBJ: 25-APP
    NAT: BUSPROG: Analytic   KEY: Bloom's: Knowledge

45. What cost concept used in applying the cost-plus approach to product pricing includes only total manufacturing costs in the "cost" amount to which the markup is added?
    a. Variable cost concept
    b. Total cost concept
    c. Product cost concept
    d. Opportunity cost concept

    ANS: C   PTS: 1   DIF: Challenging   OBJ: LO: 25-02
    NAT: BUSPROG: Analytic   KEY: Bloom's: Knowledge

46. Contractors who sell to government agencies would be most likely to use which of the following cost concepts in pricing their products?
    a. Variable cost
    b. Product cost
    c. Total cost
    d. Fixed cost

    ANS: C   PTS: 1   DIF: Easy   OBJ: 25-APP
    NAT: BUSPROG: Analytic   KEY: Bloom's: Knowledge

47. The target cost approach assumes that:
    a. markup is added to total cost
    b. the selling price is set by the marketplace

c. markup is added to variable cost
d. markup is added to product cost

ANS: B   PTS: 1   DIF: Easy   OBJ: LO: 25-02
NAT: BUSPROG: Analytic   KEY: Bloom's: Knowledge

Magpie Corporation uses the total cost concept of product pricing. Below is cost information for the production and sale of 60,000 units of its sole product. Magpie desires a profit equal to a 25% rate of return on invested assets of $700,000.

Fixed factory overhead cost	$38,700
Fixed selling and administrative costs	7,500
Variable direct materials cost per unit	4.60
Variable direct labor cost per unit	1.88
Variable factory overhead cost per unit	1.13
Variable selling and administrative cost per unit	4.50

48. The dollar amount of desired profit from the production and sale of the company's product is:
a. $175,000
b. $67,200
c. $73,500
d. $96,000

ANS: A   PTS: 1   DIF: Moderate   OBJ: 25-APP
NAT: BUSPROG: Analytic   KEY: Bloom's: Application

49. The cost per unit for the production and sale of the company's product is:
a. $12.11
b. $12.88
c. $15
d. $13.50

ANS: B   PTS: 1   DIF: Moderate   OBJ: 25-APP
NAT: BUSPROG: Analytic   KEY: Bloom's: Application

50. The markup percentage on total cost for the company's product is:
a. 21.0%
b. 22.7%
c. 15.8%
d. 24.0%

ANS: B   PTS: 1   DIF: Moderate   OBJ: 25-APP
NAT: BUSPROG: Analytic   KEY: Bloom's: Application

51. The unit selling price for the company's product is:
a. $15.00
b. $13.82
c. $15.80
d. $14.76

ANS: C   PTS: 1   DIF: Moderate   OBJ: 25-APP
NAT: BUSPROG: Analytic   KEY: Bloom's: Application

Mallard Corporation uses the product cost concept of product pricing. Below is cost information for the production and sale of 45,000 units of its sole product. Mallard desires a profit equal to a 12% rate of return on invested assets of $800,000.

Fixed factory overhead cost	$82,000
Fixed selling and administrative costs	45,000
Variable direct materials cost per unit	5.50
Variable direct labor cost per unit	7.65
Variable factory overhead cost per unit	2.25
Variable selling and administrative cost per unit	.90

52. The dollar amount of desired profit from the production and sale of the company's product is:
    a. $105,840
    b. $225,000
    c. $ 96,000
    d. $220,500

    ANS: C   PTS: 1   DIF: Moderate   OBJ: LO: 25-02
    NAT: BUSPROG: Analytic   KEY: Bloom's: Application

53. The cost per unit for the production of the company's product is:
    a. $13.15
    b. $17.22
    c. $15.40
    d. $15.75

    ANS: B   PTS: 1   DIF: Moderate   OBJ: LO: 25-02
    NAT: BUSPROG: Analytic   KEY: Bloom's: Application

54. The markup percentage on product cost for the company's product is:
    a. 23.4%
    b. 10.98%
    c. 26.1%
    d. 18%

    ANS: A   PTS: 1   DIF: Moderate   OBJ: LO: 25-02
    NAT: BUSPROG: Analytic   KEY: Bloom's: Application

55. The unit selling price for the company's product is:
    a. $19.35
    b. $15.75
    c. $22.05
    d. $21.26

    ANS: D   PTS: 1   DIF: Moderate   OBJ: LO: 25-02
    NAT: BUSPROG: Analytic   KEY: Bloom's: Application

Dotterel Corporation uses the variable cost concept of product pricing. Below is cost information for the production and sale of 35,000 units of its sole product. Dotterel desires a profit equal to a 11.2% rate of return on invested assets of $350,000.

Fixed factory overhead cost	$105,000
Fixed selling and administrative costs	35,000
Variable direct materials cost per unit	4.34
Variable direct labor cost per unit	5.18
Variable factory overhead cost per unit	.98
Variable selling and administrative cost per unit	.70

56. The dollar amount of desired profit from the production and sale of the company's product is:
    a. $89,600
    b. $39,200
    c. $70,000
    d. $84,000

    ANS: B   PTS: 1   DIF: Moderate   OBJ: 25-APP
    NAT: BUSPROG: Analytic   KEY: Bloom's: Application

57. The variable cost per unit for the production and sale of the company's product is:
    a. $14.00
    b. $12.60
    c. $9.80
    d. $11.20

    ANS: D   PTS: 1   DIF: Moderate   OBJ: 25-APP
    NAT: BUSPROG: Analytic   KEY: Bloom's: Application

58. The markup percentage for the sale of the company's product is:
    a. 14%
    b. 5.6%
    c. 45.71%
    d. 11.2%

    ANS: C   PTS: 1   DIF: Moderate   OBJ: 25-APP
    NAT: BUSPROG: Analytic   KEY: Bloom's: Application

59. The unit selling price for the company's product is:
    a. $16.32
    b. $13.44
    c. $12.10
    d. $13.72

    ANS: A   PTS: 1   DIF: Moderate   OBJ: 25-APP
    NAT: BUSPROG: Analytic   KEY: Bloom's: Application

60. What pricing concept considers the price that other providers charge for the same product?
    a. Demand-based concept
    b. Total cost concept
    c. Cost-plus concept
    d. Competition-based concept

    ANS: D   PTS: 1   DIF: Easy   OBJ: LO: 25-02
    NAT: BUSPROG: Analytic   KEY: Bloom's: Knowledge

61. What pricing concept is used if all costs are considered and a fair mark-up is added to determine the selling price?
   a. Total cost concept
   b. Demand-based concept
   c. Variable cost concept
   d. Fixed cost concept

   ANS: A   PTS: 1   DIF: Easy   OBJ: 25-APP
   NAT: BUSPROG: Analytic   KEY: Bloom's: Knowledge

62. Which equation better describes Target Costing?
   a. Selling Price − Desired Profit = Target Costs
   b. Selling Price + Profit = Target Costs
   c. Target Variable Costs + Contribution Margin = Selling Price
   d. Selling Price = Profit − Target Variable Costs

   ANS: A   PTS: 1   DIF: Easy   OBJ: LO: 25-02
   NAT: BUSPROG: Analytic   KEY: Bloom's: Knowledge

The Swan Company produces their product at a total cost of $43 per unit. Of this amount $8 per unit is selling and administrative costs. The total variable cost is $30 per unit The desired profit is $20 per unit.

63. Determine the mark up percentage on product cost.
   a. 80%
   b. 46.5%
   c. 70%
   d. 110%

   ANS: A   PTS: 1   DIF: Moderate   OBJ: LO: 25-02
   NAT: BUSPROG: Analytic   KEY: Bloom's: Application

64. Determine the mark up percentage on variable cost.
   a. 100%
   b. 110%
   c. 80%
   d. 46.5%

   ANS: B   PTS: 1   DIF: Moderate   OBJ: 25-APP
   NAT: BUSPROG: Analytic   KEY: Bloom's: Application

65. Determine the mark up percentage on total cost.
   a. 100%
   b. 110%
   c. 80%
   d. 46.5%

   ANS: D   PTS: 1   DIF: Moderate   OBJ: 25-APP
   NAT: BUSPROG: Analytic   KEY: Bloom's: Application

66. Target costing is arrived at by
   a. taking the selling price and subtracting desired profit.
   b. taking the selling price and adding desired profit.

c.   taking the selling price and subtracting the budget standard cost.
d.   taking the budget standard cost and reducing it by 10%.

ANS: A   PTS: 1   DIF: Moderate   OBJ: LO: 25-02
NAT: BUSPROG: Analytic   KEY: Bloom's: Knowledge

67.   Paint Company manufactures Paint X and Paint Y and can sell all it can make of either. Based on the
      following data, assuming the number of hours is a constraint, which statement is true,?

	X	Y
Sales Price	$32	$40
Variable Cost	22	24
Hours needed to process	5	8

a.   X is more profitable than Y
b.   Y is more profitable than X
c.   Neither X nor Y is profitable.
d.   X and Y are equally profitable.

ANS: D   PTS: 1   DIF: Moderate   OBJ: LO: 25-03
NAT: BUSPROG: Analytic   KEY: Bloom's: Application

Widgeon Co. manufactures three products: Bales; Tales; and Wales. The selling prices are: $55;
$78; and $32, respectively. The variable costs for each product are: $20; $50; and $15, respectively.
Each product must go through the same processing in a machine that is limited to 2,000 hours per
month. Bales take 5 hours to process, Tales take 7 hours, and Wales take 1 hour.

68.   Which product has the highest contribution margin per machine hour?
      a.   Bales
      b.   Tales
      c.   Wales
      d.   Bales and Tales have the same

ANS: C   PTS: 1   DIF: Moderate   OBJ: LO: 25-03
NAT: BUSPROG: Analytic   KEY: Bloom's: Application

69.   What is the contribution margin per machine hour for Bales?
      a. $5
      b. $7
      c. $35
      d. $28

ANS: B   PTS: 1   DIF: Moderate   OBJ: LO: 25-03
NAT: BUSPROG: Analytic   KEY: Bloom's: Application

70.   What is the contribution margin per machine hour for Tales?
      a. $4
      b. $7
      c. $28
      d. $35

ANS: A   PTS: 1   DIF: Moderate   OBJ: LO: 25-03
NAT: BUSPROG: Analytic   KEY: Bloom's: Application

71. What is the contribution per machine hour for Wales?
    a. $35
    b. $28
    c. $17
    d. $7

    ANS: C   PTS: 1   DIF: Moderate   OBJ: LO: 25-03
    NAT: BUSPROG: Analytic   KEY: Bloom's: Application

72. Assuming that Widgeon Co. can sell all of the products they can make, what is the maximum contribution margin they can earn per month?
    a. $49,000
    b. $70,000
    c. $56,000
    d. $34,000

    ANS: D   PTS: 1   DIF: Moderate   OBJ: LO: 25-03
    NAT: BUSPROG: Analytic   KEY: Bloom's: Application

73. Assume that Widgeon produced enough product with the highest contribution margin per unit to use 1,000 hours of machine time. Product demand does not warrant any more production of that product. What is the maximum additional contribution margin that can be realized by utilizing the remaining 1,000 hours on the product with the second highest contribution margin per hour?
    a. $35,000
    b. $7,000
    c. $4,000
    d. $28,000

    ANS: B   PTS: 1   DIF: Moderate   OBJ: LO: 25-03
    NAT: BUSPROG: Analytic   KEY: Bloom's: Application

Flyer Company sells a product in a competitive marketplace. Market analysis indicates that their product would probably sell at $48 per unit. Flyer management desires a 12.5% profit margin on sales. Their current full cost per unit for the product is $44 per unit.

74. What is the target cost of the company's product?
    a. $44
    b. $42
    c. $43
    d. $40

    ANS: B   PTS: 1   DIF: Moderate   OBJ: LO: 25-02
    NAT: BUSPROG: Analytic   KEY: Bloom's: Application

75. What is the desired profit per unit?
    a. $6
    b. $8
    c. $5
    d. $4

    ANS: A   PTS: 1   DIF: Moderate   OBJ: LO: 25-02
    NAT: BUSPROG: Analytic   KEY: Bloom's: Application

76. If the company meets the new target cost number, how much will they have to cut costs per unit, if any?
   a. $1
   b. $3
   c. $2
   d. $0

   ANS: C   PTS: 1   DIF: Moderate   OBJ: LO: 25-02
   NAT: BUSPROG: Analytic   KEY: Bloom's: Application

77. If the company can not cut costs any lower than they already are what would the profit margin on sales be if they meet the market selling price?
   a. 9.3%
   b. 7.3%
   c. 10.3%
   d. 8.3%

   ANS: D   PTS: 1   DIF: Challenging   OBJ: LO: 25-02
   NAT: BUSPROG: Analytic   KEY: Bloom's: Application

Miramar Industries manufactures two products, A and B.   The manufacturing operation involves three overhead activities - production setup, material handling, and general factory activities. Miramar uses activity-based costing to allocate overhead to products.   An activity analysis of the overhead revealed the following estimated costs and activity bases for these activities:

Activity	Cost	Activity Base
Production Setup	$250,000	Number of setups
Material Handling	$150,000	Number of parts
General Overhead	$ 80,000	Number of direct labor hours

Each product's total activity in each of the three areas are as follows:

	Product A	Product B
Number of setups	100	300
Number of parts	40,000	20,000
Number of direct labor hours	8,000	12,000

78. What is the activity rate for Production Setup?
   a. $2,500 per setup
   b. $833 per setup
   c. $625 per setup
   d. $400 per setup

   ANS: C   PTS: 1   DIF: Moderate   OBJ: LO: 25-04
   NAT: BUSPROG: Analytic   KEY: Bloom's: Application

79. What is the activity rate for Material Handling?
   a. $1.50 per part
   b. $3.75 per part
   c. $7.50 per part
   d. $2.50 per part

ANS: D   PTS: 1   DIF: Moderate   OBJ: LO: 25-04
NAT: BUSPROG: Analytic   KEY: Bloom's: Application

80. What is the activity rate for General Overhead?
    a. $4.00 per direct labor hour
    b. $60.00 per direct labor hour
    c. $6.67 per direct labor hour
    d. $10.00 per direct labor hour

ANS: A   PTS: 1   DIF: Moderate   OBJ: LO: 25-04
NAT: BUSPROG: Analytic   KEY: Bloom's: Application

81. What is the total overhead allocated to Product A using activity-based costing?
    a. $194,500
    b. $162,500
    c. $32,000
    d. $224,000

ANS: A   PTS: 1   DIF: Moderate   OBJ: LO: 25-04
NAT: BUSPROG: Analytic   KEY: Bloom's: Application

82. What is the overhead allocated to Product B using activity-based costing?
    a. $135,000
    b. $175,000
    c. $292,500
    d. $285,500

ANS: D   PTS: 1   DIF: Moderate   OBJ: LO: 25-04
NAT: BUSPROG: Analytic   KEY: Bloom's: Application

83. Using the variable cost concept determine the mark-up per unit for 30,000 units using the following
    data: Variable cost per unit $15.00, total fixed costs $90,000 and desired profit $150,000.
    a. $10   c. $8
    b. $15   d. $23

ANS: C   PTS: 1   DIF: Moderate   OBJ: LO: 25-02
NAT: BUSPROG: Analytic   KEY: Bloom's: Application

84. Using the variable cost concept determine the selling price for 30,000 units using the following data:
    Variable cost per unit $15.00, total fixed costs $90,000 and desired profit $150,000.
    a. $10   c. $8
    b. $15   d. $23

ANS: D   PTS: 1   DIF: Moderate   OBJ: LO: 25-02
NAT: BUSPROG: Analytic   KEY: Bloom's: Application

OTHER

1. The Stewart Cake Factory owns a building for its operations. Stewart uses only half of the building and is considering two options for the unused space. The Candy Store would like to purchase the half of the building that is not being used for $550,000. A 7% commission would have to be paid at the time of purchase. Ice Cream Delight would like to lease the half of the building for the next 5 years at $100,000 each year. Stewart would have to continue paying $9,000 of property taxes each year and $1,000 of yearly insurance on the property, according to the proposed lease agreement.

    Determine the differential income or loss from the lease alternative.

    ANS:

Differential revenue from alternatives:		
Revenue from lease	$500,000	
Revenue from sale	550,000	
Differential loss from lease		(50,000)
Differential cost of alternatives:		
Property tax and insurance	$ 50,000	
Commission expense	38,500	
Differential cost of lease		(11,500)
Net differential loss from the lease alternative		($61,500)

    PTS: 1   DIF: Moderate   OBJ: LO: 25-01   NAT: BUSPROG: Analytic
    KEY: Bloom's: Application

2. Crane Company Division B recorded sales of $360,000, variable cost of goods sold of $315,000, variable selling expenses of $13,000, and fixed costs of $61,000, creating a loss from operations of $29,000. Determine the differential income or loss from the sales of Division B. Should this division be discontinued?

    ANS:

Differential revenue		$360,000
Differential costs:		
Variable cost of goods sold	$315,000	
Variable selling expenses	13,000	328,000
Annual differential income Division B		32,000

    Division B should not be discontinued.

    PTS: 1   DIF: Easy   OBJ: LO: 25-01   NAT: BUSPROG: Analytic
    KEY: Bloom's: Application

3. Lockrite Security Company manufacturers home alarms. Currently it is manufacturing one of its components at a total cost of $45 which includes fixed costs of $15 per unit. An outside provider of this component has offered to sell them the component for $40. Provide a differential analysis of the outside purchase proposal.

ANS:

Differential cost to purchase:	
Purchase price of the component	$ 40
Differential cost to manufacture:	
Variable manufacturing costs ($45 − $15)	30
Cost savings from continuing to make the component	$ 10

PTS: 1   DIF: Easy   OBJ: LO: 25-01   NAT: BUSPROG: Analytic
KEY: Bloom's: Application

4. An oven with a book value of $67,000 has an estimated 5 year life. A proposal is offered to sell the oven for $8,500 and replace it with a new oven costing $110,000. The new machine has a five year life with no residual value. The new machine would reduce annual maintenance costs by $23,000. Provide a differential analysis on the proposal to replace the machine.

ANS:

Annual maintenance cost reduction	$ 23,000	
Number of years applicable	× 5	
Total differential decrease in cost	$ 115,000	
Proceeds from sale of equipment	8,500	$ 123,500
Cost of new equipment		110,000
Net differential decrease in cost from replacing equipment		$ 13,500

PTS: 1   DIF: Moderate   OBJ: LO: 25-01   NAT: BUSPROG: Analytic
KEY: Bloom's: Application

5. An unfinished desk is produced for $36.00 and sold for $65.00.   A finished desk can be sold for $75.00.   The additional processing cost to complete the finished desk is $5.95. Provide a differential analysis for further processing.

ANS:

Differential revenue from further processing:		
Revenue per unfinished desk	$ 65.00	
Revenue per finished desk	75.00	
Differential revenue		$ 10.00
Differential cost per desk:		
Additional cost for producing		5.95
Differential income from further processing		$ 4.05

PTS: 1   DIF: Easy   OBJ: LO: 25-01   NAT: BUSPROG: Analytic
KEY: Bloom's: Application

6. Rachel Cake Factory normally sells their specialty cake for $22. An offer to buy 100 cakes for $19 per cake was made by an organization hosting a national event in the city. The variable cost per cake is $11. A special decoration per cake will add another $1 to the cost. Determine the differential income or loss per cake from selling the cakes.

ANS:

Differential revenue:		
Revenue per cake		$ 19
Differential cost:		
Variable manufacturing costs	$ 11	
Additional decoration	1	12
Differential income from accepting special order		$ 7

PTS: 1   DIF: Easy   OBJ: LO: 25-01   NAT: BUSPROG: Analytic
KEY: Bloom's: Application

7. The Owl Company produces and sells Product X at a total cost of $35 per unit, of which $28 is
    product cost and $7 is selling and administrative expenses. In addition, the total cost of $35 is made
    up of $24 variable cost and $11 fixed cost.   The desired profit is $6 per unit. Determine the mark up
    percentage on product cost.

    ANS:
    Mark up percentage: ($6 + $7) / $28 = 46.4%

    PTS: 1   DIF: Easy   OBJ: LO: 25-02   NAT: BUSPROG: Analytic
    KEY: Bloom's: Application

8. Ptarmigan Company produces two products. Product A has a contribution margin of $20 and
    requires 4 machine hours. Product B has a contribution margin of $18 and requires 3 machine hours.
    Determine the most profitable product assuming the machine hours are the constraint.

    ANS:

	Product A	Product B
Contribution margin per unit	$20	$18
Machine hours	4	3
Contribution margin per bottleneck hour	$ 5	$ 6
Product B is the most profitable.		

    PTS: 1   DIF: Easy   OBJ: LO: 25-03   NAT: BUSPROG: Analytic
    KEY: Bloom's: Application

9. The Turtle Company has total estimated factory overhead for the year of $1,200,000, divided into
    four activities: Fabrication, $600,000; Assembly, $240,000; Setup, $200,000; and Materials
    Handling $160,000. Turtle manufactures two products: Boogie Boards and Surf Boards. The
    activity-base usage quantities for each product by each activity are as follows:

	Fabrication	Assembly	Setup	Materials Handling
Boogie Boards	10,000 dlh	30,000 dlh	60 setups	100 moves
Surf Boards	30,000	10,000	440	700
	40,000 dlh	40,000 dlh	500 setups	800 moves

    Each product is budgeted for 10,000 units of production for the year. Determine (a) the activity rates
    for each activity and (b) the factory overhead cost per unit for each product using activity-based
    costing.

ANS:

a.

Fabrication: $600,000 / 40,000 = $15 per dlh
Assembly: $240,000 / 40,000 = $6 per dlh
Setup: $200,000 / 500 setups = $400 per setup
Materials Handling: $160,000 / 800 moves = $200 per move

b.

	Boogie Board			Surf Board		
Activity	Activity-based Usage	Activity Rate	Activity Cost	Activity-Based Usage	Activity Rate	Activity Cost
Fabrication	10,000 dlh	$15/dlh	$150,000	30,000 dlh	$15/dlh	$450,000
Assembly	30,000 dlh	$6/dlh	180,000	10,000 dlh	$6/dlh	60,000
Setup	60 setups	$400/setup	24,000	440 setups	$400/setup	176,000
Materials Handling	100 moves	$200/move	20,000	700 moves	$200/move	140,000
Total			$374,000			$826,000
Budgeted Units			÷10,000			÷10,000
Factory overhead per unit			$ 37.40			$ 82.60

PTS: 1   DIF: Moderate   OBJ: LO: 25-04   NAT: BUSPROG: Analytic
KEY: Bloom's: Application

10. An employee of Morgan Corporation has found some partially completed units of Model X in a dusty corner of the warehouse. A job ticket attached to the units indicates that a total of $750 in manufacturing costs have been used to bring the materials to this point in the manufacturing process. The units can be sold in their current condition for $275 to a scrap metal dealer. If Morgan spends $250 to complete the units, they could be sold for $600.

Required:
    A. What should Morgan do? Why?
    B. Identify the sunk cost, if any.

ANS:
A. Morgan should finish the units because the incremental revenue of $325 ($600 − $275) is greater than the incremental cost of $250.

B. The $750 in manufacturing cost that has already been incurred is sunk and not relevant.

PTS: 1   DIF: Moderate   OBJ: LO: 25-01   NAT: BUSPROG: Analytic
KEY: Bloom's: Application

11. Olsen Company produces two products. Product A has a contribution margin of $30 and requires 10 machine hours. Product B has a contribution margin of $24 and requires 4 machine hours. Determine the most profitable product assuming the machine hours are the constraint.

ANS:

	Product A	Product B
Contribution margin per unit	$30	$24
Machine hours	10	4
Contribution margin per bottleneck hour	$ 3	$ 6
Product B is the most profitable.		

PTS: 1   DIF: Easy   OBJ: LO: 25-03   NAT: BUSPROG: Analytic
KEY: Bloom's: Application

12.   Jamison Company produces and sells Product X at a total cost of $25 per unit, of which $15 is product cost and $10 is selling and administrative expenses. In addition, the total cost of $25 is made up of $14 variable cost and $11 fixed cost.   The desired profit is $5 per unit. Determine the mark up percentage on total cost.

ANS:
Mark up percentage: $5 / $25 = 20%

PTS: 1   DIF: Easy   OBJ: 25-APP   NAT: BUSPROG: Analytic
KEY: Bloom's: Application

13.   The Canine Company has total estimated factory overhead for the year of $2,400,000, divided into four activities: Fabrication, $1,200,000; Assembly, $480,000; Setup, $400,000; and Materials Handling $320,000. Canine manufactures two products: Standard Crates and Deluxe Crates. The activity-base usage quantities for each product by each activity are as follows:

	Fabrication	Assembly	Setup	Materials Handling
Standard	20,000 dlh	60,000 dlh	120 setups	200 moves
Deluxe	60,000	20,000	880	1,400
	80,000 dlh	80,000 dlh	1,000 setups	1,600 moves

Each product is budgeted for 20,000 units of production for the year. Determine (a) the activity rates for each activity and (b) the factory overhead cost per unit for each product using activity-based costing.

ANS:
a.
Fabrication: $1,200,000 / 80,000 = $15 per dlh
Assembly: $480,000 / 80,000 = $6 per dlh
Setup: $400,000 / 1,000 setups = $400 per setup
Materials Handling: $320,000 / 1,600 moves = $200 per move

b.

	Standard			Deluxe		
Activity	Activity-based Usage	Activity Rate	Activity Cost	Activity-Based Usage	Activity Rate	Activity Cost
Fabrication	20,000 dlh	$15/dlh	$300,000	60,000 dlh	$15/dlh	$ 900,000
Assembly	60,000 dlh	$6/dlh	360,000	20,000 dlh	$6/dlh	120,000
Setup	120 setups	$400/setup	48,000	880 setups	$400/setup	352,000
Materials Handling	200 moves	$200/move	40,000	1,400 moves	$200/move	280,000
Total			$748,000			$1,652,000
Budgeted Units			÷20,000			20,000
Factory overhead per unit			$ 37.40			$ 82.60

PTS: 1   DIF: Moderate   OBJ: LO: 25-04   NAT: BUSPROG: Analytic
KEY: Bloom's: Application

14. Finch, Inc. has bought a new server and is having to decide what to do with the old one. The cost of the old server was originally $60,000 and has been depreciated $45,000. The company has received two offers that it must consider. One offer was made to purchase the equipment outright for $18,500 less a 5% sales commission. The other offer was to lease the equipment for $7,000 for the next five years but the company will be required to provide maintenance and insurance totaling $3,000 per year. What offer should Finch, Inc. accept?

ANS:
Differential Revenue:

Revenue from lease ($7,000 × 5 years)		$ 35,000
Revenue from sale		18,500
Differential revenue from lease		$ 16,500

Differential Costs

Maintenance and Insurance ($3000 × 5)	$15,000	
Commission Expense on Sale ($18,500 × 5%)	925	$ 14,075
Net differential income from the lease alternative		$ 2,425

PTS: 1   DIF: Moderate   OBJ: LO: 25-01   NAT: BUSPROG: Analytic
KEY: Bloom's: Application

15. Gull Corp. is considering selling its old popcorn machine and replacing it with a newer one. The old machine has a book value of $5,000 and its remaining useful life is 5 years. Annual costs are $4,000. A high school is willing to buy it for $2,000. New equipment would cost $18,000 and annual operating costs would be $1,500. The new machine has an estimated useful life of 5 years. Should the machine be replaced? Support your answer with calculations.

ANS:
The machine should not be replaced:

Proposal to Replace Equipment

Annual variable costs - present equipment	$ 4,000	
Annual variable costs - new equipment	1,500	
Annual differential decrease in cost	$ 2,500	
Number of years applicable	×5	
Total differential decrease in cost	$12,500	
Proceeds from sales of present equipment	2,000	$ 14,500
Cost of New Equipment		18,000
Annual net differential increase in cost - new equipment		($ 3,500)

PTS: 1   DIF: Moderate   OBJ: LO: 25-01   NAT: BUSPROG: Analytic
KEY: Bloom's: Application

16. Lark Art Company sells unfinished wooden decorations at a price of $15.00. The current profit margin is $5.00 per decoration. The company is considering taking individual orders and customizing them for sale. To finish the decoration the company would have to pay additional labor of $3.00, additional materials costing an average of $4.00 per unit and fixed costs would increase by $1,500. If the company estimates that it can sell 600 units for $25.00 each month, should they start taking the orders?

ANS:

Proposal to Process Decorations Further

Differential revenue:		
Revenue for finished decorations (600 units × $25.00)		$15,000
Revenue for unfinished decorations (600 units × $15.00)		9,000
Differential Revenue		$ 6,000
Differential cost:		
Direct Labor (600 units × $3.00)	$1,800	
Direct Materials (600 × $4.00)	2,400	
Additional Fixed Costs	1,500	$ 5,700
Differential income from further processing		$ 300

Yes, the company should take additional orders.

PTS: 1   DIF: Moderate   OBJ: LO: 25-01   NAT: BUSPROG: Analytic
KEY: Bloom's: Application

17. Using the variable cost concept determine the selling price for 30,000 units using the following data: Variable cost per unit $15.00, total fixed costs $90,000 and desired profit $150,000.

ANS:
Markup percentage = Desired profit + Total fixed costs
                              Total Variable Costs

MP = $150,000 + $90,000   = 53.3 %
                  $450,000

Mark-up $15.00 × 53.3%= $8.00
Selling Price = $15.00 + $8.00 =$23.00

PTS: 1   DIF: Moderate   OBJ: 25-APP   NAT: BUSPROG: Analytic
KEY: Bloom's: Application

18. Airflow Company sells a product in a competitive marketplace.   Market analysis indicates that their
     product would probably sell at $28.00 per unit.   Airflow management desires a profit equal to a
     20% rate of return on invested assets of $1,400,000.   They anticipate selling 50,000 units.   Their
     current full cost per unit for the product is $25 per unit.

     (1) What is the amount of profit per unit?

     (2) What is the target cost per unit if they meet the market dictated price and management's desired
     profit?

     ANS:
     (1) $28.00 − $25.00 = $3.00

     (2) $1,400,000 × 20% = $280,000/50,000 = $5.60 per unit.
         $28.00 − $5.60 = $22.40 per unit

     PTS: 1   DIF: Moderate   OBJ: LO: 25-02   NAT: BUSPROG: Analytic
     KEY: Bloom's: Application

MATCHING

Match each of the following terms with the best definition given.
a.   Demand-based concept
b.   Competition-based concept
c.   Product cost concept
d.   Target costing
e.   Production bottleneck

1.   Constraint
2.   Combines market-based pricing with a cost reduction emphasis
3.   Only costs of manufacturing are included in product cost per unit
4.   Sets the price according to competitors
5.   Sets the price according to demand

1.   ANS: E   PTS: 1   DIF: Easy   OBJ: LO: 25-03
     NAT: BUSPROG: Analytic   KEY: Bloom's: Knowledge
2.   ANS: D   PTS: 1   DIF: Easy   OBJ: LO: 25-02
     NAT: BUSPROG: Analytic   KEY: Bloom's: Knowledge
3.   ANS: C   PTS: 1   DIF: Easy   OBJ: LO: 25-02
     NAT: BUSPROG: Analytic   KEY: Bloom's: Knowledge
4.   ANS: B   PTS: 1   DIF: Easy   OBJ: LO: 25-02
     NAT: BUSPROG: Analytic   KEY: Bloom's: Knowledge
5.   ANS: A   PTS: 1   DIF: Easy   OBJ: LO: 25-02
     NAT: BUSPROG: Analytic   KEY: Bloom's: Knowledge

Match each of the following terms with the best definition given.
a. Engineering Change Order
b. Total cost concept
c. Variable cost concept
d. Normal selling price
e. Setup

6. A document that initiates a product or process change.
7. Includes manufacturing cost plus selling and administrative expenses.
8. Changing tooling when preparing for a new product.
9. Target selling price to be achieved in the long term.
10. Variable manufacturing costs plus variable selling and administrative costs are included in cost per unit.

6. ANS: A   PTS: 1   DIF: Easy   OBJ: LO: 25-04
   NAT: BUSPROG: Analytic   KEY: Bloom's: Knowledge
7. ANS: B   PTS: 1   DIF: Easy   OBJ: 25-APP
   NAT: BUSPROG: Analytic   KEY: Bloom's: Knowledge
8. ANS: E   PTS: 1   DIF: Easy   OBJ: 25-APP
   NAT: BUSPROG: Analytic   KEY: Bloom's: Knowledge
9. ANS: D   PTS: 1   DIF: Easy   OBJ: LO: 25-02
   NAT: BUSPROG: Analytic   KEY: Bloom's: Knowledge
10. ANS: C   PTS: 1   DIF: Easy   OBJ: LO: 25-04
   NAT: BUSPROG: Analytic   KEY: Bloom's: Knowledge

Match each of the following terms with the best definition.
a. Opportunity cost
b. Sunk cost
c. Theory of constraints
d. Differential analysis
e. Product cost distortion

11. Possible result of using an inappropriate overhead allocation method.
12. Revenue forgone from an alternative use of an asset.
13. Strategy that focuses on reducing bottlenecks.
14. Not relevant to future decisions.
15. Evaluation of how income will change based on an alternative course of action.

11. ANS: E   PTS: 1   DIF: Easy   OBJ: LO: 25-04
   NAT: BUSPROG: Analytic   KEY: Bloom's: Knowledge
12. ANS: A   PTS: 1   DIF: Easy   OBJ: LO: 25-01
   NAT: BUSPROG: Analytic   KEY: Bloom's: Knowledge
13. ANS: C   PTS: 1   DIF: Easy   OBJ: LO: 25-03
   NAT: BUSPROG: Analytic   KEY: Bloom's: Knowledge
14. ANS: B   PTS: 1   DIF: Easy   OBJ: LO: 25-01
   NAT: BUSPROG: Analytic   KEY: Bloom's: Knowledge
15. ANS: D   PTS: 1   DIF: Easy   OBJ: LO: 25-01
   NAT: BUSPROG: Analytic   KEY: Bloom's: Knowledge

PROBLEM

1. Carillion Company is considering the disposal of equipment that is no longer needed for operations. The equipment originally cost $600,000 and accumulated depreciation to date totals $460,000. An offer has been received to lease the machine for its remaining useful life for a total of $310,000, after which the equipment will have no salvage value. The repair, insurance, and property tax expenses that would be incurred by Carillion Company on the machine during the period of the lease are estimated at $75,800. Alternatively, the equipment can be sold through a broker for $230,000 less a 10% commission.

    Prepare a differential analysis report, dated June 15 of the current year, on whether the equipment should be leased or sold.

    ANS:

Carillion Company
Proposal to Lease or Sell Equipment
June 15, 20--

Net Revenue from leasing:		
Revenue from lease	$310,000	
Costs associated with the lease	75,800	
Net revenue from lease		$234,200
Net Revenue from selling:		
Sales price	$230,000	
Commission expense on sale	23,000	
Net from selling		207,000
Net advantage of lease alternative		$ 27,200

PTS: 1   DIF: Moderate   OBJ: LO: 25-01   NAT: BUSPROG: Analytic
KEY: Bloom's: Application

2. Product J is one of the many products manufactured and sold by Oceanside Company. An income statement by product line for the past year indicated a net loss for Product J of $12,250. This net loss resulted from sales of $275,000, cost of goods sold of $186,500, and operating expenses of $85,750. It is estimated that 30% of the cost of goods sold represents fixed factory overhead costs and that 40% of the operating expense is fixed. If Product J is retained, the revenue, costs, and expenses are not expected to change significantly from those of the current year. Because of the large number of products manufactured, the total fixed costs and expenses are not expected to decline significantly if Product J is discontinued.

    Prepare a differential analysis report, dated February 8 of the current year, on the proposal to discontinue Product J.

ANS:

Oceanside Company
Proposal to Discontinue Product J
February 8, 20--

Differential revenue from annual sales of product:		
Revenue from sales		$275,000
Differential cost of annual sales		
of product:		
Variable cost of goods sold ($186,500 × 70%)	$130,550	
Variable operating expenses ($85,750 × 60%)	51,450	182,000
Annual differential income from		
sales of Product J		$ 93,000

PTS: 1   DIF: Moderate   OBJ: LO: 25-01   NAT: BUSPROG: Analytic
KEY: Bloom's: Application

3.   Snipe Company has been purchasing a component, Part Q, for $19.20 a unit. Snipe is currently operating at 70% of capacity and no significant increase in production is anticipated in the near future. The cost of manufacturing a unit of Part Q, determined by the absorption costing method, is estimated as follows:

Direct materials	$11.50
Direct labor	4.50
Variable factory overhead	1.12
Fixed factory overhead	3.15
Total	$20.27

Prepare a differential analysis report, dated March 12 of the current year, on the decision to make or buy Part Q.

ANS:

Snipe Company
Proposal to Manufacture Part Q
March 12, 20--

Purchase price of part		$19.20
Differential cost to manufacture part:		
Direct materials	$11.50	
Direct labor	4.50	
Variable factory overhead	1.12	17.12
Cost savings from manufacturing Part Q		$ 2.08

PTS: 1   DIF: Moderate   OBJ: LO: 25-01   NAT: BUSPROG: Analytic
KEY: Bloom's: Application

4. MZE Manufacturing Company has a normal plant capacity of 37,500 units per month. Because of an extra large quantity of inventory on hand, it expects to produce only 30,000 units in May. Monthly fixed costs and expenses are $112,500 ($3 per unit at normal plant capacity) and variable costs and expenses are $8.25 per unit. The present selling price is $13.50 per unit. The company has an opportunity to sell 7,500 additional units at $9.90 per unit to an exporter who plans to market the product under its own brand name in a foreign market. The additional business is therefore not expected to affect the regular selling price or quantity of sales of MZE Manufacturing Company.

    Prepare a differential analysis report, dated April 21 of the current year, on the proposal to sell at the special price.

    ANS:

Proposal to Sell to Exporter

April 21, 20--

Differential revenue from accepting offer:	
Revenue from sale of 7,500 additional units at $9.90	$74,250
Differential cost of accepting offer:	
Variable costs and expenses of 7,500 additional units at $8.25	61,875
Differential income from accepting offer	$12,375

    PTS: 1   DIF: Moderate   OBJ: LO: 25-01   NAT: BUSPROG: Analytic
    KEY: Bloom's: Application

5. Due to Medicare reimbursement cuts, Loving Home Care is considering shutting down its Certified Nursing Assistant (CNA) Division. Fixed costs will have to be transferred to the Nursing Division if the CNA division is discontinued.   Based on the following income statement make a recommendation to the president regarding this decision.

Loving Home Care

Condensed Income Statement

For the Year Ended December 31, 20--

	Nursing	CNA's	Total
Revenues	$3,500,000	$1,000,000	$4,500,000
Variable Costs	2,000,000	700,000	2,700,000
Fixed Costs	400,000	400,000	800,000
Net Income from operations	$1,100,000	($ 100,000)	$1,000,000

    ANS:

Proposal to Discontinue CNA's

December 31, 20--

Differential revenue from annual revenue from CNA's	$1,000,000
Differential variable costs from CNA's	700,000
Annual differential income from CNA's revenue	$ 300,000

    Keep as operating income would decrease by $300,000 if the CNA division were discontinued.

6. Holiday Decorations Unique has been approached by the community college to make special decorations for the faculty and staff. The college is willing to buy 5,000 Christmas ornaments with their own design for $6.00 each. The company normally sells its decorations for $12.00 each. A break down of their costs is as follows:

Direct Materials	$2.00
Direct Labor	.50
Variable Costs	1.50
Fixed Costs	2.50
Total Cost Per Unit	$6.50

Should Holiday Decorations Unique accept the special order made by the college? The company has enough excess capacity to make this order.

ANS:

Proposal to Sell Christmas Decorations to College

Differential Revenue from accepting offer (5,000 × $6.00)	$30,000
Differential variable costs of additional units (5,000 × $4.00)	20,000
Differential income from accepting the offer	$10,000

7. The Bitterns Company produces their product at a total cost of $89 per unit. Of this amount $14 per unit is selling and administrative costs. The total variable cost is $58 per unit. The desired profit is $25 per unit. Determine the mark up percentage on (a) total cost, (b) product cost and (c) variable cost concepts.

ANS:
(a) $25 / $89 = 28.1%

(b) ($25 + $14) / $75 = 52%

(c) ($25 + $31) / $58 = 96.6%

8. Jay Company uses the total cost concept of applying the cost-plus approach to product pricing. The costs and expenses of producing and selling 38,400 units of Product E are as follows:

Variable costs:	
Direct materials	$ 4.70
Direct labor	2.50
Factory overhead	1.90
Selling and administrative expenses	2.60
Total	$ 11.70
Fixed costs:	
Factory overhead	$80,000
Selling and administrative expenses	14,000

Jay desires a profit equal to a 14% rate of return on invested assets of $640,000.

(a)   Determine the amount of desired profit from the production and sale of Product E.
(b)   Determine the total costs and the cost amount per unit for the production and sale of 38,400 units of Product E.
(c)   Determine the markup percentage for Product E.
(d)   Determine the selling price of Product E.

ANS:
(a) $89,600 ($640,000 × 14%)

(b)   Total costs:
    Variable ($11.70 × 38,400 units) $449,280
    Fixed ($80,000 + $14,000)   94,000
    Total $543,280
    Cost amount per unit: $543,280/38,400 units $ 14.15

(c)   Markup Percentage   = $\dfrac{\text{Desired Profit}}{\text{Total Costs}}$

    Markup Percentage   = $\dfrac{\$89,600}{\$543,280}$

    Markup Percentage   =   16.5%

(d)   Cost amount per unit $14.15
    Markup ($14.15 × 16.5%)   2.33
    Selling price $16.48

PTS: 1   DIF: Challenging   OBJ: 25-APP   NAT: BUSPROG: Analytic
KEY: Bloom's: Application

9.   Hummingbird Company uses the product cost concept of applying the cost-plus approach to product pricing. The costs and expenses of producing 25,000 units of Product K are as follows:

Variable costs:
   Direct materials $2.50
   Direct labor   4.25
   Factory overhead   1.25
   Selling and administrative expenses   .50
   Total $8.50

Fixed costs:
   Factory overhead $25,000
   Selling and administrative expenses   17,000

Hummingbird desires a profit equal to a 5% rate of return on invested assets of $642,500.

(a)   Determine the amount of desired profit from the production and sale of Product K.
(b)   Determine the total manufacturing costs and the cost amount per unit for the production and sale of 25,000 units of Product K.
(c)   Determine the markup percentage for Product K.
(d)   Determine the selling price of Product K.

Round your markup percentage to one decimal place, and other intermediate calculations and final answer to two decimal places.

ANS:
(a) $32,125 ($642,500 × 5%)

(b)   Total manufacturing costs:

Variable ($8.00 × 25,000 units)	$200,000
Fixed factory overhead	25,000
Total	$225,000
Cost amount per unit: $225,000/25,000 units	$ 9.00

(c)

$$\text{Markup Percentage} = \frac{\text{Desired Profit} + \text{Total Selling and Administrative Expenses}}{\text{Total Manufacturing Costs}}$$

$$\text{Markup Percentage} = \frac{\$32,125 + \$17,000 + (\$.50 \times 25,000 \text{ units})}{\$225,000}$$

$$\text{Markup Percentage} = \frac{\$32,125 + \$17,000 + \$12,500}{\$225,000}$$

$$\text{Markup Percentage} = \frac{\$ 61,625}{\$225,000} = 27.4\%$$

(d)

Cost amount per unit	$ 9.00
Markup ($9.00 × 27.4%)	2.47
Selling price	$11.47

PTS: 1   DIF: Challenging   OBJ: LO: 25-02   NAT: BUSPROG: Analytic
KEY: Bloom's: Application

10.   Moon Company uses the variable cost concept of applying the cost-plus approach to product pricing. The costs and expenses of producing and selling 75,000 units of Product T are as follows:

Variable costs:	
Direct materials	$ 7.00
Direct labor	3.50
Factory overhead	1.50
Selling and administrative expenses	3.00
Total	$ 15.00
Fixed costs:	
Factory overhead	$45,000
Selling and administrative expenses	20,000

Moon desires a profit equal to a 18% rate of return on invested assets of $1,440,000.

(a)   Determine the amount of desired profit from the production and sale of Product T.
(b)   Determine the total variable costs for the production and sale of 75,000 units of Product T.
(c)   Determine the markup percentage for Product T.
(d)   Determine the unit selling price of Product T.

Round your markup percentage to one decimal place and other intermediate calculations and final answer to two decimal places.

ANS:
(a) $259,200 ($1,440,000 × 18%)

(b)   Total variable costs: $15.00 × 75,000 units = $1,125,000

(c)   Markup Percentage = $\dfrac{\text{Desired Profit} + \text{Total Fixed Costs}}{\text{Total Variable Costs}}$

Markup Percentage = $\dfrac{\$259,200 + \$45,000 + \$20,000}{\$1,125,000}$

Markup Percentage = $\dfrac{\$324,200}{\$1,125,000}$

Markup Percentage = 28.8%

(d)
Cost amount per unit	$15.00
Markup ($15 × 28.8%)	4.32
Selling price	$19.32

PTS: 1   DIF: Challenging   OBJ: 25-APP   NAT: BUSPROG: Analytic
KEY: Bloom's: Application

11.   Falcon Inc. manufactures Product B, incurring variable costs of $15.00 per unit and fixed costs of $70,000. Falcon desires a profit equal to a 12% rate of return on assets, $785,000 of assets are devoted to producing Product B, and 100,000 units are expected to be produced and sold.

(a)   Compute the markup percentage, using the total cost concept.
(b)   Compute the selling price of Product B.

Round your intermediate calculations and final answer to two decimal places.

ANS:
(a)   Markup Percentage = $\dfrac{\text{Desired Profit}}{\text{Total Costs}}$

Markup Percentage = $\dfrac{\$785,000 \times 12\%}{(\$15 \times 100,000) + \$70,000}$

Markup Percentage = $\dfrac{\$94,200}{\$1,570,000}$

Markup Percentage = 6%

(b) Cost amount per unit $15.70
     Markup ($15.70 × 6%)   .94
     Selling price of Product B $16.64

PTS: 1   DIF: Challenging   OBJ: 25-APP   NAT: BUSPROG: Analytic
KEY: Bloom's: Application

12. Goshawks Co. produces an automotive product and incurs total manufacturing costs of $2,600,000 in the production of 80,000 units. The company desires to earn a profit equal to a 12% rate of return on assets of $960,000. Total selling and administrative expenses are $105,000.

(a) Calculate the markup percentage, using the product cost concept.
(b) Compute the price of the automotive product.

Round your markup percentage to one decimal place, and other intermediate calculations and final answer to two decimal places.

ANS:
(a) Markup Percentage = $\dfrac{\text{Desired Profit} + \text{Total Selling and Administrative Expenses}}{\text{Total Manufacturing Costs}}$

     Markup Percentage = $\dfrac{(\$960{,}000 \times 12\%) + \$105{,}000}{\$2{,}600{,}000}$

     Markup Percentage = $\dfrac{\$220{,}200}{\$2{,}600{,}000}$

     Markup Percentage = 8.5%

(b) Manufacturing Cost amount per unit ($2,600,000 / 80,000 units) $32.50
     Markup ($32.50 × 8.5%)   2.76
     Selling price $35.26

PTS: 1   DIF: Moderate   OBJ: LO: 25-02   NAT: BUSPROG: Analytic
KEY: Bloom's: Application

13. Yakking Co. manufactures mobile cellular equipment and develops a price for the product by using the variable cost concept. Yakking incurs variable costs of $1,900,000 in the production of 100,000 units while fixed costs total $50,000. The company employs $4,725,000 of assets and wishes to earn a profit equal to a 10% rate of return on assets.

(a) Compute a markup percentage based on variable cost.
(b) Determine a selling price.

Round your markup percentage to one decimal place, and other intermediate calculations and final answer to two decimal places.

ANS:
(a)

$$\text{Markup Percentage} = \frac{\text{Desired Profit} + \text{Total Fixed Costs}}{\text{Total Variable Costs}}$$

$$\text{Markup Percentage} = \frac{\$472,500 + \$50,000}{\$1,900,000}$$

$$\text{Markup Percentage} = \frac{\$522,500}{\$1,900,000}$$

Markup Percentage = 27.5%

(b) Cost amount per unit $19.00
     Markup ($19 × 27.5%)   5.22
     Selling price $24.22

PTS: 1   DIF: Challenging   OBJ: 25-APP   NAT: BUSPROG: Analytic
KEY: Bloom's: Application

14. Sensational Soft Drinks makes three products: iced tea, soda, and lemonade. The following data are
     available:

	Iced Tea	Soda	Lemonade
Sales price per unit	$.90	$.60	$.50
Variable cost per unit	.30	.15	.10
Contribution margin per unit	$.60	$.45	$.40

Sensational is experiencing a bottleneck in one of its processes that affects each product as follows:

	Iced Tea	Soda	Lemonade
Bottleneck process hours per unit	3	3	4

(a) Using a theory of constraints (TOC) approach, rank the products in terms of profitability.
(b) What price for lemonade would equate its profitability (contribution margin per bottleneck
     hour) to that of soda?

ANS:
(a)

$$\frac{\text{Contribution Margin per Unit}}{\text{Bottleneck Hours per Unit}} = \text{CM per Bottleneck Hour}$$

Rank

(1) Iced Tea: $\frac{\$.60}{3}$ = $.20 = CM per Bottleneck Hour

(2) Soda: $\frac{\$.45}{3}$ = $.15 = CM per Bottleneck Hour

(3) Lemonade: $\frac{\$.40}{4}$ = $.10 = CM per Bottleneck Hour

(b)

| Contribution margin per bottleneck hour of soda | = | Revised Price of Lemonade (L) − Variable Cost of Lemonade |

$$\text{Contribution margin per bottleneck hour of soda} = \frac{\text{Revised Price of Lemonade (L)} - \text{Variable Cost of Lemonade}}{\text{Bottleneck Hours per Unit of Lemonade}}$$

$$\$.15 = \frac{L - \$.10}{4}$$

$$\$.60 = L - \$.10$$

$$\$.60 + \$.10 = L$$

$$\$.70 = L$$

PTS: 1 DIF: Challenging OBJ: LO: 25-03 NAT: BUSPROG: Analytic
KEY: Bloom's: Application

15. The Stewart Cake Factory sells chocolate cakes, birthday decorated cakes, and specialty cakes. The factory is experiencing a bottleneck and is trying to determine which cake is more profitable. Even though the company may have to limit the orders that it takes, they are concerned about customer service and satisfaction.
(A) Calculate the contribution margin per hour per cake.
(B) Determine which cakes the company should try to sell more of first, second, and then last.

	Chocolate Cake	Birthday Cake	Specialty Cake
Sales price	$25.00	$45.00	$30.00
Variable cost per cake	$ 5.00	$12.00	$10.00
Hours needed to bake, frost, and decorate	1 hour	2.5 hours	2 hours

ANS:
(A) Chocolate $20, Birthday $13.2, Specialty $10
(B) Chocolate, Birthday, Specialty

	Chocolate Cake	Birthday Cake	Specialty Cake
Sales price	$25.00	$45.00	$30.00
Variable cost per cake	$ 5.00	$12.00	$10.00
Contribution Margin per cake	$20.00	$33.00	$20.00
Hours needed to bake, frost, and decorate	1 hour	2.5 hours	2 hours
Contribution margin per hour per cake	$20.00	$13.20	$10.00

PTS: 1 DIF: Moderate OBJ: LO: 25-03 NAT: BUSPROG: Analytic
KEY: Bloom's: Application

TRUE/FALSE

1. The process by which management plans, evaluates, and controls long-term investment decisions involving fixed assets is called capital investment analysis.

    ANS: T   PTS: 1   DIF: Easy   OBJ: LO: 26-01
    NAT: BUSPROG: Analytic   KEY: Bloom's: Knowledge

2. The process by which management plans, evaluates, and controls long-term investment decisions involving fixed assets is called cost-volume-profit analysis.

    ANS: F   PTS: 1   DIF: Easy   OBJ: LO: 26-01
    NAT: BUSPROG: Analytic   KEY: Bloom's: Knowledge

3. Care must be taken involving capital investment decisions, since normally a long-term commitment of funds is involved and operations could be affected for many years.

    ANS: T   PTS: 1   DIF: Easy   OBJ: LO: 26-01
    NAT: BUSPROG: Analytic   KEY: Bloom's: Knowledge

4. Only managers are encouraged to submit capital investment proposals because they know the processes and are able to match investments with long-term goals.

    ANS: F   PTS: 1   DIF: Easy   OBJ: LO: 26-01
    NAT: BUSPROG: Analytic   KEY: Bloom's: Knowledge

5. The methods of evaluating capital investment proposals can be grouped into two general categories that can be referred to as (1) methods that ignore present value and (2) present values methods.

    ANS: T   PTS: 1   DIF: Easy   OBJ: LO: 26-02| LO: 26-03
    NAT: BUSPROG: Analytic   KEY: Bloom's: Knowledge

6. The methods of evaluating capital investment proposals can be grouped into two general categories that can be referred to as (1) average rate of return and (2) cash payback methods.

    ANS: F   PTS: 1   DIF: Easy   OBJ: LO: 26-02
    NAT: BUSPROG: Analytic   KEY: Bloom's: Knowledge

7. Average rate of return equals average investment divided by estimated average annual income.

    ANS: F   PTS: 1   DIF: Easy   OBJ: LO: 26-02
    NAT: BUSPROG: Analytic   KEY: Bloom's: Knowledge

8. Average rate of return equals estimated average annual income divided by average investment.

    ANS: T   PTS: 1   DIF: Easy   OBJ: LO: 26-02
    NAT: BUSPROG: Analytic   KEY: Bloom's: Knowledge

9. The method of analyzing capital investment proposals in which the estimated average annual income is divided by the average investment is the average rate of return method.

    ANS: T   PTS: 1   DIF: Easy   OBJ: LO: 26-02
    NAT: BUSPROG: Analytic   KEY: Bloom's: Knowledge

10. The excess of the cash flowing in from revenues over the cash flowing out for expenses is termed net cash flow.

    ANS: T   PTS: 1   DIF: Easy   OBJ: LO: 26-02
    NAT: BUSPROG: Analytic   KEY: Bloom's: Knowledge

11. The excess of the cash flowing in from revenues over the cash flowing out for expenses is termed net discounted cash flow.

    ANS: F   PTS: 1   DIF: Easy   OBJ: LO: 26-02
    NAT: BUSPROG: Analytic   KEY: Bloom's: Knowledge

12. The computations involved in the net present value method of analyzing capital investment proposals are less involved than those for the average rate of return method.

    ANS: F   PTS: 1   DIF: Easy   OBJ: LO: 26-03
    NAT: BUSPROG: Analytic   KEY: Bloom's: Knowledge

13. The computations involved in the net present value method of analyzing capital investment proposals are more involved than those for the average rate of return method.

    ANS: T   PTS: 1   DIF: Easy   OBJ: LO: 26-03
    NAT: BUSPROG: Analytic   KEY: Bloom's: Knowledge

14. Methods that ignore present value in capital investment analysis include the cash payback method.

    ANS: T   PTS: 1   DIF: Easy   OBJ: LO: 26-02
    NAT: BUSPROG: Analytic   KEY: Bloom's: Knowledge

15. Methods that ignore present value in capital investment analysis include the average rate of return method.

    ANS: T   PTS: 1   DIF: Easy   OBJ: LO: 26-02
    NAT: BUSPROG: Analytic   KEY: Bloom's: Knowledge

16. Methods that ignore present value in capital investment analysis include the internal rate of return method.

    ANS: F   PTS: 1   DIF: Easy   OBJ: LO: 26-03
    NAT: BUSPROG: Analytic   KEY: Bloom's: Knowledge

17. Methods that ignore present value in capital investment analysis include the net present value method.

    ANS: F   PTS: 1   DIF: Easy   OBJ: LO: 26-03
    NAT: BUSPROG: Analytic   KEY: Bloom's: Knowledge

18. The average rate of return method of capital investment analysis gives consideration to the present value of future cash flows.

ANS: F   PTS: 1   DIF: Easy   OBJ: LO: 26-02
NAT: BUSPROG: Analytic   KEY: Bloom's: Knowledge

19. The cash payback method of capital investment analysis is one of the methods referred to as a present value method.

ANS: F   PTS: 1   DIF: Easy   OBJ: LO: 26-02
NAT: BUSPROG: Analytic   KEY: Bloom's: Knowledge

20. The anticipated purchase of a fixed asset for $400,000, with a useful life of 5 years and no residual value, is expected to yield total net income of $300,000 for the 5 years. The expected average rate of return is 30%.

ANS: T   PTS: 1   DIF: Moderate   OBJ: LO: 26-02
NAT: BUSPROG: Analytic   KEY: Bloom's: Application

21. The anticipated purchase of a fixed asset for $400,000, with a useful life of 5 years and no residual value, is expected to yield total net income of $300,000 for the 5 years. The expected average rate of return is 37.5%.

ANS: F   PTS: 1   DIF: Moderate   OBJ: LO: 26-02
NAT: BUSPROG: Analytic   KEY: Bloom's: Application

22. The anticipated purchase of a fixed asset for $400,000, with a useful life of 5 years and no residual value, is expected to yield total net income of $200,000 for the 5 years. The expected average rate of return on investment is 50%.

ANS: F   PTS: 1   DIF: Moderate   OBJ: LO: 26-02
NAT: BUSPROG: Analytic   KEY: Bloom's: Application

23. The anticipated purchase of a fixed asset for $400,000, with a useful life of 5 years and no residual value, is expected to yield total net income of $200,000 for the 5 years. The expected average rate of return on investment is 25.0%.

ANS: F   PTS: 1   DIF: Moderate   OBJ: LO: 26-02
NAT: BUSPROG: Analytic   KEY: Bloom's: Application

24. In net present value analysis for a proposed capital investment, the expected future net cash flows are averaged and then reduced to their present values.

ANS: F   PTS: 1   DIF: Easy   OBJ: LO: 26-03
NAT: BUSPROG: Analytic   KEY: Bloom's: Knowledge

25. The expected period of time that will elapse between the date of a capital investment and the complete recovery in cash of the amount invested is called the discount period.

ANS: F   PTS: 1   DIF: Easy   OBJ: LO: 26-03
NAT: BUSPROG: Analytic   KEY: Bloom's: Knowledge

26. The expected period of time that will elapse between the date of a capital investment and the complete recovery in cash of the amount invested is called the cash payback period.

ANS: T   PTS: 1   DIF: Easy   OBJ: LO: 26-02
NAT: BUSPROG: Analytic   KEY: Bloom's: Knowledge

27. If a proposed expenditure of $70,000 for a fixed asset with a 4-year life has an annual expected net cash flow and net income of $32,000 and $12,000, respectively, the cash payback period is 2.5 years.

ANS: F   PTS: 1   DIF: Moderate   OBJ: LO: 26-02
NAT: BUSPROG: Analytic   KEY: Bloom's: Application

28. If a proposed expenditure of $80,000 for a fixed asset with a 4-year life has an annual expected net cash flow and net income of $32,000 and $12,000, respectively, the cash payback period is 4 years.

ANS: F   PTS: 1   DIF: Moderate   OBJ: LO: 26-02
NAT: BUSPROG: Analytic   KEY: Bloom's: Application

29. For years one through five, a proposed expenditure of $250,000 for a fixed asset with a 5-year life has expected net income of $40,000, $35,000, $25,000, $25,000, and $25,000, respectively, and net cash flows of $90,000, $85,000, $75,000, $75,000, and $75,000, respectively. The cash payback period is 3 years.

ANS: T   PTS: 1   DIF: Moderate   OBJ: LO: 26-02
NAT: BUSPROG: Analytic   KEY: Bloom's: Application

30. For years one through five, a proposed expenditure of $500,000 for a fixed asset with a 5-year life has expected net income of $40,000, $35,000, $25,000, $25,000, and $25,000, respectively, and net cash flows of $90,000, $85,000, $75,000, $75,000, and $75,000, respectively. The cash payback period is 5 years.

ANS: F   PTS: 1   DIF: Moderate   OBJ: LO: 26-02
NAT: BUSPROG: Analytic   KEY: Bloom's: Application

31. In net present value analysis for a proposed capital investment, the expected future net cash flows are reduced to their present values.

ANS: T   PTS: 1   DIF: Easy   OBJ: LO: 26-03
NAT: BUSPROG: Analytic   KEY: Bloom's: Knowledge

32. If in evaluating a proposal by use of the net present value method there is a deficiency of the present value of future cash inflows over the amount to be invested, the proposal should be rejected.

ANS: T   PTS: 1   DIF: Easy   OBJ: LO: 26-03
NAT: BUSPROG: Analytic   KEY: Bloom's: Knowledge

33. If in evaluating a proposal by use of the net present value method there is a deficiency of the present value of future cash inflows over the amount to be invested, the proposal should be accepted.

ANS: F   PTS: 1   DIF: Easy   OBJ: LO: 26-03
NAT: BUSPROG: Analytic   KEY: Bloom's: Knowledge

34. If in evaluating a proposal by use of the net present value method there is an excess of the present value of future cash inflows over the amount to be invested, the rate of return on the proposal exceeds the rate used in the analysis.

ANS: T   PTS: 1   DIF: Moderate   OBJ: LO: 26-03
NAT: BUSPROG: Analytic   KEY: Bloom's: Knowledge

35. If in evaluating a proposal by use of the net present value method there is an excess of the present value of future cash inflows over the amount to be invested, the rate of return on the proposal is less than the rate used in the analysis.

ANS: F   PTS: 1   DIF: Moderate   OBJ: LO: 26-03
NAT: BUSPROG: Analytic   KEY: Bloom's: Knowledge

36. A present value index can be used to rank competing capital investment proposals when the net present value method is used.

ANS: T   PTS: 1   DIF: Easy   OBJ: LO: 26-03
NAT: BUSPROG: Analytic   KEY: Bloom's: Knowledge

37. The internal rate of return method of analyzing capital investment proposals uses the present value concept to compute an internal rate of return expected from the proposals.

ANS: T   PTS: 1   DIF: Easy   OBJ: LO: 26-03
NAT: BUSPROG: Analytic   KEY: Bloom's: Knowledge

38. A series of equal cash flows at fixed intervals is termed an annuity.

ANS: T   PTS: 1   DIF: Easy   OBJ: LO: 26-03
NAT: BUSPROG: Analytic   KEY: Bloom's: Knowledge

39. A qualitative characteristic that may impact upon capital investment analysis is the impact of investment proposals on product quality.

ANS: T   PTS: 1   DIF: Easy   OBJ: LO: 26-04
NAT: BUSPROG: Analytic   KEY: Bloom's: Knowledge

40. A qualitative characteristic that may impact upon capital investment analysis is manufacturing flexibility.

ANS: T   PTS: 1   DIF: Easy   OBJ: LO: 26-04
NAT: BUSPROG: Analytic   KEY: Bloom's: Knowledge

41. A qualitative characteristic that may impact upon capital investment analysis is employee morale.

ANS: T   PTS: 1   DIF: Easy   OBJ: LO: 26-04
NAT: BUSPROG: Analytic   KEY: Bloom's: Knowledge

42. A qualitative characteristic that may impact upon capital investment analysis is manufacturing productivity.

ANS: T   PTS: 1   DIF: Easy   OBJ: LO: 26-04
NAT: BUSPROG: Analytic   KEY: Bloom's: Knowledge

43. A qualitative characteristic that may impact upon capital investment analysis is manufacturing control.

    ANS: T   PTS: 1   DIF: Easy   OBJ: LO: 26-04
    NAT: BUSPROG: Analytic   KEY: Bloom's: Knowledge

44. The process by which management allocates available investment funds among competing capital investment proposals is termed present value analysis.

    ANS: F   PTS: 1   DIF: Easy   OBJ: LO: 26-05
    NAT: BUSPROG: Analytic   KEY: Bloom's: Knowledge

45. The process by which management allocates available investment funds among competing capital investment proposals is termed capital rationing.

    ANS: T   PTS: 1   DIF: Easy   OBJ: LO: 26-05
    NAT: BUSPROG: Analytic   KEY: Bloom's: Knowledge

46. The payback method can be used only when net cash inflows are the same for each period.

    ANS: F   PTS: 1   DIF: Moderate   OBJ: LO: 26-02
    NAT: BUSPROG: Analytic   KEY: Bloom's: Knowledge

47. The accounting rate of return method of analyzing capital budgeting decisions measures the average rate of return from using the asset over its entire life.

    ANS: T   PTS: 1   DIF: Moderate   OBJ: LO: 26-02
    NAT: BUSPROG: Analytic   KEY: Bloom's: Knowledge

48. The accounting rate of return is a measure of profitability computed by dividing the average annual cash flows from an asset by the average amount invested in the asset.

    ANS: F   PTS: 1   DIF: Moderate   OBJ: LO: 26-02
    NAT: BUSPROG: Analytic   KEY: Bloom's: Knowledge

49. Net present value and the payback period are examples of discounted cash flow methods used in capital budgeting decisions.

    ANS: F   PTS: 1   DIF: Moderate   OBJ: LO: 26-03
    NAT: BUSPROG: Analytic   KEY: Bloom's: Knowledge

50. In calculating the net present value of an investment in equipment, the required investment and its terminal residual value should be subtracted from the present value of all future cash inflows.

    ANS: F   PTS: 1   DIF: Moderate   OBJ: LO: 26-03
    NAT: BUSPROG: Analytic   KEY: Bloom's: Knowledge

51. In calculating the present value of an investment in equipment, the present value of the terminal residual value should be added to the cash inflows.

    ANS: T   PTS: 1   DIF: Moderate   OBJ: LO: 26-03
    NAT: BUSPROG: Analytic   KEY: Bloom's: Knowledge

52. The time expected to pass before the net cash flows from an investment would return its initial cost is called the amortization period.

ANS: F   PTS: 1   DIF: Easy   OBJ: LO: 26-02
NAT: BUSPROG: Analytic   KEY: Bloom's: Knowledge

53. A company is considering purchasing a machine for $21,000. The machine will generate income from operations of $2,000; annual cash flows from the machine will be $3,500. The payback period for the new machine is 10.5 years.

ANS: F   PTS: 1   DIF: Moderate   OBJ: LO: 26-02
NAT: BUSPROG: Analytic   KEY: Bloom's: Application

54. A company is considering purchasing a machine for $21,000. The machine will generate income from operations of $2,000; annual cash flows from the machine will be $3,500. The payback period for the new machine is 6 years.

ANS: T   PTS: 1   DIF: Moderate   OBJ: LO: 26-02
NAT: BUSPROG: Analytic   KEY: Bloom's: Application

55. A company is considering the purchase of a new piece of equipment for $90,000. Predicted annual cash inflows from the investment are $36,000 (year 1), $30,000 (year 2), $18,000 (year 3), $12,000 (year 4), and $6,000 (year 5). The average income from operations over the 5-year life is $20,400. The payback period is 3.5 years.

ANS: T   PTS: 1   DIF: Moderate   OBJ: LO: 26-02
NAT: BUSPROG: Analytic   KEY: Bloom's: Application

56. A company is considering the purchase of a new machine for $48,000. Management expects that the machine can produce sales of $16,000 each year for the next 10 years. Expenses are expected to include direct materials, direct labor, and factory overhead totaling $8,000 per year plus depreciation of $4,000 per year. All revenues and expenses except depreciation are on a cash basis. The payback period for the machine is 6 years.

ANS: T   PTS: 1   DIF: Moderate   OBJ: LO: 26-02
NAT: BUSPROG: Analytic   KEY: Bloom's: Application

57. A company is considering the purchase of a new machine for $48,000. Management expects that the machine can produce sales of $16,000 each year for the next 10 years. Expenses are expected to include direct materials, direct labor, and factory overhead totaling $8,000 per year plus depreciation of $4,000 per year. All revenues and expenses except depreciation are on a cash basis. The payback period for the machine is 12 years.

ANS: F   PTS: 1   DIF: Moderate   OBJ: LO: 26-02
NAT: BUSPROG: Analytic   KEY: Bloom's: Application

58. A company is planning to purchase a machine that will cost $24,000, have a six-year life, and have no salvage value. The company expects to sell the machine's output of 3,000 units evenly throughout each year. Total income over the life of the machine is estimated to be $12,000. The machine will generate cash flows per year of $6,000. The payback period for the machine is 4 years.

ANS: T   PTS: 1   DIF: Moderate   OBJ: LO: 26-02
NAT: BUSPROG: Analytic   KEY: Bloom's: Application

59. A company is planning to purchase a machine that will cost $24,000, have a six-year life, and have no salvage value. The company expects to sell the machine's output of 3,000 units evenly throughout each year. Total income over the life of the machine is estimated to be $12,000. The machine will generate cash flows per year of $6,000. The payback period for the machine is 12 years.

ANS: F   PTS: 1   DIF: Moderate   OBJ: LO: 26-02
NAT: BUSPROG: Analytic   KEY: Bloom's: Application

60. A company is planning to purchase a machine that will cost $24,000, have a six-year life, and have no salvage value. The company expects to sell the machine's output of 3,000 units evenly throughout each year. Total income over the life of the machine is estimated to be $12,000. The machine will generate cash flows per year of $6,000. The accounting rate of return for the machine is 16.7%.

ANS: T   PTS: 1   DIF: Moderate   OBJ: LO: 26-02
NAT: BUSPROG: Analytic   KEY: Bloom's: Application

61. A company is planning to purchase a machine that will cost $24,000, have a six-year life, and have no salvage value. The company expects to sell the machine's output of 3,000 units evenly throughout each year. Total income over the life of the machine is estimated to be $12,000. The machine will generate cash flows per year of $6,000. The accounting rate of return for the machine is 50%.

ANS: F   PTS: 1   DIF: Moderate   OBJ: LO: 26-02
NAT: BUSPROG: Analytic   KEY: Bloom's: Application

MULTIPLE CHOICE

1. The process by which management plans, evaluates, and controls long-term investment decisions involving fixed assets is called:
   a. absorption cost analysis
   b. variable cost analysis
   c. capital investment analysis
   d. cost-volume-profit analysis

ANS: C   PTS: 1   DIF: Easy   OBJ: LO: 26-01
NAT: BUSPROG: Analytic   KEY: Bloom's: Knowledge

2. Decisions to install new equipment, replace old equipment, and purchase or construct a new building are examples of
   a. sales mix analysis.
   b. variable cost analysis.
   c. capital investment analysis.
   d. variable cost analysis.

ANS: C   PTS: 1   DIF: Easy   OBJ: LO: 26-01
NAT: BUSPROG: Analytic   KEY: Bloom's: Knowledge

3. Which of the following is important when evaluating long-term investments?
   a. Investments must earn a reasonable rate of return
   b. The useful life of the asset

    c.   Proposals should match long term goals.
    d.   All of the above.

ANS: D   PTS: 1   DIF: Easy   OBJ: LO: 26-01
NAT: BUSPROG: Analytic   KEY: Bloom's: Knowledge

4.   Which of the following are present value methods of analyzing capital investment proposals?
    a.   Internal rate of return and average rate of return
    b.   Average rate of return and net present value
    c.   Net present value and internal rate of return
    d.   Net present value and payback

ANS: C   PTS: 1   DIF: Easy   OBJ: LO: 26-03
NAT: BUSPROG: Analytic   KEY: Bloom's: Knowledge

5.   Which of the following is a present value method of analyzing capital investment proposals?
    a.   Average rate of return
    b.   Cash payback method
    c.   Accounting rate of return
    d.   Net present value

ANS: D   PTS: 1   DIF: Easy   OBJ: LO: 26-03
NAT: BUSPROG: Analytic   KEY: Bloom's: Knowledge

6.   By converting dollars to be received in the future into current dollars, the present value methods take into consideration that money:
    a.   has an international rate of exchange
    b.   is the language of business
    c.   is the measure of assets, liabilities, and stockholders' equity on financial statements
    d.   has a time value

ANS: D   PTS: 1   DIF: Easy   OBJ: LO: 26-03
NAT: BUSPROG: Analytic   KEY: Bloom's: Knowledge

7.   Which of the following are two methods of analyzing capital investment proposals that both ignore present value?
    a.   Internal rate of return and average rate of return
    b.   Net present value and average rate of return
    c.   Internal rate of return and net present value
    d.   Average rate of return and cash payback method

ANS: D   PTS: 1   DIF: Easy   OBJ: LO: 26-02
NAT: BUSPROG: Analytic   KEY: Bloom's: Knowledge

8.   The method of analyzing capital investment proposals that divides the estimated average annual income by the average investment is:
    a.   cash payback method
    b.   net present value method
    c.   internal rate of return method
    d.   average rate of return method

ANS: D   PTS: 1   DIF: Easy   OBJ: LO: 26-02
NAT: BUSPROG: Analytic   KEY: Bloom's: Knowledge

9. The primary advantages of the average rate of return method are its ease of computation and the fact that:
    a. it is especially useful to managers whose primary concern is liquidity
    b. there is less possibility of loss from changes in economic conditions and obsolescence when the commitment is short-term
    c. it emphasizes the amount of income earned over the life of the proposal
    d. rankings of proposals are necessary

    ANS: C   PTS: 1   DIF: Easy   OBJ: LO: 26-02
    NAT: BUSPROG: Analytic   KEY: Bloom's: Knowledge

10. The expected average rate of return for a proposed investment of $600,000 in a fixed asset, with a useful life of four years, straight-line depreciation, no residual value, and an expected total net income of $240,000 for the 4 years, is:
    a. 40%
    b. 20%
    c. 60%
    d. 24%

    ANS: B   PTS: 1   DIF: Moderate   OBJ: LO: 26-02
    NAT: BUSPROG: Analytic   KEY: Bloom's: Knowledge

11. The amount of the average investment for a proposed investment of $90,000 in a fixed asset, with a useful life of four years, straight-line depreciation, no residual value, and an expected total net income of $21,600 for the 4 years, is:
    a. $10,800
    b. $21,600
    c. $ 5,400
    d. $45,000

    ANS: D   PTS: 1   DIF: Easy   OBJ: LO: 26-02
    NAT: BUSPROG: Analytic   KEY: Bloom's: Knowledge

12. The amount of the estimated average income for a proposed investment of $90,000 in a fixed asset, giving effect to depreciation (straight-line method), with a useful life of four years, no residual value, and an expected total income yield of $21,600, is:
    a. $10,800
    b. $21,600
    c. $ 5,400
    d. $45,000

    ANS: C   PTS: 1   DIF: Easy   OBJ: LO: 26-02
    NAT: BUSPROG: Analytic   KEY: Bloom's: Knowledge

13. An anticipated purchase of equipment for $580,000, with a useful life of 8 years and no residual value, is expected to yield the following annual net incomes and net cash flows:

Year	Net Income	Net Cash Flow
1	$60,000	$110,000
2	50,000	100,000
3	50,000	100,000
4	40,000	90,000
5	40,000	90,000
6	40,000	90,000
7	40,000	90,000
8	40,000	90,000

What is the cash payback period?
a. 5 years
b. 4 years
c. 6 years
d. 3 years

ANS: C   PTS: 1   DIF: Moderate   OBJ: LO: 26-02
NAT: BUSPROG: Analytic   KEY: Bloom's: Knowledge

14. Which method for evaluating capital investment proposals reduces the expected future net cash
flows originating from the proposals to their present values and computes a net present value?
a. Net present value
b. Average rate of return
c. Internal rate of return
d. Cash payback

ANS: A   PTS: 1   DIF: Easy   OBJ: LO: 26-03
NAT: BUSPROG: Analytic   KEY: Bloom's: Knowledge

15. Which of the following can be used to place capital investment proposals involving different
amounts of investment on a comparable basis for purposes of net present value analysis?
a. Price-level index
b. Future value index
c. Rate of investment index
d. Present value index

ANS: D   PTS: 1   DIF: Easy   OBJ: LO: 26-03
NAT: BUSPROG: Analytic   KEY: Bloom's: Knowledge

16. An analysis of a proposal by the net present value method indicated that the present value of future
cash inflows exceeded the amount to be invested. Which of the following statements best describes
the results of this analysis?
a. The proposal is desirable and the rate of return expected from the proposal exceeds the
minimum rate used for the analysis.
b. The proposal is desirable and the rate of return expected from the proposal is less than the
minimum rate used for the analysis.
c. The proposal is undesirable and the rate of return expected from the proposal is less than the
minimum rate used for the analysis.
d. The proposal is undesirable and the rate of return expected from the proposal exceeds the
minimum rate used for the analysis.

ANS: A   PTS: 1   DIF: Moderate   OBJ: LO: 26-03
NAT: BUSPROG: Analytic   KEY: Bloom's: Knowledge

17. Which method of evaluating capital investment proposals uses the concept of present value to
compute a rate of return?
a. Average rate of return
b. Accounting rate of return
c. Cash payback period
d. Internal rate of return

ANS: D   PTS: 1   DIF: Easy   OBJ: LO: 26-03
NAT: BUSPROG: Analytic   KEY: Bloom's: Knowledge

18. Which of the following is a method of analyzing capital investment proposals that ignores present value?
    a. Internal rate of return
    b. Net present value
    c. Discounted cash flow
    d. Average rate of return

ANS: D   PTS: 1   DIF: Easy   OBJ: LO: 26-02
NAT: BUSPROG: Analytic   KEY: Bloom's: Knowledge

19. The methods of evaluating capital investment proposals can be separated into two general groups--present value methods and:
    a. past value methods
    b. straight-line methods
    c. reducing value methods
    d. methods that ignore present value

ANS: D   PTS: 1   DIF: Easy   OBJ: LO: 26-02
NAT: BUSPROG: Analytic   KEY: Bloom's: Knowledge

20. The rate of earnings is 10% and the cash to be received in three years is $10,000. Determine the present value amount, using the following partial table of present value of $1 at compound interest:

Year	6%	10%	12%
1	.943	.909	.893
2	.890	.826	.797
3	.840	.751	.712
4	.792	.683	.636

    a. $13,316
    b. $6,830
    c. $7,510
    d. $8,260

ANS: C   PTS: 1   DIF: Moderate   OBJ: LO: 26-03
NAT: BUSPROG: Analytic   KEY: Bloom's: Application

21. Using the following partial table of present value of $1 at compound interest, determine the present value of $20,000 to be received four years hence, with earnings at the rate of 10% a year:

Year	6%	10%	12%
1	.943	.909	.893
2	.890	.826	.797
3	.840	.751	.712
4	.792	.683	.636

    a. $13,660
    b. $12,720
    c. $15,840
    d. $10,400

ANS: A   PTS: 1   DIF: Moderate   OBJ: LO: 26-03
NAT: BUSPROG: Analytic   KEY: Bloom's: Knowledge

22. When several alternative investment proposals of the same amount are being considered, the one with the largest net present value is the most desirable. If the alternative proposals involve different amounts of investment, it is useful to prepare a relative ranking of the proposals by using a(n):
    a. average rate of return
    b. consumer price index
    c. present value index
    d. price-level index

    ANS: C PTS: 1 DIF: Easy OBJ: LO: 26-03
    NAT: BUSPROG: Analytic KEY: Bloom's: Knowledge

23. Which method of evaluating capital investment proposals uses present value concepts to compute the rate of return from the net cash flows expected from capital investment proposals?
    a. Internal rate of return
    b. Cash payback
    c. Net present value
    d. Average rate of return

    ANS: A PTS: 1 DIF: Easy OBJ: LO: 26-03
    NAT: BUSPROG: Analytic KEY: Bloom's: Knowledge

24. A series of equal cash flows at fixed intervals is termed a(n):
    a. present value index
    b. price-level index
    c. net cash flow
    d. annuity

    ANS: D PTS: 1 DIF: Easy OBJ: LO: 26-03
    NAT: BUSPROG: Analytic KEY: Bloom's: Knowledge

25. The present value index is computed using which of the following formulas?
    a. Amount to be invested/Average rate of return
    b. Total present value of net cash flow/Amount to be invested
    c. Total present value of net cash flow/Average rate of return
    d. Amount to be invested/Total present value of net cash flow

    ANS: B PTS: 1 DIF: Easy OBJ: LO: 26-03
    NAT: BUSPROG: Analytic KEY: Bloom's: Knowledge

26. Hazard Company is considering the acquisition of a machine that costs $525,000. The machine is expected to have a useful life of 6 years, a negligible residual value, an annual cash flow of $150,000, and annual operating income of $87,500. What is the estimated cash payback period for the machine?
    a. 3 years
    b. 4.3 years
    c. 3.5 years
    d. 5 years

    ANS: C PTS: 1 DIF: Easy OBJ: LO: 26-02
    NAT: BUSPROG: Analytic KEY: Bloom's: Application

27. The expected average rate of return for a proposed investment of $8,000,000 in a fixed asset, using straight line depreciation, with a useful life of 20 years, no residual value, and an expected total net income of $12,000,000 is:
    a. 15%
    b. 12%
    c. 40%
    d. 7.5%

    ANS: A   PTS: 1   DIF: Moderate   OBJ: LO: 26-02
    NAT: BUSPROG: Analytic   KEY: Bloom's: Application

28. The present value factor for an annuity of $1 is determined using which of the following formulas?
    a. Amount to be invested/Annual average net income
    b. Annual net cash flow/Amount to be invested
    c. Annual average net income/Amount to be invested
    d. Amount to be invested/Equal annual net cash flows

    ANS: D   PTS: 1   DIF: Easy   OBJ: LO: 26-03
    NAT: BUSPROG: Analytic   KEY: Bloom's: Knowledge

The management of Nebraska Corporation is considering the purchase of a new machine costing $490,000. The company's desired rate of return is 10%. The present value factors for $1 at compound interest of 10% for 1 through 5 years are 0.909, 0.826, 0.751, 0.683, and 0.621, respectively. In addition to the foregoing information, use the following data in determining the acceptability in this situation:

Year	Income from Operations	Net Cash Flow
1	$100,000	$180,000
2	40,000	120,000
3	40,000	100,000
4	10,000	90,000
5	10,000	120,000

29. The cash payback period for this investment is:
    a. 5 years
    b. 4 years
    c. 2 years
    d. 3 years

    ANS: B   PTS: 1   DIF: Easy   OBJ: LO: 26-02
    NAT: BUSPROG: Analytic   KEY: Bloom's: Application

30. The average rate of return for this investment is:
    a. 18%
    b. 16%
    c. 58%
    d. 10%

    ANS: B   PTS: 1   DIF: Moderate   OBJ: LO: 26-02
    NAT: BUSPROG: Analytic   KEY: Bloom's: Application

31. The management of Arkansas Corporation is considering the purchase of a new machine costing $490,000. The company's desired rate of return is 10%. The present value factors for $1 at compound interest of 10% for 1 through 5 years are 0.909, 0.826, 0.751, 0.683, and 0.621, respectively. In addition to the foregoing information, use the following data in determining the acceptability in this situation:

Year	Income from Operations	Net Cash Flow
1	$100,000	$180,000
2	40,000	120,000
3	40,000	100,000
4	10,000	90,000
5	10,000	120,000

The net present value for this investment is:
a. positive $36,400
b. positive $55,200
c. Negative $16,170
d. Negative $126,800

ANS: C   PTS: 1   DIF: Moderate   OBJ: LO: 26-03
NAT: BUSPROG: Analytic   KEY: Bloom's: Application

32. The management of California Corporation is considering the purchase of a new machine costing $400,000. The company's desired rate of return is 10%. The present value factors for $1 at compound interest of 10% for 1 through 5 years are 0.909, 0.826, 0.751, 0.683, and 0.621, respectively. In addition to the foregoing information, use the following data in determining the acceptability in this situation:

Year	Income from Operations	Net Cash Flow
1	$100,000	$180,000
2	40,000	120,000
3	20,000	100,000
4	10,000	90,000
5	10,000	90,000

The present value index for this investment is:
a. .88
b. 1.45
c. 1.14
d. .70

ANS: C   PTS: 1   DIF: Moderate   OBJ: LO: 26-03
NAT: BUSPROG: Analytic   KEY: Bloom's: Application

The management of Wyoming Corporation is considering the purchase of a new machine costing $375,000. The company's desired rate of return is 6%. The present value factor for an annuity of $1 at interest of 6% for 5 years is 4.212. In addition to the foregoing information, use the following data in determining the acceptability in this situation:

Year	Income from Operations	Net Cash Flow
1	$18,750	$93,750
2	18,750	93,750
3	18,750	93,750
4	18,750	93,750
5	18,750	93,750

33. The cash payback period for this investment is:
   a. 4 years
   b. 5 years
   c. 20 years
   d. 3 years

   ANS: A   PTS: 1   DIF: Easy   OBJ: LO: 26-02
   NAT: BUSPROG: Analytic   KEY: Bloom's: Application

34. The average rate of return for this investment is:
   a. 5%
   b. 10%
   c. 25%
   d. 15%

   ANS: B   PTS: 1   DIF: Easy   OBJ: LO: 26-02
   NAT: BUSPROG: Analytic   KEY: Bloom's: Application

35. The net present value for this investment is:
   a. Negative $118,145
   b. Positive $118,145
   c. Positive $19,875
   d. Negative $19,875

   ANS: C   PTS: 1   DIF: Moderate   OBJ: LO: 26-03
   NAT: BUSPROG: Analytic   KEY: Bloom's: Application

36. The present value index for this investment is:
   a. 1.00
   b. .95
   c. 1.25
   d. 1.05

   ANS: D   PTS: 1   DIF: Easy   OBJ: LO: 26-03
   NAT: BUSPROG: Analytic   KEY: Bloom's: Application

37. Motel Corporation is analyzing a capital expenditure that will involve a cash outlay of $208,240.
   Estimated cash flows are expected to be $40,000 annually for seven years. The present value factors
   for an annuity of $1 for 7 years at interest of 6%, 8%, 10%, and 12% are 5.582, 5.206, 4.868, and
   4.564, respectively. The internal rate of return for this investment is:
   a. 10%
   b. 6%
   c. 12%
   d. 8%

ANS: D   PTS: 1   DIF: Easy   OBJ: LO: 26-03
NAT: BUSPROG: Analytic   KEY: Bloom's: Application

38. Tennessee Corporation is analyzing a capital expenditure that will involve a cash outlay of $109,332. Estimated cash flows are expected to be $36,000 annually for four years. The present value factors for an annuity of $1 for 4 years at interest of 10%, 12%, 14%, and 15% are 3.170, 3.037, 2.914, and 2.855, respectively. The internal rate of return for this investment is:
a. 9%
b. 10%
c. 12%
d. 3%

ANS: C   PTS: 1   DIF: Easy   OBJ: LO: 26-03
NAT: BUSPROG: Analytic   KEY: Bloom's: Application

Below is a table for the present value of $1 at Compound interest.

Year	6%	10%	12%
1	.943	.909	.893
2	.890	.826	.797
3	.840	.751	.712
4	.792	.683	.636
5	.747	.621	.567

Below is a table for the present value of an annuity of $1 at compound interest.

Year	6%	10%	12%
1	.943	.909	.893
2	1.833	1.736	1.690
3	2.673	2.487	2.402
4	3.465	3.170	3.037
5	4.212	3.791	3.605

39. Using the tables above, what would be the present value of $15,000 (rounded to the nearest dollar) to be received four years from today, assuming an earnings rate of 10%?
a. $11,250
b. $10,245
c. $3,750
d. $47,550

ANS: B   PTS: 1   DIF: Easy   OBJ: LO: 26-03
NAT: BUSPROG: Analytic   KEY: Bloom's: Application

40. Using the tables above, what would be the present value of $10,000 (rounded to the nearest dollar) to be received three years from today, assuming an earnings rate of 6%?
a. $8,400
b. $8,900
c. $7,920
d. $11,905

ANS: A   PTS: 1   DIF: Moderate   OBJ: LO: 26-03
NAT: BUSPROG: Analytic   KEY: Bloom's: Application

41. Using the tables above, what is the present value of $4,000 (rounded to the nearest dollar) to be received at the end of <u>each</u> of the next four years, assuming an earnings rate of 12%?
     a. $2,544
     b. $1,000
     c. $12,148
     d. $14,420

     ANS: C   PTS: 1   DIF: Moderate   OBJ: LO: 26-03
     NAT: BUSPROG: Analytic   KEY: Bloom's: Application

42. Using the tables above, if an investment is made now for $23,500 that will generate a cash inflow of $8,000 a year for the next 4 years, what would be the net present value (rounded to the nearest dollar) of the investment, (assuming an earnings rate of 10%)?
     a. $23,500
     b. $16,050
     c. $25,360
     d. $1,860

     ANS: D   PTS: 1   DIF: Moderate   OBJ: LO: 26-03
     NAT: BUSPROG: Analytic   KEY: Bloom's: Application

43. Using the tables above, what would be the internal rate of return of an investment that required an investment of $189,550, and would generate an annual cash inflow of $50,000 for the next 5 years?
     a. 6%
     b. 10%
     c. 12%
     d. cannot be determined from the data given.

     ANS: B   PTS: 1   DIF: Moderate   OBJ: LO: 26-03
     NAT: BUSPROG: Analytic   KEY: Bloom's: Application

44. Using the tables above, what would be the internal rate of return of an investment of $294,840 that would generate an annual cash inflow of $70,000 for the next 5 years?
     a. 6%
     b. 10%
     c. 12%
     d. cannot be determined from the data given.

     ANS: A   PTS: 1   DIF: Moderate   OBJ: LO: 26-03
     NAT: BUSPROG: Analytic   KEY: Bloom's: Knowledge

45. The expected average rate of return for a proposed investment of $500,000 in a fixed asset, with a useful life of four years, straight-line depreciation, no residual value, and an expected total net income of $240,000 for the 4 years, is:
     a. 18%
     b. 48%
     c. 24%
     d. 12%

     ANS: C   PTS: 1   DIF: Moderate   OBJ: LO: 26-02
     NAT: BUSPROG: Analytic   KEY: Bloom's: Application

46. Which of the following is not an advantage of the average rate of return method?
    a. It is easy to use.
    b. It takes into consideration the time value of money.
    c. It includes the amount of income earned over the entire life of the proposal.
    d. It emphasizes accounting income.

    ANS: B   PTS: 1   DIF: Easy   OBJ: LO: 26-02
    NAT: BUSPROG: Analytic   KEY: Bloom's: Knowledge

47. Which of the following is an advantage of the cash payback method?
    a. It is easy to use.
    b. It takes into consideration the time value of money.
    c. It includes the cash flow over the entire life of the proposal.
    d. It emphasizes accounting income.

    ANS: A   PTS: 1   DIF: Easy   OBJ: LO: 26-02
    NAT: BUSPROG: Analytic   KEY: Bloom's: Knowledge

48. An anticipated purchase of equipment for $600,000, with a useful life of 8 years and no residual value, is expected to yield the following annual net incomes and net cash flows:

Year	Net Income	Net Cash Flow
1	$60,000	$120,000
2	50,000	110,000
3	50,000	110,000
4	40,000	100,000
5	40,000	80,000
6	40,000	80,000
7	40,000	60,000
8	40,000	60,000

    What is the cash payback period?
    a. 5 years
    b. 4 years
    c. 6 years
    d. 3 years

    ANS: C   PTS: 1   DIF: Moderate   OBJ: LO: 26-02
    NAT: BUSPROG: Analytic   KEY: Bloom's: Application

49. Using the following partial table of present value of $1 at compound interest, determine the present value of $30,000 to be received three years hence, with earnings at the rate of 12% a year:

Year	6%	10%	12%
1	.943	.909	.893
2	.890	.826	.797
3	.840	.751	.712
4	.792	.683	.636

    a. $14,240
    b. $16,800
    c. $21,360
    d. $15,840

ANS: C   PTS: 1   DIF: Moderate   OBJ: LO: 26-03
NAT: BUSPROG: Analytic   KEY: Bloom's: Application

50. The rate of earnings is 10% and the cash to be received in two year is $10,000. Determine the present value amount, using the following partial table of present value of $1 at compound interest:

Year	6%	10%	12%
1	.943	.909	.893
2	.890	.826	.797
3	.840	.751	.712
4	.792	.683	.636

a. $8,900
b. $9,090
c. $7,970
d. $8,260

ANS: D   PTS: 1   DIF: Moderate   OBJ: LO: 26-03
NAT: BUSPROG: Analytic   KEY: Bloom's: Application

51. Heather Company is considering the acquisition of a machine that costs $432,000. The machine is expected to have a useful life of 6 years, a negligible residual value, an annual cash flow of $120,000, and annual operating income of $83,721. What is the estimated cash payback period for the machine?
a. 3.6 years
b. 4.3 years
c. 5.2 years
d. 6 years

ANS: A   PTS: 1   DIF: Easy   OBJ: LO: 26-02
NAT: BUSPROG: Analytic   KEY: Bloom's: Application

52. The expected average rate of return for a proposed investment of $4,800,000 in a fixed asset, using straight line depreciation, with a useful life of 20 years, no residual value, and an expected total net income of $10,560,000 is:
a. 24%
b. 22%
c. 45%
d. 10%

ANS: B   PTS: 1   DIF: Moderate   OBJ: LO: 26-02
NAT: BUSPROG: Analytic   KEY: Bloom's: Application

53. The management of Zesty Corporation is considering the purchase of a new machine costing $400,000. The company's desired rate of return is 10%. The present value factors for $1 at compound interest of 10% for 1 through 5 years are 0.909, 0.826, 0.751, 0.683, and 0.621, respectively. In addition to the foregoing information, use the following data in determining the acceptability in this situation:

Year	Income from Operations	Net Cash Flow
1	$100,000	$180,000
2	40,000	120,000
3	20,000	100,000
4	10,000	90,000
5	10,000	90,000

The cash payback period for this investment is:
a. 5 years
b. 4 years
c. 2 years
d. 3 years

ANS: D   PTS: 1   DIF: Easy   OBJ: LO: 26-02
NAT: BUSPROG: Analytic   KEY: Bloom's: Application

54. The management of Indiana Corporation is considering the purchase of a new machine costing $400,000. The company's desired rate of return is 10%. The present value factors for $1 at compound interest of 10% for 1 through 5 years are 0.909, 0.826, 0.751, 0.683, and 0.621, respectively. In addition to the foregoing information, use the following data in determining the acceptability in this situation:

Year	Income from Operations	Net Cash Flow
1	$100,000	$180,000
2	60,000	120,000
3	30,000	100,000
4	10,000	90,000
5	10,000	90,000

The average rate of return for this investment is:
a. 18%
b. 21%
c. 53%
d. 10%

ANS: B   PTS: 1   DIF: Moderate   OBJ: LO: 26-02
NAT: BUSPROG: Analytic   KEY: Bloom's: Application

55. The management of Idaho Corporation is considering the purchase of a new machine costing $430,000. The company's desired rate of return is 10%. The present value factors for $1 at compound interest of 10% for 1 through 5 years are 0.909, 0.826, 0.751, 0.683, and 0.621, respectively. In addition to the foregoing information, use the following data in determining the acceptability in this situation:

Year	Income from Operations	Net Cash Flow
1	$100,000	$180,000
2	40,000	120,000
3	20,000	100,000
4	10,000	90,000
5	10,000	90,000

The net present value for this investment is:
a. positive $16,400
b. positive $25,200
c. Negative $99,600
d. Negative $126,800

ANS: B   PTS: 1   DIF: Moderate   OBJ: LO: 26-03
NAT: BUSPROG: Analytic   KEY: Bloom's: Application

56. The management of Dakota Corporation is considering the purchase of a new machine costing $420,000. The company's desired rate of return is 10%. The present value factors for $1 at compound interest of 10% for 1 through 5 years are 0.909, 0.826, 0.751, 0.683, and 0.621, respectively. In addition to the foregoing information, use the following data in determining the acceptability in this situation:

Year	Income from Operations	Net Cash Flow
1	$100,000	$180,000
2	40,000	120,000
3	20,000	100,000
4	10,000	90,000
5	10,000	90,000

The present value index for this investment is:
a. 1.08
b. 1.45
c. 1.14
d. .70

ANS: A   PTS: 1   DIF: Moderate   OBJ: LO: 26-03
NAT: BUSPROG: Analytic   KEY: Bloom's: Application

57. The management of Charlton Corporation is considering the purchase of a new machine costing $380,000. The company's desired rate of return is 6%. The present value factor for an annuity of $1 at interest of 6% for 5 years is 4.212. In addition to the foregoing information, use the following data in determining the acceptability in this situation:

Year	Income from Operations	Net Cash Flow
1	$20,000	$95,000
2	20,000	95,000
3	20,000	95,000
4	20,000	95,000
5	20,000	95,000

The cash payback period for this investment is:
a. 4 years
b. 5 years
c. 19 years
d. 3.3 years

ANS: A   PTS: 1   DIF: Easy   OBJ: LO: 26-02
NAT: BUSPROG: Analytic   KEY: Bloom's: Application

The management of River Corporation is considering the purchase of a new machine costing $380,000. The company's desired rate of return is 6%. The present value factor for an annuity of $1 at interest of 6% for 5 years is 4.212. In addition to the foregoing information, use the following data in determining the acceptability in this situation:

Year	Income from Operations	Net Cash Flow
1	$20,000	$95,000
2	20,000	95,000
3	20,000	95,000
4	20,000	95,000
5	20,000	95,000

58. The cash payback period for this investment is:
   a. 4 years
   b. 5 years
   c. 20 years
   d. 3 years

   ANS: A   PTS: 1   DIF: Easy   OBJ: LO: 26-02
   NAT: BUSPROG: Analytic   KEY: Bloom's: Application

59. The average rate of return for this investment is:
   a. 5%
   b. 10.5%
   c. 25%
   d. 15%

   ANS: B   PTS: 1   DIF: Easy   OBJ: LO: 26-02
   NAT: BUSPROG: Analytic   KEY: Bloom's: Application

60. The net present value for this investment is:
   a. Positive $20,140
   b. Negative $20,140
   c. Positive $19,875
   d. Negative $19,875

   ANS: A   PTS: 1   DIF: Easy   OBJ: LO: 26-03
   NAT: BUSPROG: Analytic   KEY: Bloom's: Application

Below is a table for the present value of $1 at compound interest.

Year	6%	10%	12%
1	.943	.909	.893
2	.890	.826	.797
3	.840	.751	.712
4	.792	.683	.636
5	.747	.621	.567

Below is a table for the present value of an annuity of $1 at compound interest.

Year	6%	10%	12%
1	.943	.909	.893
2	1.833	1.736	1.690
3	2.673	2.487	2.402
4	3.465	3.170	3.037
5	4.212	3.791	3.605

61. Using the tables above, what would be the present value of $15,000 (rounded to the nearest dollar) to be received at the end of each of the next two years, assuming an earnings rate of 6%?
     a. $27,495
     b. $26,040
     c. $30,000
     d. $25,350

     ANS: A   PTS: 1   DIF: Easy   OBJ: LO: 26-03
     NAT: BUSPROG: Analytic   KEY: Bloom's: Application

62. Using the tables above, what would be the present value of $8,000 (rounded to the nearest dollar) to be received one year from today, assuming an earnings rate of 12%?
     a. $7,544
     b. $7,120
     c. $7,272
     d. $7,144

     ANS: D   PTS: 1   DIF: Moderate   OBJ: LO: 26-03
     NAT: BUSPROG: Analytic   KEY: Bloom's: Application

63. Using the tables above, what is the present value of $6,000 (rounded to the nearest dollar) to be received at the end of each of the next 4 years, assuming an earnings rate of 10%?
     a. $20,790
     b. $19,020
     c. $14,412
     d. $25,272

     ANS: B   PTS: 1   DIF: Moderate   OBJ: LO: 26-03
     NAT: BUSPROG: Analytic   KEY: Bloom's: Application

64. Using the tables above, if an investment is made now for $20,000 that will generate a cash inflow of $7,000 a year for the next 4 years, what would be the present value (rounded to the nearest dollar) of the investment cash inflows, (assuming an earnings rate of 12%)?
     a. $20,352
     b. $3,969
     c. $22,190
     d. $21,259

     ANS: D   PTS: 1   DIF: Moderate   OBJ: LO: 26-03
     NAT: BUSPROG: Analytic   KEY: Bloom's: Application

65. The production department is proposing the purchase of an automatic insertion machine. They have identified 3 machines and have asked the accountant to analyze them to determine the best average rate of return.

	Machine A	Machine B	Machine C
Estimated Average Income	$ 40,000	$ 50,000	$ 75,000
Average Investment	$300,000	$250,000	$500,000

     a. Machine B
     b. Machine C

    c.   Machine B or C
    d.   Machine A

ANS: A   PTS: 1   DIF: Easy   OBJ: LO: 26-02
NAT: BUSPROG: Analytic   KEY: Bloom's: Application

66.   The production department is proposing the purchase of an automatic insertion machine. They have identified 3 machines and have asked the accountant to analyze them to determine the best cash payback.

	Machine A	Machine B	Machine C
Annual Cash Flow	$ 40,000	$ 50,000	$ 75,000
Average Investment	$300,000	$250,000	$500,000

    a.   Machine A
    b.   Machine C
    c.   Machine B
    d.   All are equal.

ANS: C   PTS: 1   DIF: Easy   OBJ: LO: 26-02
NAT: BUSPROG: Analytic   KEY: Bloom's: Application

67.   Which of the following is true of the cash payback period?
    a.   The longer the payback, the longer the estimated life of the asset.
    b.   The longer the payback, the sooner the cash spent on the investment is recovered.
    c.   The shorter the payback, the less likely the possibility of obsolescence.
    d.   All of the above are correct.

ANS: C   PTS: 1   DIF: Easy   OBJ: LO: 26-02
NAT: BUSPROG: Analytic   KEY: Bloom's: Knowledge

68.   The production department is proposing the purchase of an automatic insertion machine. They have identified 3 machines and have asked the accountant to analyze them to determine which of the proposals (if any) meet or exceed the company's policy of a minimum desired rate of return of 10% using the net present value method. Each of the assets has a estimated useful life of 10 years.

	Machine A	Machine B	Machine C
Present Value of Future Cash Flows computed using 10% rate of return	$305,000	$295,000	$300,000
Amount of initial investment	$300,000	$300,000	$300,000

    a.   A & C
    b.   B & C
    c.   B
    d.   A only

ANS: A   PTS: 1   DIF: Moderate   OBJ: LO: 26-03
NAT: BUSPROG: Analytic   KEY: Bloom's: Application

69. The production department is proposing the purchase of an automatic insertion machine. They have identified 3 machines, each with an estimated life of 10 years. Which machine offers the best internal rate of return?

	Machine A	Machine B	Machine C
Annual net cash flows	$ 50,000	$ 40,000	$ 75,000
Average investment	$250,000	$300,000	$500,000

    a. Machine B
    b. Machine C
    c. Machine A and B
    d. Machine A

ANS: D   PTS: 1   DIF: Moderate   OBJ: LO: 26-03
NAT: BUSPROG: Analytic   KEY: Bloom's: Application

70. All of the following qualitative considerations may impact upon capital investment analysis except:
    a. manufacturing productivity
    b. manufacturing sunk cost
    c. manufacturing flexibility
    d. market opportunities

ANS: B   PTS: 1   DIF: Easy   OBJ: LO: 26-04
NAT: BUSPROG: Analytic   KEY: Bloom's: Knowledge

71. All of the following qualitative considerations may impact upon capital investment analysis except:
    a. time value of money
    b. employee morale
    c. the impact on product quality
    d. manufacturing flexibility

ANS: A   PTS: 1   DIF: Easy   OBJ: LO: 26-04
NAT: BUSPROG: Analytic   KEY: Bloom's: Knowledge

72. Which of the following provisions of the Internal Revenue Code can be used to reduce the amount of the income tax expense arising from capital investment projects?
    a. Deductions for individuals
    b. Depreciation deduction
    c. Minimum tax provision
    d. Charitable contributions

ANS: B   PTS: 1   DIF: Easy   OBJ: LO: 26-04
NAT: BUSPROG: Analytic   KEY: Bloom's: Knowledge

73. Assume in analyzing alternative proposals that Proposal F has a useful life of six years and Proposal J has a useful life of nine years. What is one widely used method that makes the proposals comparable?
    a. Ignore the fact that Proposal F has a useful life of six years and treat it as if it has a useful life of nine years.
    b. Adjust the life of Proposal J to a time period that is equal to that of Proposal F by estimating a residual value at the end of year six.

    c. Ignore the useful lives of six and nine years and find an average (7 1/2 years).
    d. Ignore the useful lives of six and nine years and compute the average rate of return.

ANS: B   PTS: 1   DIF: Easy   OBJ: LO: 26-04
NAT: BUSPROG: Analytic   KEY: Bloom's: Application

74.   Periods in time that experience increasing price levels are known as periods of:
    a. inflation
    b. recession
    c. depression
    d. deflation

ANS: A   PTS: 1   DIF: Easy   OBJ: LO: 26-04
NAT: BUSPROG: Analytic   KEY: Bloom's: Knowledge

75.   Which of the following is not considered as a complicating factor in capital investment decisions?
    a. Income tax
    b. Lease versus capital investment
    c. Equal proposed lives
    d. Qualitative considerations

ANS: C   PTS: 1   DIF: Easy   OBJ: LO: 26-04
NAT: BUSPROG: Analytic   KEY: Bloom's: Knowledge

76.   Which of the following would not be considered a good managerial tool in making a decision for determining a capital investment?
    a. Further evaluate assets that are dissimilar in nature or have different useful lives.
    b. Using only quantitative measures to purchase an asset.
    c. Analyzing the lease vs purchase option.
    d. Considering income tax ramifications.

ANS: B   PTS: 1   DIF: Easy   OBJ: LO: 26-04
NAT: BUSPROG: Analytic   KEY: Bloom's: Knowledge

77.   All of the following are factors that may complicate capital investment analysis except:
    a. possible leasing alternatives.
    b. changes in price levels.
    c. sunk costs.
    d. federal income tax ramifications.

ANS: C   PTS: 1   DIF: Moderate   OBJ: LO: 26-05
NAT: BUSPROG: Analytic   KEY: Bloom's: Knowledge

78.   The process by which management allocates available investment funds among competing investment proposals is called:
    a. investment capital
    b. investment rationing
    c. cost-volume-profit analysis
    d. capital rationing

ANS: D   PTS: 1   DIF: Easy   OBJ: LO: 26-05
NAT: BUSPROG: Analytic   KEY: Bloom's: Knowledge

79. In capital rationing, an initial screening of alternative proposals is usually performed by establishing minimum standards. Which of the following evaluation method(s) are often used?
   a. Cash payback method and average rate of return method
   b. Average rate of return method and net present value method
   c. Net present value method and cash payback method
   d. Internal rate of return and net present value methods

   ANS: A   PTS: 1   DIF: Easy   OBJ: LO: 26-05
   NAT: BUSPROG: Analytic   KEY: Bloom's: Knowledge

80. In capital rationing, alternative proposals that survive initial and secondary screening are normally evaluated in terms of:
   a. present value
   b. non-financial factors
   c. maximum cost
   d. net cash flow

   ANS: B   PTS: 1   DIF: Easy   OBJ: LO: 26-05
   NAT: BUSPROG: Analytic   KEY: Bloom's: Knowledge

81. A company is contemplating investing in a new piece of manufacturing machinery. The amount to be invested is $150,000. The present value of the future cash flows is $143,000. Should the company invest in this project?
   a. yes, because net present value is +$7,000
   b. yes, because net present value is -$7,000
   c. no, because net present value is +$7,000
   d. no, because net present value is -$7,000

   ANS: D   PTS: 1   DIF: Moderate   OBJ: LO: 26-03
   NAT: BUSPROG: Analytic   KEY: Bloom's: Application

82. A company is contemplating investing in a new piece of manufacturing machinery. The amount to be invested is $150,000. The present value of the future cash flows generated by the project is $145,000. Should they invest in this project?
   a. yes, because the rate of return on the project exceeds the desired rate of return used to calculate the present value of the future cash flows.
   b. no, because the rate of return on the project is less than the desired rate of return used to calculate the present value of the future cash flows.
   c. no, because net present value is +$5,000
   d. yes, because the rate of return on the project is equal to the desired rate of return used to calculate the present value of the future cash flows.

   ANS: B   PTS: 1   DIF: Moderate   OBJ: LO: 26-03
   NAT: BUSPROG: Analytic   KEY: Bloom's: Application

83. A company is contemplating investing in a new piece of manufacturing machinery. The amount to be invested is $170,000. The present value of the future cash flows is $185,000. The company's desired rate of return used in the present value calculations was 10%. Which of the following statements is true?
   a. The project should not be accepted because the net present value is negative.
   b. The internal rate of return on the project is less than 10%.
   c. The internal rate of return on the project is more than 10%.
   d. The internal rate of return on the project is equal to 10%.

ANS: C   PTS: 1   DIF: Moderate   OBJ: LO: 26-03
NAT: BUSPROG: Analytic   KEY: Bloom's: Application

84. A company is contemplating investing in a new piece of manufacturing machinery. The amount to be invested is $100,000. The present value of the future cash flows at the company's desired rate of return is $105,000. The IRR on the project is 12%. Which of the following statements is true?
    a. The project should not be accepted because the net present value is negative.
    b. The desired rate of return used to calculate the present value of the future cash flows is less than 12%.
    c. The desired rate of return used to calculate the present value of the future cash flows is more than 12%.
    d. The desired rate of return used to calculate the present value of the future cash flows is equal to 12%.

ANS: B   PTS: 1   DIF: Moderate   OBJ: LO: 26-03
NAT: BUSPROG: Analytic   KEY: Bloom's: Application

85. A company is contemplating investing in a new piece of manufacturing machinery. The amount to be invested is $100,000. The present value of the future cash flows at the company's desired rate of return is $100,000. The IRR on the project is 12%. Which of the following statements is true?
    a. The project should not be accepted because the net present value is negative.
    b. The desired rate of return used to calculate the present value of the future cash flows is less than 12%.
    c. The desired rate of return used to calculate the present value of the future cash flows is more than 12%.
    d. The desired rate of return used to calculate the present value of the future cash flows is equal to 12%.

ANS: D   PTS: 1   DIF: Moderate   OBJ: LO: 26-03
NAT: BUSPROG: Analytic   KEY: Bloom's: Application

OTHER

1. Determine the average rate of return for a project that is estimated to yield total income of $400,000 over four years, cost $720,000, and has a $70,000 residual value. Round answers in percentage to one decimal place.

ANS:

Estimated average annual income:	$100,000	($400,000 / 4 years)
Average investment:	$ 395,000	($720,000 + $70,000) / 2
Average rate of return	25.3%	($100,000 / $395,000)

PTS: 1   DIF: Easy   OBJ: LO: 26-02   NAT: BUSPROG: Analytic
KEY: Bloom's: Application

2. Determine the average rate of return for a project that is estimated to yield total income of $250,000 over four years, cost $480,000, and has a $20,000 residual value.

ANS:

Estimated average annual income:	$62,500	($250,000 / 4 years)
Average investment:	$250,000	($480,000 + $20,000) / 2
Average rate of return	25%	($62,500 / $250,000)

PTS: 1   DIF: Easy   OBJ: LO: 26-02   NAT: BUSPROG: Analytic
KEY: Bloom's: Application

3. An 8-year project is estimated to cost $400,000 and have no residual value. If the straight-line depreciation method is used and the average rate of return is 5%, determine the estimated annual net income.

ANS:

$$\frac{\text{Estimated Average Annual Income}}{\text{Average Investment}} = \frac{\$X}{(\$400,000 + \$0)/2} = 5\%$$

$$\$X = .05(\$200,000)$$

$$\$X = \$10,000$$

PTS: 1   DIF: Easy   OBJ: LO: 26-02   NAT: BUSPROG: Analytic
KEY: Bloom's: Application

4. An 6-year project is estimated to cost $350,000 and have no residual value. If the straight-line depreciation method is used and the average rate of return is 12%, determine the estimated annual net income.

ANS:

$$\frac{\text{Estimated Average Annual Income}}{\text{Average Investment}} = \frac{\$X}{(\$350,000 + \$0)/2} = 12\%$$

$$\$X = .12(\$175,000)$$

$$\$X = \$21,000$$

PTS: 1   DIF: Easy   OBJ: LO: 26-02   NAT: BUSPROG: Analytic
KEY: Bloom's: Application

5. A project has estimated annual net cash flows of $50,000. It is estimated to cost $180,000. Determine the cash payback period.

ANS:
3.6 years ($180,000 / $50,000)

PTS: 1   DIF: Easy   OBJ: LO: 26-02   NAT: BUSPROG: Analytic
KEY: Bloom's: Application

6. A project has estimated annual net cash flows of $90,000. It is estimated to cost $324,000. Determine the cash payback period.

ANS:
3.6 years ($324,000 / $90,000)

PTS: 1   DIF: Easy   OBJ: LO: 26-02   NAT: BUSPROG: Analytic
KEY: Bloom's: Application

7. A project has estimated annual cash flows of $95,000 for four years and is estimated to cost $260,000. Assume a minimum acceptable rate of return of 10%. Using the following tables determine the (a) net present value of the project and (b) the present value index, rounded to two decimal places.

Below is a table for the present value of $1 at compound interest.

Year	6%	10%	12%
1	.943	.909	.893
2	.890	.826	.797
3	.840	.751	.712
4	.792	.683	.636
5	.747	.621	.567

Below is a table for the present value of an annuity of $1 at compound interest.

Year	6%	10%	12%
1	.943	.909	.893
2	1.833	1.736	1.690
3	2.673	2.487	2.402
4	3.465	3.170	3.037
5	4.212	3.791	3.605

ANS:
(a) $41,150   [$95,000 × 3.170) − $260,000]
(b) 1.16   ($301,150 / $260,000)

PTS: 1   DIF: Moderate   OBJ: LO: 26-03   NAT: BUSPROG: Analytic
KEY: Bloom's: Application

8. A project has estimated annual cash flows of $90,000 for three years and is estimated to cost $250,000. Assume a minimum acceptable rate of return of 10%. Using the following tables determine the (a) net present value of the project and (b) the present value index, rounded to two decimal places.

Below is a table for the present value of $1 at compound interest.

Year	6%	10%	12%
1	.943	.909	.893
2	.890	.826	.797
3	.840	.751	.712
4	.792	.683	.636
5	.747	.621	.567

Below is a table for the present value of an annuity of $1 at compound interest.

Year	6%	10%	12%
1	.943	.909	.893
2	1.833	1.736	1.690
3	2.673	2.487	2.402
4	3.465	3.170	3.037
5	4.212	3.791	3.605

ANS:
(a) −$26,170   [$90,000 × 2.487) − $250,000]
(b) .90   ($223,830 / $250,000)

PTS: 1   DIF: Moderate   OBJ: LO: 26-03   NAT: BUSPROG: Analytic
KEY: Bloom's: Application

9. A project is estimated to cost $273,840 and provide annual cash flows of $60,000 for seven years.
    Determine the internal rate of return for this project, using the following table.

Year	6%	10%	12%
1	.943	.909	.893
2	1.833	1.736	1.690
3	2.673	2.487	2.402
4	3.465	3.170	3.037
5	4.212	3.791	3.605
6	4.917	4.355	4.111
7	5.582	4.868	4.564
8	6.210	5.335	4.968
9	6.802	5.759	5.328
10	7.360	6.145	5.650

ANS:
12% [($273,840 / $60,000) = 4.564, the present value of an annuity factor for seven periods at 12%.

PTS: 1   DIF: Moderate   OBJ: LO: 26-03   NAT: BUSPROG: Analytic
KEY: Bloom's: Application

10. A project is estimated to cost $248,400 and provide annual cash flows of $50,000 for eight years.
     Determine the internal rate of return for this project, using the following table.

Year	6%	10%	12%
1	.943	.909	.893
2	1.833	1.736	1.690
3	2.673	2.487	2.402
4	3.465	3.170	3.037
5	4.212	3.791	3.605
6	4.917	4.355	4.111
7	5.582	4.868	4.564
8	6.210	5.335	4.968
9	6.802	5.759	5.328
10	7.360	6.145	5.650

ANS:
12% [($248,400 / $50,000) = 4.968, the present value of an annuity factor for eight periods at 12%.]

PTS: 1   DIF: Moderate   OBJ: LO: 26-03   NAT: BUSPROG: Analytic
KEY: Bloom's: Application

11. Project A requires an original investment of $65,000. The project will yield cash flows of $15,000 per year for seven years. Project B has a calculated net present value of $5,500 over a five year life. Project A could be sold at the end of five years for a price of $30,000. (a) Using the proper table below determine the net present value of Project A over a five-year life with salvage value assuming a minimum rate of return of 12%. (b) Which project provides the greatest net present value?

Below is a table for the present value of $1 at compound interest.

Year	6%	10%	12%
1	.943	.909	.893
2	.890	.826	.797
3	.840	.751	.712
4	.792	.683	.636
5	.747	.621	.567

Below is a table for the present value of an annuity of $1 at compound interest.

Year	6%	10%	12%
1	.943	.909	.893
2	1.833	1.736	1.690
3	2.673	2.487	2.402
4	3.465	3.170	3.037
5	4.212	3.791	3.605

ANS:
(a)

Present value of a $15,000 five year annuity at 12%:	$54,075 *
Present value of a $30,000 amount, five years at 12%	17,010**
Total present value of Project A:	$ 71,085
Total cost of Project A:	65,000
Net present value of Project A	$ 6,085

*[$15,000 × 3.605 (Present value of an annuity of $1)]
**[$30,000 × .567 (Present value of $1)]

(b) Project A's net present value of $6,085 is greater than the net present value of Project B, $5,500.

PTS: 1   DIF: Moderate   OBJ: LO: 26-03   NAT: BUSPROG: Analytic
KEY: Bloom's: Application

12. Project A requires an original investment of $50,000. The project will yield cash flows of $15,000 per year for seven years. Project B has a calculated net present value of $13,500 over a four year life. Project A could be sold at the end of four years for a price of $25,000. (a) Using the proper table below determine the net present value of Project A over a four-year life with salvage value assuming a minimum rate of return of 12%. (b) Which project provides the greatest net present value?

Below is a table for the present value of $1 at compound interest.

Year	6%	10%	12%
1	.943	.909	.893
2	.890	.826	.797
3	.840	.751	.712
4	.792	.683	.636
5	.747	.621	.567

Below is a table for the present value of an annuity of $1 at compound interest.

Year	6%	10%	12%
1	.943	.909	.893
2	1.833	1.736	1.690
3	2.673	2.487	2.402
4	3.465	3.170	3.037
5	4.212	3.791	3.605

ANS:

(a)

Present value of a $15,000 four year annuity at 12%:	$45,555 *
Present value of a $25,000 amount, four years at 12%	15,900**
Total present value of Project A:	$ 61,455
Total cost of Project A:	50,000
Net present value of Project A	$ 11,455

*[$15,000 × 3.037 (Present value of an annuity of $1)]
**[$25,000 × .636 (Present value of $1)]

(b) Project B's present value of $13,500 is greater than the net present value of Project A of $11,455.

PTS: 1   DIF: Moderate   OBJ: LO: 26-03   NAT: BUSPROG: Analytic
KEY: Bloom's: Application

13.   What is the present value of $8,000 to be received at the end of six years, if the required rate of return
      is 15%?

Below is a table for the present value of $1 at compound interest.

Year	15%	Year	15%
1	0.87	6	0.432
2	0.756	7	0.376
3	0.658	8	0.327
4	0.572	9	0.284
5	0.497	10	0.247

Below is a table for the present value of an annuity of $1 at compound interest.

Year	15%	Year	15%
1	0.87	6	3.785
2	1.626	7	4.16
3	2.283	8	4.487
4	2.855	9	4.772
5	3.353	10	5.019

ANS:

$8,000 * 0.432 = $3,456.00

PTS: 1   DIF: Moderate   OBJ: LO: 26-03   NAT: BUSPROG: Analytic
KEY: Bloom's: Application

14. Norton Company is considering a project that will require an initial investment of $750,000 and will return $200,000 each year for five years.

Required:

If taxes are ignored and the required rate of return is 9%, what is the project's net present value? Based on this analysis, should Norton Company proceed with the project?

Below is a table for the present value of $1 at compound interest.

Year	9%	Year	9%
1	0.917	6	0.596
2	0.842	7	0.547
3	0.772	8	0.502
4	0.708	9	0.460
5	0.650	10	0.422

Below is a table for the present value of an annuity of $1 at compound interest.

Year	9%	Year	9%
1	0.917	6	4.486
2	1.759	7	5.033
3	2.531	8	5.535
4	3.240	9	5.995
5	3.890	10	6.418

ANS:

($200,000 * 3.89) − $750,000 = $28,000
Yes, since the net present value is greater than zero, Norton Company should proceed with the project.

PTS: 1   DIF: Moderate   OBJ: LO: 26-03   NAT: BUSPROG: Analytic
KEY: Bloom's: Application

15. An investment of $185,575 is expected to generate returns of $65,000 per year for each of the next four years.   What is the investment's internal rate of return?

Below is a table for the present value of $1 at compound interest.

Year	6%	10%	12%	15%
1	0.943	0.909	0.893	0.87
2	0.89	0.826	0.797	0.756
3	0.84	0.751	0.712	0.658
4	0.792	0.683	0.636	0.572
5	0.747	0.621	0.567	0.497

Below is a table for the present value of an annuity of $1 at compound interest.

Year	6%	10%	12%	15%
1	0.943	0.909	0.893	0.87
2	1.833	1.736	1.69	1.626
3	2.673	2.487	2.402	2.283
4	3.465	3.17	3.037	2.855
5	4.212	3.791	3.605	3.353

ANS:

$185,575 / $65,000 = 2.855 at 4 years = 15%

PTS: 1   DIF: Moderate   OBJ: LO: 26-03   NAT: BUSPROG: Analytic
KEY: Bloom's: Application

16.   Dickerson Co. is evaluating a project requiring a capital expenditure of $810,000. The project has an
      estimated life of four years and no salvage value. The estimated net income and net cash flow from
      the project are as follows:

Year	Net Income	Net Cash Flow
1	$ 75,000	$285,000
2	100,000	290,000
3	109,000	190,000
4	36,000	125,000
	$320,000	$890,000

      The company's minimum desired rate of return is 12%. The present value of $1 at compound
      interest of 12% for 1, 2, 3, and 4 years is .893, .797, .712, and .636, respectively.

      Required:

      Determine the average rate of return on investment, including the effect of depreciation on the
      investment.

      ANS:
      $$\frac{\$320,000 \,/\, 4}{(\$810,000 + \$0)/2} = \frac{\$80,000}{\$405,000} = 19.8\%$$

      PTS: 1   DIF: Moderate   OBJ: LO: 26-02   NAT: BUSPROG: Analytic
      KEY: Bloom's: Application

17.   Dickerson Co. is evaluating a project requiring a capital expenditure of $810,000. The project has an
      estimated life of four years and no salvage value. The estimated net income and net cash flow from
      the project are as follows:

Year	Net Income	Net Cash Flow
1	$ 75,000	$280,000
2	100,000	300,000
3	109,000	200,000
4	36,000	120,000
	$320,000	$900,000

      The company's minimum desired rate of return is 12%. The present value of $1 at compound
      interest of 12% for 1, 2, 3, and 4 years is .893, .797, .712, and .636, respectively.

      Required:

      Determine the net present value.

ANS:

Year	Present Value of $1 at 12%	Net Cash Flow	Present Value of Net Cash Flow
1	.893	$280,000	$ 250,040
2	.797	300,000	239,100
3	.712	200,000	142,400
4	.636	120,000	76,320
Total		$900,000	$ 707,860
Amount to be invested			810,000
Net present value			$(102,140)

PTS: 1   DIF: Moderate   OBJ: LO: 26-03   NAT: BUSPROG: Analytic
KEY: Bloom's: Application

MATCHING

Match each of the following methods with the correct category.
   a.   Methods that do not use Present value.
   b.   Methods that use Present value.

1.   Cash payback method
2.   Internal rate of return method
3.   Average rate of return method
4.   Net present value method

1.   ANS: A   PTS: 1   DIF: Easy   OBJ: LO: 26-02
     NAT: BUSPROG: Analytic   KEY: Bloom's: Knowledge
2.   ANS: B   PTS: 1   DIF: Easy   OBJ: LO: 26-03
     NAT: BUSPROG: Analytic   KEY: Bloom's: Knowledge
3.   ANS: A   PTS: 1   DIF: Easy   OBJ: LO: 26-02
     NAT: BUSPROG: Analytic   KEY: Bloom's: Knowledge
4.   ANS: B   PTS: 1   DIF: Easy   OBJ: LO: 26-03
     NAT: BUSPROG: Analytic   KEY: Bloom's: Knowledge

Match each of the following terms with the best definition given below.
   a.   Capital investment analysis   d.   Average rate of return
   b.   Time value of money concept   e.   Cash payback period
   c.   Net present value method

5.   Recognizes that a dollar today is worth more than a dollar tomorrow.
6.   The investment analysis method that is most often used by large U.S. companies.
7.   Capital budgeting
8.   Average income as a percentage of average investment
9.   Initial cost divided by Annual net cash inflow of an investment

5. ANS: B   PTS: 1   DIF: Easy   OBJ: LO: 26-03
    NAT: BUSPROG: Analytic   KEY: Bloom's: Knowledge
6. ANS: C   PTS: 1   DIF: Easy   OBJ: LO: 26-03
    NAT: BUSPROG: Analytic   KEY: Bloom's: Knowledge
7. ANS: A   PTS: 1   DIF: Easy   OBJ: LO: 26-01
    NAT: BUSPROG: Analytic   KEY: Bloom's: Knowledge
8. ANS: D   PTS: 1   DIF: Easy   OBJ: LO: 26-02
    NAT: BUSPROG: Analytic   KEY: Bloom's: Knowledge
9. ANS: E   PTS: 1   DIF: Easy   OBJ: LO: 26-02
    NAT: BUSPROG: Analytic   KEY: Bloom's: Knowledge

Match the term with the correct definition.
a. net present value
b. annuity
c. capital investment analysis
d. internal rate of return
e. payback period
f. accounting rate of return

10. A measure of profitability computed by dividing the average operating income that an asset generates by the average amount of the investment in the asset.
11. The decision model that computes the expected net monetary gain or loss from a project by discounting all expected future cash inflows and outflows to their present value, using a minimum desired rate of return.
12. A stream of equal cash flow amounts.
13. A formal means of analyzing long-range investment decisions.
14. The rate of return that makes the net present value of a project equal to zero.
15. The length of time it will take to recover through cash inflows the dollars of a capital outlay.

10. ANS: F   PTS: 1   DIF: Easy   OBJ: LO: 26-02
    NAT: BUSPROG: Analytic   KEY: Bloom's: Knowledge
11. ANS: A   PTS: 1   DIF: Easy   OBJ: LO: 26-03
    NAT: BUSPROG: Analytic   KEY: Bloom's: Knowledge
12. ANS: B   PTS: 1   DIF: Easy   OBJ: LO: 26-03
    NAT: BUSPROG: Analytic   KEY: Bloom's: Knowledge
13. ANS: C   PTS: 1   DIF: Easy   OBJ: LO: 26-01
    NAT: BUSPROG: Analytic   KEY: Bloom's: Knowledge
14. ANS: D   PTS: 1   DIF: Easy   OBJ: LO: 26-03
    NAT: BUSPROG: Analytic   KEY: Bloom's: Knowledge
15. ANS: E   PTS: 1   DIF: Easy   OBJ: LO: 26-02
    NAT: BUSPROG: Analytic   KEY: Bloom's: Knowledge

PROBLEM

1. Jimmy Co. is considering a 12-year project that is estimated to cost $1,050,000 and has no residual value. Jimmy Co. seeks to earn an average rate of return of 18% on all capital projects. Determine the necessary average annual income (using straight-line depreciation) that must be achieved on this project for this project to be acceptable to Jimmy Co.

   ANS:

   $$\frac{\text{Estimated Average Annual Income}}{\text{Average Investment}} = \text{Average Rate of Return}$$

   $$\frac{\times}{(\$1,050,000 + \$0)/2} = .18$$

   $$\frac{\times}{\$525,000} = .18$$

   $$x = \$94,500$$

   PTS: 1   DIF: Moderate   OBJ: LO: 26-02   NAT: BUSPROG: Analytic
   KEY: Bloom's: Application

2. Proposals L and K each cost $500,000, have 6-year lives, and have expected total cash flows of $720,000. Proposal L is expected to provide equal annual net cash flows of $140,000, while the net cash flows for Proposal K are as follows:

Year 1	$250,000
Year 2	200,000
Year 3	100,000
Year 4	90,000
Year 5	60,000
Year 6	20,000
	$720,000

   Determine the cash payback period for each proposal. Round your answers to two decimal places.

   ANS:
   Proposal L: $500,000/$140,000 = 3.57 years

   Proposal K: $250,000 + $200,000 + .5 ($100,000) = $500,000 = 2.5 years

   PTS: 1   DIF: Easy   OBJ: LO: 26-02   NAT: BUSPROG: Analytic
   KEY: Bloom's: Application

3. Proposals M and N each cost $600,000, have 6-year lives, and have expected total cash flows of $750,000. Proposal M is expected to provide equal annual net cash flows of $125,000, while the net cash flows for Proposal N are as follows:

Year 1	$250,000
Year 2	$200,000
Year 3	$150,000
Year 4	$ 75,000
Year 5	$ 50,000
Year 6	$ 25,000

Determine the cash payback period for each proposal.

ANS:
Proposal M: $600,000/$125,000 = 4.8 years

Proposal N: $250,000 + $200,000 + $150,000 = $600,000 = 3 years

PTS: 1   DIF: Easy   OBJ: LO: 26-02   NAT: BUSPROG: Analytic
KEY: Bloom's: Application

4. A $550,000 capital investment proposal has an estimated life of four years and no residual value.
    The estimated net cash flows are as follows:

Year	Net Cash Flow
1	$300,000
2	280,000
3	208,000
4	180,000

The minimum desired rate of return for net present value analysis is 12%. The present value of $1 at
compound interest of 12% for 1, 2, 3, and 4 years is .893, .797, .712, and .636, respectively.
Determine the net present value.

ANS:

Year	Present Value of $1 at 12%	Net Cash Flow	Present Value of Net Cash Flow
1	.893	$300,000	$267,900
2	.797	280,000	223,160
3	.712	208,000	148,096
4	.636	180,000	114,480
Total		$968,000	$753,636
Amount to be invested			550,000
Net present value			$203,636

PTS: 1   DIF: Moderate   OBJ: LO: 26-03   NAT: BUSPROG: Analytic
KEY: Bloom's: Application

5. Sunrise Inc. is considering a capital investment proposal that costs $227,500 and has an estimated
    life of four years and no residual value. The estimated net cash flows are as follows:

Year	Net Cash Flow
1	$97,500
2	$80,000
3	$60,000
4	$40,000

The minimum desired rate of return for net present value analysis is 10%. The present value of $1 at
compound interest rates of 10% for 1, 2, 3, and 4 years is .909, .826, .751, and .683, respectively.
Determine the net present value.

ANS:

Year	Present Value of $1 at 10%	Net Cash Flow	Present Value of Net Cash Flows
1	.909	$ 97,500	$ 88,628
2	.826	80,000	66,080
3	.751	60,000	45,060
4	.683	40,000	27,320
Total		$277,500	$227,088
Amount to be invested			227,500
Net present value			$ (412)

PTS: 1   DIF: Moderate   OBJ: LO: 26-03   NAT: BUSPROG: Analytic
KEY: Bloom's: Application

6.   The net present value has been computed for Proposals P and Q. Relevant data are as follows:

	Proposal P	Proposal Q
Amount to be invested	$245,000	$460,000
Total present value of net cash flow	296,500	425,000

Determine the present value index for each proposal. Round your answers to two decimal places.

ANS:
Proposal P: $\dfrac{\$296,500}{\$245,000} = 1.21$

Proposal Q: $\dfrac{\$425,000}{\$460,000} = 0.92$

PTS: 1   DIF: Moderate   OBJ: LO: 26-03   NAT: BUSPROG: Analytic
KEY: Bloom's: Application

7.   Vanessa Company is evaluating a project requiring a capital expenditure of $480,000. The project has an estimated life of 4 years and no salvage value. The estimated net income and net cash flow from the project are as follows:

Year	Net Income	Net Cash Flow
1	$ 90,000	$210,000
2	80,000	200,000
3	40,000	160,000
4	30,000	150,000
	$ 240,000	$720,000

The company's minimum desired rate of return for net present value analysis is 15%. The present value of $1 at compound interest of 15% for 1, 2, 3, and 4 years is .870, .756, .658, and .572, respectively.

Determine (a) the average rate of return on investment, using straight line depreciation, and (b) the net present value.

ANS:

(a)

$$\frac{\$240,000/4}{(\$480,000 + \$0)/2} = \frac{\$60,000}{\$240,000} = 25\%$$

(b)

Year	Present Value of $1 at 15%	Net Cash Flow	Present Value of Net Cash Flow
1	.870	$ 210,000	$ 182,700
2	.756	200,000	151,200
3	.658	160,000	105,280
4	.572	150,000	85,800
Total		$ 720,000	$ 524,980
Amount to be invested			480,000
Net present value			$ 44,980

PTS: 1   DIF: Challenging   OBJ: LO: 26-02 | LO: 26-03
NAT: BUSPROG: Analytic   KEY: Bloom's: Application

8.   BAM Co. is evaluating a project requiring a capital expenditure of $806,250. The project has an estimated life of four years and no salvage value. The estimated net income and net cash flow from the project are as follows:

Year	Net Income	Net Cash Flow
1	$ 75,000	$285,000
2	102,000	290,000
3	109,500	190,000
4	36,000	125,000
	$322,500	$890,000

The company's minimum desired rate of return is 12%. The present value of $1 at compound interest of 12% for 1, 2, 3, and 4 years is .893, .797, .712, and .636, respectively.

Determine: (a) the average rate of return on investment, including the effect of depreciation on the investment, and (b) the net present value.

ANS:

(a)

$$\frac{\$322,500/4}{(\$806,250 + \$0)/2} = \frac{\$80,625}{\$403,125} = 20\%$$

(b)

Year	Present Value of $1 at 12%	Net Cash Flow	Present Value of Net Cash Flow
1	.893	$285,000	$ 254,505
2	.797	290,000	231,130
3	.712	190,000	135,280
4	.636	125,000	79,500
Total		$890,000	$ 700,415
Amount to be invested			806,250
Net present value			$(105,835)

PTS: 1 DIF: Challenging OBJ: LO: 26-02 | LO: 26-03
NAT: BUSPROG: Analytic KEY: Bloom's: Application

9. The internal rate of return method is used to analyze a $946,250 capital investment proposal with annual net cash flows of $250,000 for each of the six years of its useful life.

(a) Determine a present value factor for an annuity of $1 which can be used in determining the internal rate of return.

(b) Based on the factor determined in (a) and the portion of the present value of an annuity of $1 table presented below, determine the internal rate of return for the proposal.

Year	10%	15%	20%
1	0.909	0.870	0.833
2	1.736	1.626	1.528
3	2.487	2.283	2.106
4	3.170	2.855	2.589
5	3.791	3.353	2.991
6	4.355	3.785	3.326
7	4.868	4.160	3.605

ANS:
(a)
$\frac{\$946,250}{\$250,000} = 3.785$

(b)
15%

PTS: 1 DIF: Moderate OBJ: LO: 26-03 NAT: BUSPROG: Analytic
KEY: Bloom's: Application

10. Tipper Co. is considering a 10-year project that is estimated to cost $700,000 and has no residual value. Tipper seeks to earn an average rate of return of 15% on all capital projects. Determine the necessary average annual income (using straight-line depreciation) that must be achieved on this project for this project to be acceptable to Tipper Co.

ANS:
$\frac{\text{Estimated Average Annual Income}}{\text{Average Investment}}$ = Average Rate of Return

$\frac{\times}{(\$700,000 + \$0)/2}$ = .15

$\frac{\times}{\$350,000}$ = .15

$\times$ = $52,500

PTS: 1 DIF: Moderate OBJ: LO: 26-02 NAT: BUSPROG: Analytic
KEY: Bloom's: Application

11.   Proposals A and B each cost $500,000 and have 5-year lives.   Proposal A is expected to provide
      equal annual net cash flows of $109,000, while the net cash flows for Proposal B are as follows:

      Year 1 $150,000
      Year 2   140,000
      Year 3   110,000
      Year 4   50,000
      Year 5   50,000
                                                               $500,000

      Determine the cash payback period for each proposal. Round answers to two decimal places.

      ANS:
      Proposal A: $500,000/$109,000 = 4.59 years

      Proposal B: ($150,000 + $140,000 + $110,000 + $50,000 + $50,000) = $500,000 = 5 years

      PTS: 1   DIF: Easy   OBJ: LO: 26-02   NAT: BUSPROG: Analytic
      KEY: Bloom's: Application

12.   A $400,000 capital investment proposal has an estimated life of four years and no residual value.
      The estimated net cash flows are as follows:

Year	Net Cash Flow
1	$200,000
2	150,000
3	90,000
4	80,000

      The minimum desired rate of return for net present value analysis is 12%. The present value of $1 at
      compound interest of 12% for 1, 2, 3, and 4 years is .893, .797, .712, and .636, respectively.
      Determine the net present value.

      ANS:

Year	Present Value of $1 at 12%	Net Cash Flow	Present Value of Net Cash Flow
1	.893	$200,000	$178,600
2	.797	150,000	119,550
3	.712	90,000	64,080
4	.636	80,000	50,880
Total		$520,000	$413,110
Amount to be invested			400,000
Net present value			$ 13,110

      PTS: 1   DIF: Moderate   OBJ: LO: 26-03   NAT: BUSPROG: Analytic
      KEY: Bloom's: Application

13. Mundall Company is considering a project that will require an initial investment of $600,000 and is expected to generate the following cash flows:

Year 1	$100,000
Year 2	$250,000
Year 3	$250,000
Year 4	$200,000
Year 5	$100,000

A. What is the project's payback period?

B. If the required rate of return is 20% and taxes are ignored, what is the project's net present value? The present value of $1 at compound interest of 20% for 1, 2, 3, 4 and 5 years is .8333, .6944, .5787, .4823 and .4019, respectively.

ANS:

A. $100,000 + $250,000 + $250,000 = $600,000, so the payback period is three years.

B.

($600,000) * 1.000 =	($600,000)
$100,000 * 0.8333 =	83,330
$250,000 * 0.6944 =	173,600
$250,000 * 0.5787 =	144,675
$200,000 * 0.4823 =	96,460
$100,000 * 0.4019 =	40,190
Net present value	$(61,745)

PTS: 1   DIF: Challenging   OBJ: LO: 26-03   NAT: BUSPROG: Analytic
KEY: Bloom's: Application

14. Identify four capital investment analysis models discussed in the chapter and discuss the strengths and weaknesses of each model.

ANS:
The four capital investment models discussed in the chapter are the payback method, the accounting rate of return model, the net present value model, and the internal rate of return model.

Following are strengths and weaknesses of each:

The payback model is easy to understand and is based on cash flows, which are of primary concern to many businesses. However, it ignores profitability and the time value of money.

The accounting rate of return model measures profitability, but it ignores the time value of money.

The net present value model and the internal rate of return model are both based on cash flows, profitability and the time value of money. These models don't have any of the weaknesses identified with the payback model and the accounting rate of return model.

PTS: 1   DIF: Moderate   OBJ: LO: 26-02 | LO: 26-03
NAT: BUSPROG: Analytic   KEY: Bloom's: Knowledge

15.   What is capital investment analysis?   Why are capital investment analysis decisions often difficult and risky?

      ANS:
      Capital investment analysis is the process of analyzing alternative long-term investments and deciding which assets to acquire and/or sell.   Capital investment analysis decisions are difficult because they are usually based on predictions about an uncertain future.   These decisions involve large sums of money committed for long periods of time and may be irreversible.

      PTS: 1   DIF: Easy   OBJ: LO: 26-01   NAT: BUSPROG: Analytic
      KEY: Bloom's: Knowledge

16.   Briefly describe the time value of money.   Why is the time value of money important in capital investment analysis?

      ANS:
      The time value of money means that a dollar today is worth more than a dollar in the future.   Since capital investment analysis decisions are often based on cash flows which will be received in the future, managers often use a process called discounting in order to measure future cash flows in the value of today's dollar.

      PTS: 1   DIF: Easy   OBJ: LO: 26-03   NAT: BUSPROG: Analytic
      KEY: Bloom's: Knowledge